PRINCIPLES
of
PENETRANTS

by

CARL E. BETZ

Vice President, Magnaflux Corporation
Member, American Society for Metals
American Welding Society
American Society for Testing and Materials
Society for Nondestructive Testing

Second Edition

Published by Magnaflux Corporation
Chicago, Illinois 60656

PUBLISHED BY
MAGNAFLUX CORPORATION
CHICAGO, ILLINOIS 60656

MANUFACTURED IN THE UNITED STATES
BY STEWART PRINTING COMPANY
CHICAGO, ILLINOIS 60605

LIBRARY OF CONGRESS
CATALOG CARD NUMBER: 76-95933

Dedication
To

F. B. (Bic) Doane

In recollection of thirty-five years of association and friendship.

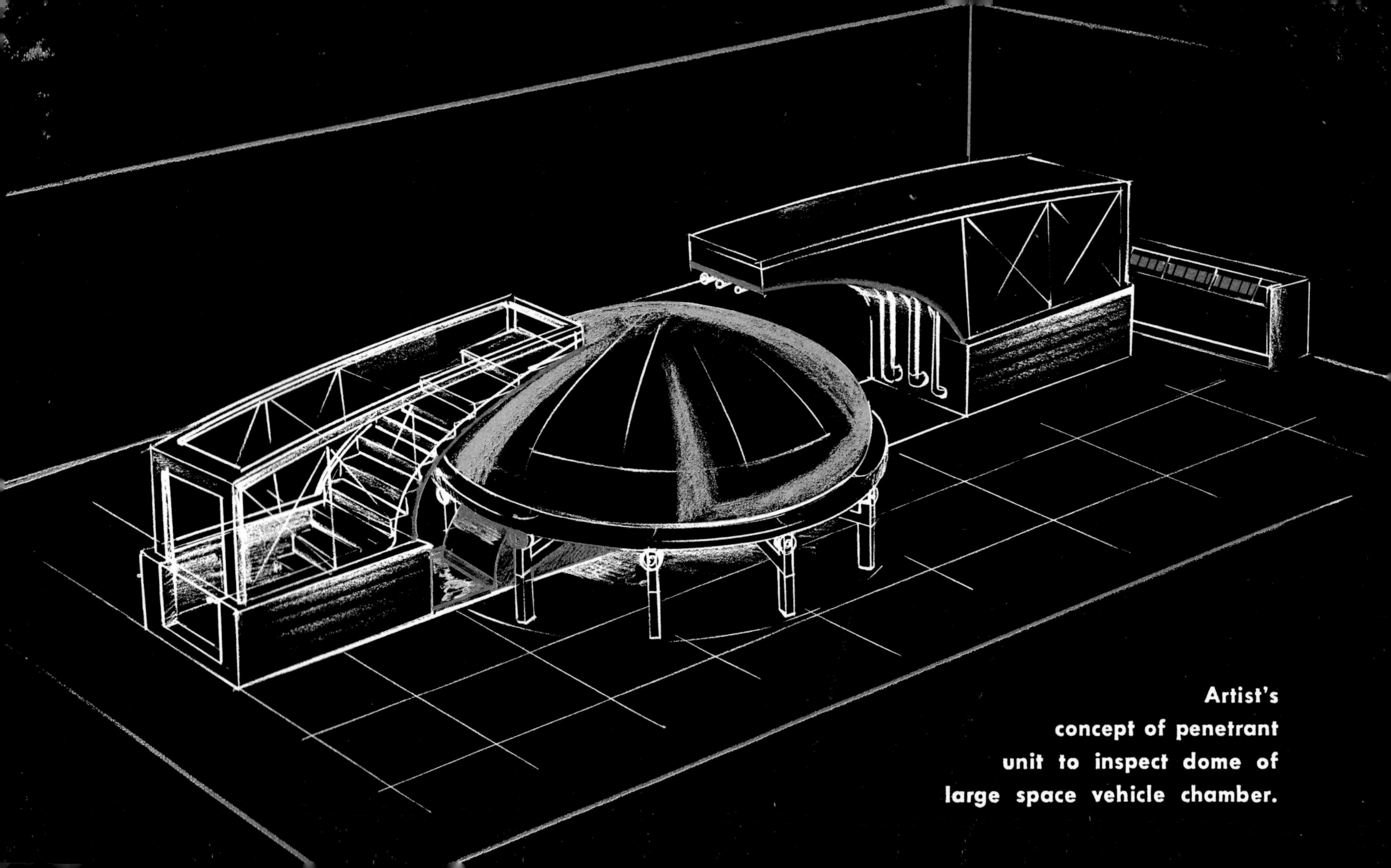

Artist's concept of penetrant unit to inspect dome of large space vehicle chamber.

PRINCIPLES OF PENETRANTS

LIST OF CHAPTERS

TABLE OF CONTENTS

CHAPTER 1

HISTORY OF PENETRANTS

CHAPTER 4

NATURE AND PROPERTIES OF PENETRANTS

CHAPTER 5

NATURE & PROPERTIES OF DEVELOPERS

CHAPTER 6

THE PENETRANT METHOD—FACTORS AFFECTING ITS OPERATION

CHAPTER 7

WATER WASHABLE FLUORESCENT PENETRANTS MATERIALS AND TECHNIQUES

CHAPTER 8

POST-EMULSIFIABLE FLUORESCENT PENETRANT MATERIALS AND TECHNIQUES

CHAPTER 9

BLACK LIGHT—ITS NATURE, SOURCES AND REQUIREMENTS

CHAPTER 10

COLOR-CONTRAST PENETRANTS—MATERIALS AND TECHNIQUES

CHAPTER 11

EQUIPMENT FOR CONDUCTING PENETRANT INSPECTION

CHAPTER 12

DETECTABLE DEFECTS

CHAPTER 13

INDUSTRIAL APPLICATIONS

CHAPTER 14

DETECTION OF LEAKS WITH PENETRANTS

CHAPTER 15

INTERPRETATION OF RESULTS

CHAPTER 16

STANDARDS AND SPECIFICATIONS FOR PENETRANT INSPECTION

CHAPTER 17

TESTS FOR EVALUATION AND CONTROL OF PENETRANTS EMULSIFIERS AND DEVELOPERS

APPENDIX I

PENETRANTS

APPENDIX II

DEVELOPERS

APPENDIX III

EVALUATION TESTS FOR PENETRANTS AND DEVELOPERS

APPENDIX IV

COLOR-CONTRAST TECHNIQUES

APPENDIX V

REMOVERS, CLEANING TECHNIQUES

APPENDIX VI

EQUIPMENT

LIST OF TABLES

LIST OF ILLUSTRATIONS

CHAPTER 5

CHAPTER 6

CHAPTER 7

Page

CHAPTER 8

CHAPTER 9

CHAPTER 10 *Page*

CHAPTER 11

CHAPTER 12

CHAPTER 13

CHAPTER 14

CHAPTER 15

CHAPTER 17

APPENDIX I

APPENDIX II

APPENDIX IV

PREFACE

At the time this is written it has been just over 20 years since Fluorescent Penetrant methods were first offered to Industry by Magnaflux Corporation in the summer of 1942. During the first few years of its use the method and techniques were quite simple and only a single penetrant, of the water-washable type, was available.

As use of the Penetrant Method expanded during and just after the war, variations in techniques and a multiplicity of materials made their appearance, and this development continued through the 1950-1960 decade and still goes on. The addition of color contrast penetrants, post-emulsification techniques, wet developers, and automated equipment have changed a fundamentally simple inspection process into one requiring considerable knowledge and experience to apply properly to the vastly more complex inspection problems of today.

Until recent years there seemed to be no need for a comprehensive treatise on Penetrant Inspection and information for new users seemed to be adequately furnished by relatively simple operating instructions prepared by various interested users or furnished by Magnaflux Corporation to purchasers of its products. However, as the complexity of the method grew so did the need for a compilation of all available knowledge and experience regarding the materials, techniques, equipment and uses of Penetrant testing.

This book was consequently conceived and has been written in an attempt to fill this need. It is not intended to be an operating handbook, but rather a source of detailed information regarding the state of the art at this time. The effort to treat each phase of the subject as completely as possible within its own context has resulted in what may appear to be some tedious repetition, especially to the reader who may undertake to read the book straight through. Realizing that this is true, it still seemed the only way to present each of these phases in its proper perspective, and not divert the reader's attention by the need to follow too many distracting cross references although many are nevertheless included. Still, the reader who comes across too many references to the various steps of the process, such as washing precautions, developer applications or drying techniques, is advised to skip over material which he thinks he has read before, but only at the risk of missing an implication in context.

As in any technology, numerous new terms are invented or special meanings are assigned to words or phrases. Chapter 3 attempts to define some of those in general use in Penetrant testing. Two terms are perhaps new and should be explained. In reference to the non-fluorescent dye penetrants, it seemed that some name other than "Visible" or "Dye" or "Visible Dye" penetrant was desirable, and the term "Color-Contrast Penetrant" has been used in reference to this type throughout the book. The term "seeability" is a coined word not found in the dictionary, but seems to be particularly expressive to refer to all those characteristics of an indication that help the inspector to detect its presence. The factors of brightness, color, contrast, size, all have a part in making an indication "seeable."

The bibliography added as an Appendix is not intended as a comprehensive list of all literature bearing on Penetrant Inspection, but rather as a list of useful publications which have come to our attention over the years, which contribute in one way or another to our knowledge and experience of the subject. References to specific publications where pertinent to a given discussion, are given in the body of the text, or as footnotes.

As the book goes to press the author is acutely conscious of the fact that what he has written is thereby frozen for an indefinite period of time. Developments will continue, however, and knowledge and experience advance so that the contents of this volume can be regarded only as a cross-section of Penetrant Testing technology as of this date. It is hoped, nevertheless, that its value to users of the method will lie in the basic information it contains, on which the developments of the future can be superimposed.

To make adequate acknowledgment to all those who have contributed in some degree to this work would involve a list of a high percentage of my fellow-workers in Magnaflux Corporation as well as many others who have used and contributed to the method over the years. More specifically, the comments and suggestions of Dr. D. T. O'Connor, J. E. Clarke, Bruce Graham, D. W. Parker and J. T. Schmidt of the Magnaflux technical staff have been most helpful. J. T. Schmidt has supplied most of the material for Chapter

17 on tests. F. S. Catlin is responsible for producing most of the illustrations as well as contributing many helpful suggestions. Others of Magnaflux who have contributed comments and encouragement include R. O. Schiebel, R. G. Strother, W. D. Reid, A. E. Christensen, H. G. Bogart, R. P. Turner, F. B. Stern, Taber de Forest, R. C. Eichin, H. Migel, K. A. Skeie, D. P. Walsh, L. B. Haller, A. R. Lindgren, J. T. Kent, R. N. Baughman, Marc Van Baalen, and W. E. Durack. Drawings and graphs are the work of J. Scittine. Outside of Magnaflux, the careful review of the text and detailed helpful suggestions of R. C. Switzer, E. S. Mathews, R. A. Ward, and Robert Uhler, of Switzer Brothers, Inc., have been greatly appreciated. Finally, special thanks are due to W. E. Thomas whose help and support for this undertaking has contributed greatly to its coming finally to completion.

Carl E. Betz
Chicago, January 7, 1963.

PREFACE TO THE SECOND EDITION OF "PRINCIPLES OF PENETRANTS"

To designate this re-issue of the book Principles of Penetrants as a new edition is probably misleading, since it is not in any sense a revision of the original text. Some new material has been added in a series of new appendices, but the text itself has been revised only slightly. A few minor corrections or insertions are the extent of such revision. In order to call attention to the new material, footnotes specifically referring the reader to one of the six appendices have been added on pages at points where the appended new information is pertinent. It is hoped that by this device the new material will be read in the proper context and not be lost as is often the case when readers ignore the appendices entirely as unimportant.

In preparing the new material the author acknowledges with thanks the help given him by F. S. Catlin, Bruce Graham, Dr. G. O. McClurg and John E. Clarke. Especial thanks go to Tom Schmidt who is responsible for the revisions regarding evaluation tests given in Appendix III. Thanks also are due to W. E. Thomas and D. T. O'Connor for their support in producing this new edition.

Carl E. Betz

Greentree Farm, Indiana
June 14, 1969

CHAPTER 1

HISTORY OF PENETRANTS

1. EARLY NONDESTRUCTIVE TESTING. The use of penetrants for finding flaws in structural materials became a factor in Industry in 1942, when the complete system of Fluorescent Penetrant Inspection under the trade name of Zyglo* was first introduced by Magnaflux Corporation. This was an important landmark in the progress of nondestructive testing. In the years just preceding World War II the use of aluminum, magnesium, stainless steels and other nonmagnetic materials was very rapidly expanding. This expansion was immeasurably accelerated after the start of the War. A reliable, rapid and inexpensive test method for finding imperfections, flaws and defects in such materials was urgently needed.

During the previous decade—1930 to 1940—nondestructive testing had made a great deal of progress and some industries were coming to regard it an important—not to say vital—process, both for manufacture and for maintenance. In the transportation industry and most especially in the manufacture and maintenance of aircraft engines and air frames, such methods were eagerly accepted. The aircraft industry was so safety-conscious that for many years expense was a secondary consideration to any testing that would help assure the integrity and safe life of engines and structures.

2. RADIOGRAPHY AND MAGNETIC PARTICLE TESTING. In the 1920's radiography was practically the only truly nondestructive test that could give really critical and accurate information about the soundess of a part. It was to be improved tremendously in the years ahead, but even at that time it was an excellent method for finding internal flaws, as in welds, castings and forgings. It had more difficulty, at first, with steel than with the lighter nonferrous metals. As time went on, higher powered equipment and better techniques permitted penetration of quite heavy sections of iron and steel. The use of highly penetrating gamma radiation—largely from radium—also expanded these applications.

*Zyglo. Trademark registered in U.S. Patent Office. Property of Magnaflux Corporation. Also registered in Canada, Great Britain and numeous other countries.

As speeds and loads in aircraft and other transportation equipment were stepped up, it became increasingly urgent to be able to locate fine surface discontinuities—seams, heat cracks, fatigue cracks, etc.—quickly and reliably, and on a 100% basis. Radiography could see inside a casting or forging, but it was less than fully reliable for finding all *surface* cracks. On the basis of 100% inspection of many small parts, radiography became quite expensive because of film and processing costs.

It was during this period—the 1930's—that the magnetic particle method was introduced under the trade name of "Magnaflux"*, and rapidly came into wide use. With it, surface cracks and other surface discontinuities could be located in magnetic materials quickly and reliably, and the cost of the test was gratifyingly low. Supplies were not expensive so operating costs were minimized, and equipment and techniques were not particularly critical. Inspectors easily learned to use the method and liked it because indications were immediately visible directly on the surface of each part being tested.

These visible indications were most convincing to inspectors—so much so that at first non-relevant conditions were often misinterpreted as defects and often good material was rejected as a result. Some years of experience and tests by many users were necessary to accumulate the knowledge needed to correct this situation and to develop realistic standards for acceptance and rejection. Still, the use of the magnetic particle method constantly increased, since what it *could* do far outweighed in importance the things it failed to do, or the over-inspection that occurred.

3. NEED FOR TEST METHOD FOR NON-MAGNETIC MATERIALS. With the growth of the use of aluminum and other non-magnetic metals and materials, the lack of a good nondestructive test method to find critical surface defects in them was increasingly felt. What was wanted was a method as quick, easy and inexpensive, and as reliable, as the magnetic particle method—but one which would work on non-magnetic material.

The list of available methods to locate surface cracks in non-magnetic parts such as castings and forgings was not impressive prior to 1942. Some had merit in special or limited applications.

---

*Magnaflux. Trademark registered in U.S. Patent Office. Property of Magnaflux Corporation. Also registered in Canada, Great Britain and numerous other countries.

Most were able to find *some* defects and were used for that reason. Some users of such methods no doubt thought they were getting good inspection and either did not know or did not care about the flaws they missed. Others certainly knew the results were less than perfect, but used the methods because they *did* find some defects, and no more thorough methods were available.

4. AVAILABLE METHODS BEFORE PENETRANTS. The following methods were in use for the testing of non-magnetic materials in the years prior to 1942. The magnetic particle method is not included in the list, since it is applicable only to magnetic materials.

(a) RADIOGRAPHY. This was certainly an excellent and generally reliable method, but admittedly it could not locate with certainty the shallow surface cracks—especially fatigue cracks —which were looming as so important at that time. The method had the additional disadvantage of being slow and expensive, particularly when used on 100% of parts.

Modern techniques have made radiography rapid enough for many production applications and cost has also been reduced materially. The main disadvantage—the inability to find fine surface cracks in all circumstances—is inherent in the method. Techniques, such as multiple-angle shots, have been devised to increase the likelihood that all cracks will be found; still, complete reliability is not achieved and cost is multiplied.

So, in spite of its excellent abilities in many areas, radiography did not, and does not now, meet the need for surface crack detection.

(b) ETCHING METHODS. By etching or pickling the surface of a part suspected of being cracked, the surface is attacked by the corrosive liquid. At the edges of a crack the attack is more rapid, the edges of the crack itself being eaten away. This widens and enlarges the crack at the surface and makes it much more easily seen with the eye.

The method has very many disadvantages. The use of acid or alkali on a large scale presents operating problems and discourages the use of the process on a production basis. All cracks must still be sought by a careful visual inspection, with magnifier if the part is critical—and fine cracks are still often missed. If used on highly finished parts, damage to the surface often results. Still, the method has value and is used today in certain applications. For instance, inspection of aluminum forgings in the as-forged condition is difficult, because forging laps are tight and likely to be filled with oxide so that penetrants may be unable to enter. An alkali etch will dissolve both metal and oxide at the crack and render the crack or lap more visible to the eye, or more certain to be found with penetrants.

Etching is also useful in confirming a crack found by other methods—or a suspected area may be lightly polished and etched and examined with a microscope. For the most part, however, etching is inferior today to modern penetrant methods *except* when the defect is so tightly filled with foreign material that the penetrant cannot enter. Today eddy current methods are being used to replace etching in situations of this sort.

The deficiencies of the etching method and its limited applications were fully realized and it did not furnish a satisfactory answer to the testing problems of the early 1940's.

(c) ANODIZING. This variation of the etching method is a by-product of the anodizing process and similar processes used

Fig. 1—Indications of defects produced by anodizing. a) Anodizing indications of cracks. b) Same specimen, indications produced by fluorescent penetrant.

on alumnium and magnesium. When the surface of these metals is treated with an oxidizing agent, such as a chromate or chromic acid, a corrosion-resistant surface film is produced.

Where a crack or other open defect exists, the oxidizing liquid enters and later makes the crack visible either by the etching action at the crack edges or by the stain produced by the liquid at the defect. This might be said to be a combination etching and penetrant method.

The method is quite effective on certain cracks and surface defects, but is reliable only on the larger cracks. It has been proven to be unable to find very fine defects because they are bridged over by the protective film. The anodizing and similar processes are used today as protective finishes but are seldom considered dependable where a critical inspection for cracks is required.

(d) OIL AND WHITING METHOD. This method is definitely a forerunner of the modern penetrant methods. It was in use for finding gross cracks in railroad equipment and will be described in detail in a following section. In the form in which it was being used it was useful only for large cracks and no one up to that time had thought of improving it. A version of it called the "Hot Oil" method was later developed and will also be described in another section.

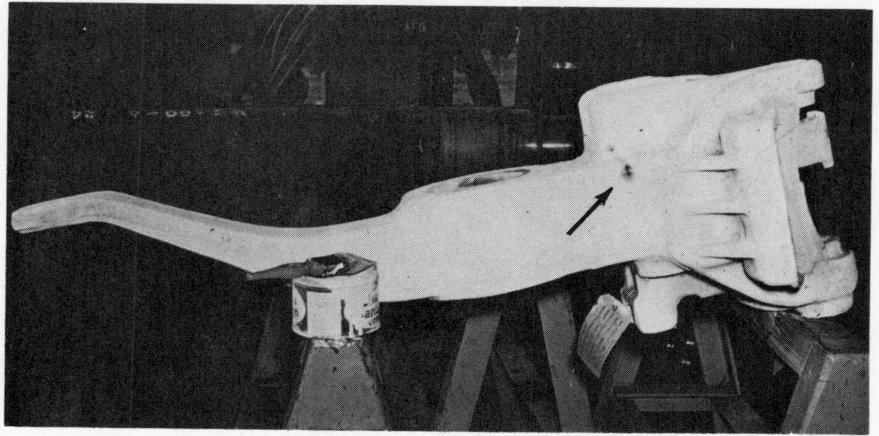

Courtesy Santa Fe Railway.

Fig. 2—Oil and whiting method as used in a railroad shop on a locomotive coupler. Bleeding of oil indicates crack. (Early 1930's)

The "Oil and Whiting" method possessed the nucleus of an answer to the problem of finding defects in non-magnetic metals, but it was not realized at the time.

(e) BRITTLE LACQUER METHOD. An interesting method was suggested about 1940 and actually was offered to industry under the trade name "Vitroflux"*. In this method the surface to be inspected was coated with a very brittle lacquer. When the lacquer film was fully dry, the surface was given a sharp blow, causing the part to vibrate. Stress concentrations due to the impact occurred at cracks, and caused the lacquer to crack also. With suitable illumination the cracks in the lacquer could be seen by careful visual inspection.

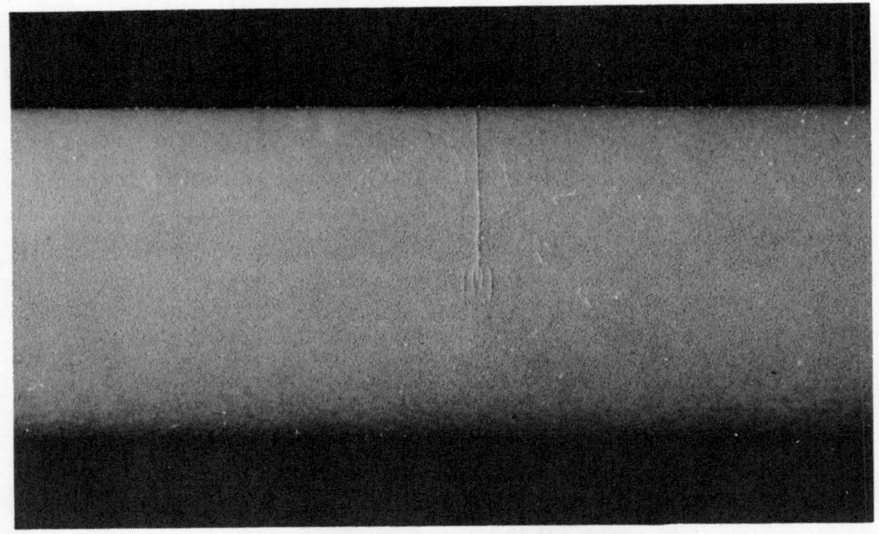

Fig. 3—Indication of crack with Vitroflux.

Experience quickly showed the method was not reliable on complicated shapes, and visibility of the lacquer cracks was poor except over a smooth, bright surface. In addition the method was slow and clumsy and involved a difficult cleaning operation to remove the lacquer after inspection.

The method was used briefly on a few special applications, such as finding cracks in aluminum alloy propellor blades. It was then dropped in favor of other methods.

*Vitroflux. Trademark registered in U.S. Patent Office. Property of Magnaflux Corporation.

(f) RINGING METHODS. The practice of ringing a casting or a piece of china to determine whether it is sound is an ancient method for telling whether a gross crack exists or not. When a part is held suspended at one point and struck a blow, only an uncracked part will give off a clear ringing note—otherwise it "sounds cracked."

The method is insensitive to fine cracks and cracks of unfavorable direction. It gives no indication as to *where* the crack is located. It is not a reliable method of inspection, except for a few very special shaped parts—for example, bells.

(g) VISUAL METHODS. Careful examination of a surface with or without a magnifier, special illumination or polarized light often is used as a method of inspection intended to locate the presence of cracks. Experienced inspectors are often quite skillful, especially on smooth ground or polished surfaces. But the method is slow, tedious and requires painstaking attention on the part of the inspector. The human factor is so large that the method simply cannot compete in dependability with more positive methods of crack detection.

(h) PROOF TESTING. Proof-testing—such as hydrostatic tests on pipe—were used long ago and are still a requirement in many specifications. Welded pipe, tanks and other structures are loaded usually to some point above expected operating stress. Such tests do serve a purpose somewhat different from a nondestructive test for defects. They indicate that the pipe or structure can initially take the designed-for load.

Such tests however, give no indication of the presence of cracks which may grow in service and cause failure. A defect severe enough to cause failure under a proof-load test is likely to be found by suitable nondestructive inspection before the proof-load is applied. When found instead under proof-loading the whole structure is often destroyed or so damaged that rework or salvage may be impossible. Although proof tests of this type certainly have a place in the category of tests, they are in no sense an answer to the demand for a nondestructive flaw-finding test for non-magnetic materials.

5. ADVENT OF PENETRANT INSPECTION. It was into such an environment that modern penetrant methods were introduced in the summer of 1942. Since the original materials and techniques had been well worked out in the laboratory and had been field-tested, it is not surprising that the method was at once put to work and in a matter of months was in use in dozens of installations.

6. OIL AND WHITING METHOD. The idea of using penetrating substances to find cracks in metal parts was by no means a new one. In the railroad industry, for the maintenance of steam locomotives, a method known as the "Oil and Whiting" method had been in use for at least 50 years and probably longer.

In this method the "penetrant" was a heavy lubricating oil available in all railroad shops—"600 W." It was usually thinned with kerosene or other light oil, giving a thin dark-colored mixture. Often used oil was employed, giving a darker, dirtier colored liquid. Locomotive parts—rods, axles, crank pins, eccentric parts, etc.—were first cleaned, usually by boiling in a caustic soda solution, dried, and then immersed in a tank of the diluted 600-W oil.

The "penetration time" was anything from a few hours to twenty-four or more, after which the parts were removed, and swabbed off with waste moistened with kerosene. When the surfaces were clean and dry they were painted all over with a mixture of whiting (chalk) in denatured alcohol. This coating dried rapidly and left a dead-white and quite uniform surface.

Usually the parts were then vibrated by striking with a sledge or by means of an air-hammer. The vibration was intended to cause the cracks to "work," and squeeze the dirty oil of the penetrant back out to the surface. Wherever oil came back to the surface, whether as the result of the vibration or simply by "creeping" out, the white coating would be stained a dirty brown and a crack would be indicated.

The method left much to be desired. Unquestionably it found many cracks and to the extent that it did so, it was probably worth more than the effort that it cost. But it was completely inadequate to locate fine cracks, and especially, fine shallow fatigue cracks at the stage where salvage of the part is nearly always possible. The reasons for poor results lay perhaps largely in the way the test was performed, and perhaps to a considerable degree also in the lack of control of materials.

The mixture of oil and kerosene probably made a fair "penetrant," but since both constituents and their proportions were left to the individual operator—usually a machinist or helper—no uniformity was possible. The same was true of the whiting mixture. Also the "swab" cleaning, if overdone, would clean out cracks; too much whiting could be applied, etc. In other words, the variables which determined whether or not a crack would be shown were not controlled at all. Also, and of perhaps greater importance, the color of the penetrant did not produce enough contrast against the white background to present sharply visible indications. Only a little oil came out from a fine crack, not enough to make a readily visible stain on the layer of whiting.

That the method failed to show significant cracks was easily and quickly demonstrated when results were compared with those of the magnetic particle method. On one Western road on which the oil and whiting method was regularly used, while failures still occurred, 40% of all side rods were found to be cracked when the magnetic particle method was first employed. On an Eastern road, six axles, on which no cracks were found with oil and whiting, were *all* shown to be cracked when tested with magnetic particles.

The oil and whiting method was used mostly on steel parts, and by 1940 had been largely discredited for this use by the magnetic particle method. No one seems to have been successful in applying the principle of this method to solve the non-magnetic materials flaw-finding problem until the fluorescent penetrant test method came along in 1942.

It is certainly interesting at this time to observe by hindsight the parallel between the old oil-and-whiting method and modern penetrant methods. The parallel is most marked when color-contrast methods—red dye penetrants—are considered. It is not known whether oil-and-whiting furnished any inspiration to any early workers on modern penetrants, but it is entirely possible. Still, as will be evident as we proceed with the story, the contributions necessary to make a really dependable inspection method out of the penetrant idea required a tremendous amount of time, effort and creative thought and work.

7. EARLY WORK. Work on the problem of finding flaws in non-magnetic materials goes back at least as far as 1935. Carl E. Betz and F. B. Doane, working at Magnaflux Corporation to improve the magnetic particle method, were conscious of the need for a similar method for non-ferrous metals. A method was actually worked out based on electrolysis and color contrast which, however, proved to be entirely impractical.

In 1938 Taber de Forest, again in the research laboratories of Magnaflux Corporation, experimented with color contrast penetrants. But with the materials and techniques he was able to develop the results were not sufficiently satisfactory for the method to be offered commercially.

It was in this general period of time that Robert C. Switzer of Switzer Brothers, Inc. (now of Day-Glo Color Corp., Cleveland, Ohio) began his experiments independently of Magnaflux Corporation. Among other objectives, his work was directed toward location of defects by penetrants using colored dyes in the penetrants to increase the color contrast of indications against a background. Since he was particularly interested in applications of fluorescent colors, he realized that superior contrasts (over mere color-contrast) could be secured by means of fluorescent dyes and the use of black light to cause them to fluoresce, and his initial development was concentrated in the fluorescent dye area.

8. THE SWITZER DEVELOPMENT. The work of R. C. Switzer led him to apply for a patent on various penetrant methods of finding flaws in solid materials, which application resulted in U.S. Patent #2,259,400 issued on October 14, 1941. The original application covered the use of both fluorescent penetrants and color-contrast penetrants; the Patent Office required division and the fluorescent method was first prosecuted as being much more important to industry than the color-contrast version.

Patent #2,259,400 was a basic patent covering methods of finding flaws or discontinuities in solid bodies by use of penetrants containing fluorescent dyes or additives. The claims were broad and the patent formed the basis for the development of penetrant inspection as it is known today.

R. C. Switzer offered Magnaflux Corporation a license under this patent and in February of 1942 an exclusive license was given to Magnaflux Corporation with full rights to sublicense users under the methods.

9. DEVELOPMENT OF THE FLUORESCENT PENETRANT METHODS. Magnaflux Corporation was fully aware of the potential value and usefulness of the methods to which it had secured rights, but also realized that much more developmental work needed to be done before a practical industrial test system could be offered for economic use. In the next few months a tremendous amount of work was done, both by Magnaflux and by the Switzer brothers. Many formulations were made and many different techniques were tried. At Magnaflux the developmental work was led by Greer Ellis and Taber de Forest and later by F. S. Catlin; while R. A. Ward and J. L. Switzer did most of the Switzer research

From this intensive work, the water-wash fluorescent penetrant materials and technique, in practically the form in which they are used today, were perfected, tested and produced for industrial use.

In July of 1942 the new method was offered commercially. The trade name of Zyglo was selected to designate the method and materials. A second patent was applied for, covering the water-wash technique and the materials. This patent, U.S. No. 2,405,078 issued July 30, 1946 to R. A. Ward.

10. "HOT OIL" METHOD. It is interesting to note that the demand for a method of this type was so keen that some companies worked up a version of fluorescent penetrant inspection on the basis of information transmitted during field trials of the work the Switzers were doing, in advance of any direct offering of the method by Magnaflux. This interim method used hot lubricating oil as a penetrant, a quick cleaning with solvent, and black light to find defects using the natural fluorescence of the lubricating oil as it came back out of the defect as an indicator.

Almost the only purpose for which this version was used was in the inspection of bearings for lack of bond between the backing and the silver lining, and for pores in the lining. Here development of indications was obtained by heating the bearings on a hot plate, and inspecting them, *on the hot plate,* with black light. In spite of the method's many drawbacks, a number of companies engaged in the making of aircraft and marine engines found a fairly satisfactory answer to a war-pressured production problem by this means. The method was also tried on aluminum castings and forgings but with indifferent success.

The hot oil method was low in sensitivity, due mainly to the low order of visibility afforded by the fluorescence of the oil. Penetrants containing intensely fluorescent dyes in a balanced formulation were demonstrably superior and the "Hot Oil" method was largely supplanted in a relatively short time.

11. EARLY USERS. Since the Air Arms of the Army and Navy were directing aircraft production in 1942, the new fluorescent penetrant method was first taken to them for evaluation, and it was quickly approved for use for the location of surface flaws in non-magnetic materials. Early users were practically all engaged in war production of some sort, mostly in the aircraft area.

Some of the early applications were the following:

Lack of bond in bearings, and porosity
Stainless steel super-charger impeller wheels
Stellite tools
Hard-faced exhaust valves for aircraft engines

Fig. 4—First fluorescent penetrant unit—1942.

Sintered tungsten carbide tools
Aircraft propellers
Aircraft engine cylinder heads
Aircraft engine crank cases
Aluminum and magnesium castings
Leaks in electronic tubes

The first engineered and integrated piece of equipment for fluorescent penetrant inspection was delivered to Aluminum Industries, Cincinnati, Ohio, on October 23, 1942, for the inspection of aluminum castings. With this equipment development it was realized that control of the method required equipment design control as well as control of the materials used in the inspection. With many variables being possible, consistent test results depended on this control as a vital element of a test system.

12. EXPANSION OF USE OF FLUORESCENT METHODS. During the decade following the introduction of the fluorescent water-wash method in 1942, some improvements in techniques and materials were made. However, greatest effort was devoted to adapting the method to the large number of applications in many industries where it seemed to offer a solution to inspection problems. Many special penetrants were developed and tried for special uses. Equipment for both general use and for special testing problems was developed and built. It was a period during which the method was proved out—its abilities explored and its limitations marked out and studied.

13. COLOR-CONTRAST PENETRANTS. The color-contrast penetrant system had been considered by Magnaflux Corporation in the late 1930's and extensively investigated by R. C. Switzer in his early work. However, emphasis was placed on the fluorescent version because of its greater sensitivity and wider applicability. In the mid-1940's work was done by Rebecca (Smith) Sparling and others on the color-contrast type of penetrant, although the method did not come at once into general use. However, with increased knowledge of penetrants and techniques, the color-contrast method, though less sensitive than the fluorescent, has since found a great many useful applications. (See also Chapter 10, Section 1).

The patent situation with respect to the color-contrast penetrant field has not been as clear as is the case with fluorescent penetrants. Over the years a number of patents having to do with color-contrast penetrant methods have been issued to various persons, resulting in a rather confused situation.

This situation was somewhat clarified by issuance to R. C. Switzer in 1958 of U.S. Patent No. 2,839,918 on the color-contrast penetrant method, following a lengthy interference proceeding in the Patent Office with a patent to Ralph Bloom Jr., et al. A patent to L. W. Sockman et al was involved in interference proceedings with an application which stemmed from a filing by R. A. Ward and R. C. Switzer in 1945. In spite of this confused patent situation, however, color-contrast penetrants are in wide use in industry today.

The great advantage of the color-contrast system lies in its extreme portability, there usually being no need for even an electrical outlet, since no black light is needed. In many small shops, for limited application, the color-contrast system now offers a very useful and convenient tool. In large shops, too, it is widely used as a quick, local checking method. It has found extremely wide acceptance in a great many types of industry for manufacturing and maintenance testing needs.

14. MODERN STATUS OF PENETRANTS. After over twenty years of use the Penetrant Methods have proven to be very valuable and in many instances indispensible testing tools. Penetrant testing is one of the three most widely used nondestructive testing methods today—the other two being Radiography and Magnetic Particle Testing.

In the course of years of work with the penetrant methods, a great deal has been learned about how to secure the best possible results from the use of penetrants under all manner of conditions. To meet special situations and to solve special problems, research and experiment as well as engineering development have produced numerous materials, various techniques and a great many types of equipment, both general purpose and special.

A new method—the post-emulsification or P. E. method—was developed in the Magnaflux Laboratories to meet the critical needs of the jet engine industry for the inspection of turbine buckets and blades. Donald W. Parker and Taber de Forest led the research on the method, achieving greatly increased sensitivity for all types of defects, as well as increased ability to locate fairly open and shallow types. New materials were developed for this application and were offered under the trade name Pentrex.* On September 17, 1957, U.S. Patent 2,806,959 issued covering the post-emulsification method.

Equipment for fluorescent penetrant inspection has been produced to inspect huge airframe and rocket components requiring stations sixty and even eighty feet long. Also, automatic equipment now

Fig. 5—Automatic unit for inspecting various jet engine parts.

processes complicated parts up to the point of inspection under black light so that the inspector need only examine the parts for indications. (Fig. 5). Even this step may one day be eliminated as automatic scanning equipment is further developed from work which has already been under way for several years.

In the realm of process improvement considerable work has been done on self-developing penetrant materials which eliminate the need for the application of separate developers. These systems use materials and techniques which tend to immobilize exuded penetrant indications along the edge of the defect.**

Continuing improvements can be looked for as new problems

*Pentrex. Trademark registered U.S. Patent Office. Property of Magnaflux Corporation. Also registered in Canada, Great Britain and many other countries.

**At this point turn to Appendices I and V for further discussion of developments in penetrants and cleaning techniques.

stimulate further research and development. New metallic and non-metallic fabrication materials are constantly offering a challenge to the nondestructive testing engineer, and penetrants can be expected to offer their share of solutions for the many and varied flaw-detection requirements so created. The penetrant methods have found a permanent place in nondestructive testing technology and will continue to play a vital part in this increasingly important field.

CHAPTER 2

GENERAL CONSIDERATIONS

1. WHAT IS THE PENETRANT METHOD? The Penetrant Method of nondestructive testing is a method for finding discontinuities open to the surface in solid and essentially nonporous bodies. The method employs a penetrating liquid which is applied over the surface and enters the discontinuity or crack. Subsequently, after the excess of penetrant has been cleaned from the surface, the penetrant which exudes or is drawn back out of the crack is observed, indicating the presence and location of the discontinuity.

2. HOW DOES IT WORK? There are five essential steps in employing the penetrant method, with one important sub-step. The five steps are the following:

(a) PRE-CLEANING OR SURFACE PREPARATION: As a preliminary step, the surface of the part must be clean and dry, and the discontinuity itself must be free of water, oil or other con-

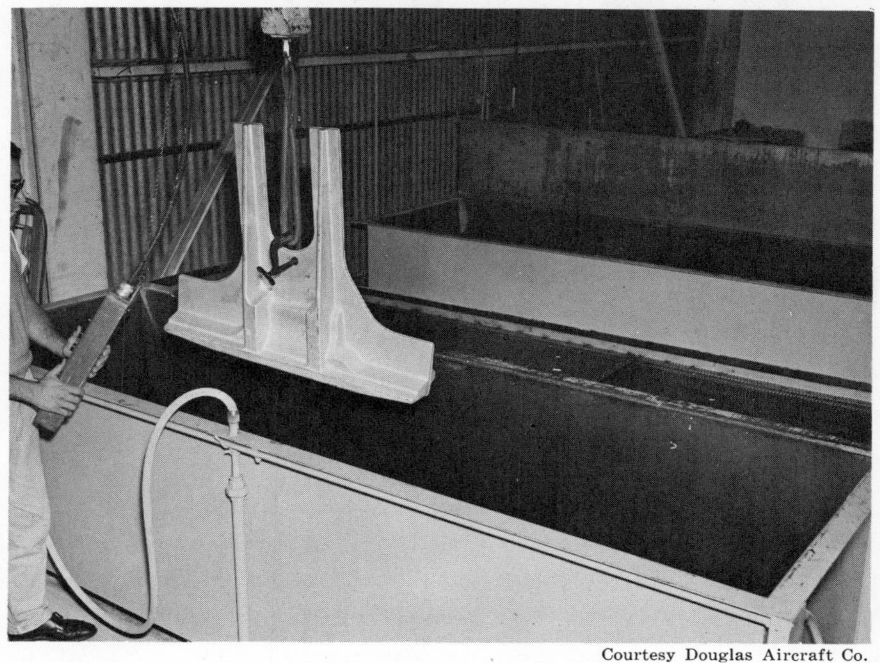

Courtesy Douglas Aircraft Co.

Fig. 6—Dipping part in penetrant.

taminant, so *pre-cleaning* of the part with a solvent is almost always required.

(b) PENETRATION: This involves applying the penetrant to form a film over the surface so that it can enter the discontinuity. This may be done by dipping, spraying or painting on with a brush. A sufficient amount of time must then be allowed to elapse to permit the penetrant to enter, as completely as it will, the discontinuities which may be present.

(c) REMOVING EXCESS PENETRANT. This step, often called "wash" or "rinse," involves the removal of the excess penetrant from the surface by some means, after time for full penetration has been allowed. Cleaning may be simply a wiping off, with or without the use of a solvent, or it may be a washing, most often with water.

(Courtesy Douglas Aircraft Co.)

Fig. 7—Washing part with water.

The purpose of the cleaning is to free the surface of all penetrant so that when the penetrant which has entered a discontinuity begins to exude or creep back out, it will be visible against a clean background.

In order that the penetrant form a proper clean-cut indication the surface should be dry. If the surface has been wiped or a volatile solvent used, it will be dry about as soon as that operation is complete. If water has been used to wash the surface a more positive means of drying must be employed. Since water-washing is a common method of cleaning after penetration, a sub-step—drying—is usually a necessary part of the inspection.

Drying can sometimes be accomplished by wiping dry with a cloth or towel, but more often a special hot-air dryer is used since warming has added advantages in facilitating the forming of indications.

(d) DEVELOPING. The fourth step is to apply a developing film over the dry surface. The developer acts as a blotting agent to speed the penetrant's natural tendency to come back out of the discontinuity and spread slightly at the edges of the

(Courtesy Douglas Aircraft Co.)

Fig. 8—Dipping part into wet developer.

crack. The developer helps both to draw the penetrant out and to spread it.

The developer is usually a fine powder, white or slightly colored, and may be applied dry or suspended in a liquid. The end result of its application is a light film of powder

(Courtesy Douglas Aircraft Co.)

Fig. 9—Placing part into drier.

evenly spread over the surface of the part. After applying (and drying if applied wet), developing time is permitted to elapse to allow penetrant to come to the surface of the part in sufficient amount to form an indication which the inspector can see.*

(e) INSPECTION. When the surface has been sufficiently developed, the inspector must examine the part to see any indications which are present. This is done in good white light if the penetrant is of the color-contrast type. If a fluorescent penetrant was used, inspection is carried out in a darkened area with a "black" light to cause the penetrant to fluoresce, or emit visible light.

"Black" light is near-ultraviolet light which, when directed toward a fluorescent penetrant, causes the latter to

*Here see Appendix II regarding further discussion of developers and developer action.

GENERAL CONSIDERATIONS

(Courtesy Douglas Aircraft Co.)

Fig. 10—Inspecting part under black light.

glow with a light of its own. In a dark area the glowing indication is readily seen.

The inspector usually marks the location of indications, and may or may not accept or reject the part on the spot. Interpretation of the indication and evaluation of the condition indicated is often the function of a special quality control man or salvage group. (See Chapter 15)

Many variations of materials and techniques are in use for each of these steps and will be discussed in detail in the following chapters.

3. WHAT CAN IT FIND? Since the penetrant method produces indications by means of liquid exuding from a discontinuity, it follows that it can only detect defects which have an opening to the surface into which the liquid can originally penetrate. The method, then, excells in finding any discontinuity, whether crack, seam, lap or porous area, which is open to the surface on which the inspection is made.

The method works best on clean cracks or tears—even very fine cracks—or on porosity such as is common close to the surface of many non-ferrous castings. The crack may be shallow if it is tight and the porosity need have only minute openings connecting it to the surface.

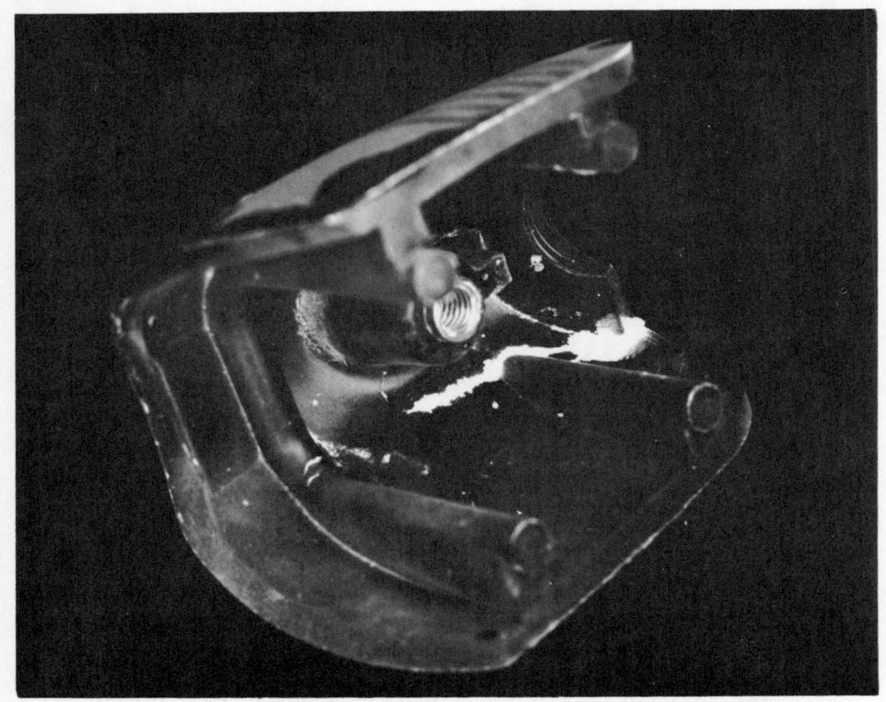

Fig. 11—Typical indication of a crack produced with fluorescent penetrant.

It works least well on shallow and fairly wide open discontinuities, since penetrant is retained less well in such openings during the cleaning or washing operation. It also performs less well on tight cracks which are filled with some foreign material such as oxide or carbon. In such cases sufficient penetrant may not be able to enter the crack in the first place. However, modern materials (Pentrex) and the techniques of post-emulsification have extended the ability of the method into these areas also, so that today open shallow defects can usually be indicated and many filled cracks can be sufficiently penetrated to give good indications.

Another type of defect which penetrants find exceptionally well is the through-leak in tanks, piping, welds, etc. Here the penetrant applied on one surface follows the path of the leak, to appear on the opposite surface where it can be readily seen. This is an area of usefulness in itself which will be treated separately in Chapter 14.

Chapter 2

GENERAL CONSIDERATIONS

(Courtesy Mojonnier Brothers Co.)

Fig. 12—Testing for leaks on outside of welded special industrial tank.

4. On What Kind of Materials is it Applicable? The Penetrant method is effective on any relatively hard, generally non-porous solid material. Its widest usefulness is in finding flaws in non-magnetic metals, such as aluminum, magnesium, stainless steels, copper, brass and various other metals and alloys, including titanium, beryllium and zirconium. It is also applicable to vitrified ceramics, to glass and to plastics of all kinds, although special penetrants must be used for some of these materials.

The method will, of course, also work on ferrous metals—i.e., magnetic materials. There are numerous reasons, however, why the magnetic particle method is preferable in most cases on such material, although penetrants *are* properly used on magnetic materials in some special instances.

Some of the reasons for preferring magnetic particles are:

(a) they will detect both surface and near-to-surface discontinuities.

(b) they will detect cracks filled with carbon or oxide or other contaminant.
(c) they will detect cracks under thin films of paint or plating.
(d) in general, magnetic particles are faster and more economical than penetrants, and less cleaning is required.

Some instances when penetrants do find application on iron and steel parts are:

(a) when it is desired to demonstrate that a discontinuity actually does come to the surface, or actually does penetrate from one surface through to another.
(b) in some cases (castings for example) when large numbers of small parts of complex geometry are to be inspected and the cracks expected are known to be clean and easily penetrated. In such a case penetrants may be faster since individual handling for magnetization is avoided.

5. WHAT ARE THE GENERAL ADVANTAGES OF THE METHOD? The penetrant method has many advantages that have caused it to be so widely used. Possibly one of the most important is that it is essentially a simple method—simple in principle and simple in application. As is so often the case, however, there is always a tendency to oversimplify and this can lead to trouble. There are certain rules and principles that must be observed if consistent and reliable results are to be obtained.

To say—as has been said—that all that is needed to operate the method is a bucket, a rag and a black light is dangerous oversimplification. True, results can sometimes be obtained with such minimum facilities, but the operator attempting to use the method on this basis should at least know what limitations he is placing upon himself. If such simplification were safe there would be no need for this book on the subject of penetrant inspection.

But simple in principle and easily understood the method certainly is. Also it is convincing to the inspector in its results, since indications, as in the magnetic particle method, appear as a direct delineation of the defect on the surface of the part itself.

Furthermore, there is no limitation whatever on the size or shape of the article to be inspected, nor on the composition so long as the surface is non-porous in nature. Inspections are made in the

Fig. 13—Indication of lap in .150″ tungsten rod. (Enlarged).

field on large tanks, turbine rotors and other structures, and in the plant on such tiny things as fine tungsten wire leads for vacuum tubes.

Another most important advantage is the adaptability of the method to production inspection of small parts, and in this, as has been said, it sometimes has an advantage over magnetic particle methods. Basket processing through the penetrant method enables the preparation often of hundreds of small parts at a time, with no need for individual handling till the step of examination by the inspector for indications.

It was stated that the method is essentially simple in application. Equipment to handle many large or odd-shaped parts often becomes quite complicated, but this is mainly due to the need for cutting down on the *time* required and to facilitate handling of the parts in the interests of time-saving. Minimum equipment in the form of portable kits offers the basic facilities for conducting inspections by the method, and in such cases no other equipment whatever is needed, except a black light if fluorescent penetrant is being used.

Another advantage is the fact that penetrants inherently have a tremendous ability for getting into very fine cracks, as will be discussed in detail in Chapter 4. This sensitivity to extremely fine

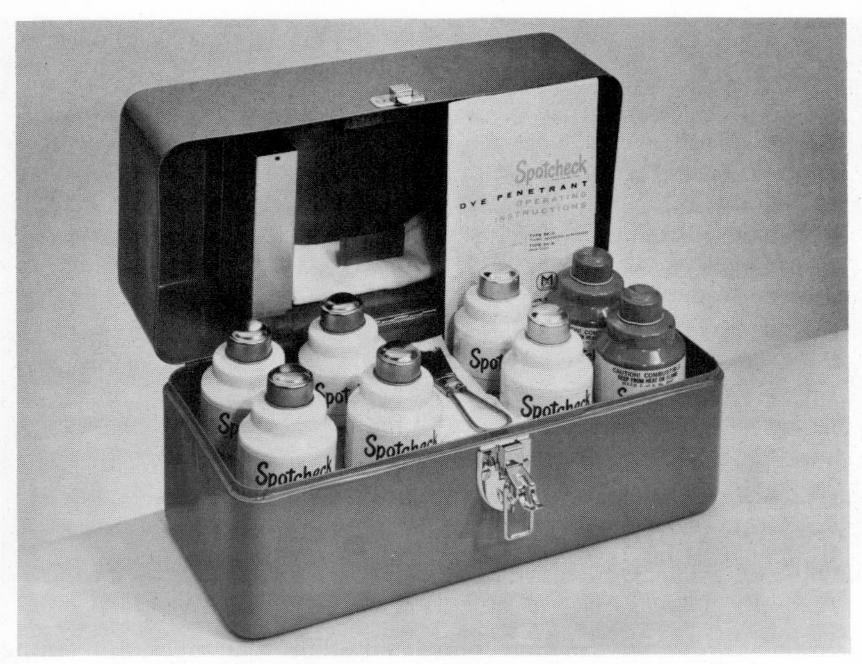

Fig. 14—Minimum equipment. Kit for color-contrast method.

cracks that cannot be seen by any other means is an important ability of the method. Magnetic particles are perhaps equally sensitive in forming an indication at exceedingly fine cracks, but even Magnaglo,* the fluorescent form of magnetic particles, does not produce the brilliant contrast in indications presented by the very high-brightness fluorescent penetrants. None of the other methods based merely on visual contrast or visual aids have a comparable ability.

Penetrants lend themselves to many variations in type and composition which makes possible their adaptation to the inspection of many different materials under a variety of conditions. For instance, some types of penetrants will attack some kinds of plastics and special formulations are available or can be readily developed to meet this condition. Some penetrants do not properly "wet" certain surfaces and again a variation in formulation is possible.

Magnetic particle methods often require two or more separate inspections to make sure that cracks in every possible orientation

*Magnaglo. Trademark registered in U.S. Patent Office. Property of Magnaflux Corporation. Also registered in Canada and Great Britain.

have been tested for. This is not true of penetrants, which can find defects in one operation no matter what their direction in the part.

In addition to the above technical advantages, the penetrant method has the merit of being relatively inexpensive, reasonably rapid (especially compared to certain other methods such as radiography) and to present minimum problems of interpretation. Because there are few if any false or non-relevant indications, interpretation is in the main perhaps easier than with magnetic particles. And finally, operators find no great difficulty in learning to apply the penetrant method properly and no special advance knowledge or skill is required of an operator. He must, of course, as in any inspection operation, have good, tested eyesight, be intelligent and honest and do a painstaking, conscientious job. But the skill needed is mainly the skill of manipulation of what is usually fairly simple equipment. This can usually be acquired in a relatively short period of training and instruction under an experienced operator.

6. WHAT ARE THE GENERAL LIMITATIONS OF THE METHOD? Since in any process there are things it will not or cannot do, as well as those which it can do, it is well to look at the limitations and disadvantages of the method in an appraisal such as this.

First of all, the method can find *only* discontinuities which have openings to the surface on which the penetrant is applied. Penetrant must be able to get into the defect else no indication can possibly be formed later. And by the same token, the defect must not be so filled with foreign material that penetrant cannot enter the opening. Cracks filled with oxide, oil or grease or even water, for example, will make it difficult if not impossible for the penetrant to enter.

Furthermore, the surface of the material must be impervious to the penetrant. If the surface is porous or tends to absorb penetrant in any way, the excess penetrant cannot be removed completely and a background remains against which indications of defects are difficult to see. This limitation excludes from the method porous materials such as non-vitrified clay ware and unsintered powder compresses, although the porous surface of a casting reveals its porosity by this very circumstance. However, a crack in the midst of excessive porosity on the surface of a casting may be difficult to identify.

If the penetrant tends to soften or dissolve the material being tested then again the method cannot be used, both because the surface of the part cannot be cleaned of background and because the surface may be damaged. In most cases however special penetrants which do not react with the material are available. Oily penetrants attack rubber, where water- or alcohol-base penetrants will not. Alcohol-base penetrants will attack some plastics, as will also oil-base penetrants, but usually a suitable liquid can be found which will be inert with respect to the material being tested. Water base penetrants have been extensively used for glass and some plastics.

Although the temperature range at which penetrants are effective is in general pretty wide, circumstances do arise when temperature prevents good inspection. Very cold and very hot temperatures are not compatible with proper operation of the method. (See Chapters 7, 8 and 10)

There is a cleaning problem following penetrant inspection in some cases. If the process following penetrant inspection, or the future service of the part can be affected by traces of penetrant or developer remaining after inspection, special precautions must be taken to clean the part thoroughly. In inspection of food machinery for example no trace of an oily penetrant should remain. Sometimes welding, brazing or soldering operations may be interfered with by residual penetrant or developer.

The penetrant itself suffers from contamination by foreign materials—especially water—necessitating in some instances special precautions in preparing parts for inspection or in protecting the penetrant containers from moisture, dirt or other substances.

There are very few inspection processes that are free of the hazard introduced by the human factor. Penetrant inspection depends on the eye of the inspector and his constant vigilance if it is to be reliable. In this respect it differs in no way from radiography, ultrasonic or magnetic particle methods. As in these methods, penetrant techniques do all possible to minimize the chance of error due to human fallibility. Automatic scanning and sorting devices are being developed, have been tried out in some applications, and offer promise for the future.

With penetrant inspection, the greatest safeguard against missing an indication of a defect lies in the great brilliance of the fluorescent material. It is hard *not* to see a bright light in a darkened space.

7. COMPARISON WITH OTHER METHODS. Since there are three other major nondestructive methods capable of finding discontinuities or flaws in non-magnetic materials—which is the prime field of use for penetrants—a quick comparison with these methods is of interest.

(a) Penetrants are much more reliable for finding surface discontinuities than radiography, and are faster and cheaper to use. Geometry and size of parts do not limit the use of the penetrant method.

(b) Penetrants are faster for overall scanning of parts for surface discontinuities, and are also more reliable for this purpose than ultrasonic methods in nearly all cases. Penetrants are not limited by shape or other part geometry and are cheaper for mass production. They will find shallower and shorter discontinuities.

(c) Penetrants are more flexible than eddy-current methods and are not restricted by part geometry as are the latter. They are not as fast on bars or tubing for certain classes of defect. Eddy currents however cannot reliably locate as wide a variety of discontinuities as regards width, depth and direction, as can penetrants.

(d) Penetrants yield to all three of the above methods in the area of internal defects. In this respect they also yield to the magnetic particle method, but are practically the equal of the latter in all applications in which the discontinuity is open at the surface and is not filled with some blocking contamination.

(e) Since the penetrant method excels all three of the other methods in locating fine, short and shallow cracks in the surface of parts, it is the most reliable method available in most applications for detecting the presence of fatigue cracks in nonmagnetic materials. The magnetic particle method is its equal in this respect on magnetic materials, and is more reliable on cracks which may be filled with foreign substances.

Fatigue cracks almost invariably start at the *surface* of parts which are highly stressed in service, and propagate through the cross section until complete failure occurs. If they can be detected in their early or incipient stages failure can be prevented and the machine part can often be saved. Because of its special ability in locating such surface cracks penetrant inspection is superior to the other methods in most instances for maintenance inspection of machinery of all kinds.

CHAPTER 3

SOME DEFINITIONS OF TERMS

Before proceeding to a more detailed discussion of penetrants and the penetrant method, it seems appropriate to give a brief definition of some of the various terms peculiar to the subject. Many of these terms will be defined more precisely in later discussions, but before the reader gets very far he will find certain words used in somewhat special senses. Rather than interrupt the text to define each of these terms when it is first used we give here a limited list of the more common ones, and their meanings when used in connection with penetrant nondestructive testing.

The list is not all-inclusive and is not intended to be a full glossary of all terms. Rather it is a list which, if understood in advance, will make the understanding of the text of the next few chapters easier for the reader.

1. PENETRANT. This is the fluid—usually a liquid but it can be a gas—that is caused to enter the discontinuity in order to produce an indication at the flaw.

2. PENETRABILITY. The property of a *Penetrant* that causes it to find its way into very fine openings, such as cracks.

3. FLUORESCENT PENETRANT. A penetrant incorporating a flourescent dye to improve the visibility of indications at the flaw.

4. FLUORESCENT DYE. A dye which becomes fluorescent, giving off light, when it is exposed to short wave radiation such as ultraviolet or near ultraviolet light.

5. COLOR-CONTRAST PENETRANT. A penetrant incorporating a dye—usually nonfluorescent—sufficiently intense to give good visibility to flaw indications under white light.

6. COLOR-CONTRAST DYE. A dye which can be used in a penetrant to impart sufficient color intensity to give good color contrast in indications against the background of the surface being tested, when viewed under white light.

7. LEAKER-PENETRANT. A type of penetrant especially designed for leak detection.

8. WATER-WASH PENETRANT. A type of penetrant which incorporates an emulsifier, thus making it possible to clean a surface coated with such a penetrant by means of water.

9. POST-EMULSIFICATION PENETRANT. A type of penetrant containing no emulsifier, but which is cleaned from a surface with water after applying an emulsifier as a separate step. The term is often abbreviated as "P.E." penetrant, or "P.E." method.

10. EMULSIFIER. A material which, applied over the film of penetrant on the surface of a part, mixes with the penetrant and enables it to be washed off the surface with water.

11. WATER-WASHABILITY. The property of a penetrant which permits it to be cleaned from the surface of a part by washing with water.

12. SOLVENT CLEANING. The process of removing the excess penetrant from the surface of a part by washing or wiping with a solvent for the penetrant.

13. PENETRATING TIME. The time allowed, after penetrant has been applied to a surface, for the penetrant to enter discontinuities which may be present.

14. DRAIN TIME. Penetrating time, when the part is not kept immersed in the penetrant but is set aside on a rack permitting excess penetrant to drain away.

15. EMULSIFICATION TIME. The time allowed for the emulsifier to act on the penetrant before the part is washed, after emulsifier is applied as a separate step.

16. DRYING TIME. The time during which a washed or wet-developed part is in the hot air drying oven.

17. DEVELOPING TIME. The time between the application of the developer and the examination of the part for indications.

18. DEVELOPER. A finely divided material applied over the surface of a part to help bring out penetrant indications.

19. DRY DEVELOPER. A developer in which the developing powder is applied dry.

20. WET DEVELOPER. A developer in which the developing powder is applied as a suspension or solution in a liquid, usually water.

CHAPTER 3

SOME DEFINITIONS OF TERMS

21. SOLVENT DEVELOPER. A developer in which the developing powder is applied as a suspension in a quick-drying solvent.

22. PART. A term used to refer to a manufactured article which is being inspected.

23. DISCONTINUITY. An opening in a part representing an actual break in continuity, permitting penetrant to enter when it breaks the surface. The term is usually applied to material flaws rather than to intended openings resulting from design, or assembly of separate parts.

24. FINE CRACK. A discontinuity in a solid material with a very fine opening to the surface, but possessing length and depth greater than the width of this opening; usually depth is many times the width.

25. SHALLOW DISCONTINUITY. A discontinuity open to the surface of a solid object which possesses little depth in proportion to the width of this opening. A scratch or nick may be a "shallow discontinuity" in this sense.

26. FILLED CRACK. A crack-like discontinuity, open to the surface, but filled with some foreign material—oxide, grease, etc.—which tends to prevent penetrants from entering.

27. CRACK CONTAMINANT. Material which fills a crack and which may prevent penetrants from entering.

28. FLUORESCENCE. The property of a substance which enables it to receive light energy of one wave length, convert a portion of it to a different and longer wave length and re-emit the energy as visible light.

29. BLACK LIGHT. Light energy just below the visible range of violet light, usually predominantly of about 3650 Angstrom units. This wave length reacts strongly on certain dyes to make them fluoresce in a range visible to the eye.

30. BLACK LIGHT INTENSITY. Foot-candles of *black light* at any given point in an inspection area.*

31. DARK ADAPTATION. The adjustment of the pupils of the eyes and internal eye changes, when one passes from a bright to a dark-

*Here see Appendix III for additional information on measurement of Black Light intensity.

ened space. This adjustment permits maximum seeing in the dim area. Also called "dark adaption."

32. INDICATION. The visible evidence of penetrant which has come out of a discontinuity, indicating to the inspector that some sort of surface opening is present.

33. DEFECT. A discontinuity the size, shape, orientation or location of which makes it detrimental to the useful service of the part in which it occurs.

34. FALSE INDICATION. A penetrant indication on the surface of a part not caused by an actual discontinuity but by some other and non-relevant circumstance.

35. CONTRAST RATIO. The relative amount of light emitted or reflected as between an indication and its background.

36. BACKGROUND. The background against which an indication must be viewed. It may be the natural surface of the part, or may be modified by developer or the residual color of the penetrant not fully removed by washing.

37. "SEEABILITY." The characteristic of an indication that enables an observer to see it against the adverse conditions of background, outside light, etc.

38. INTERPRETATION. The process of judging from an *indication* of a discontinuity what the cause of the indication and the nature of the discontinuity actually are.

39. EVALUATION. The process of deciding as to the severity of the condition after the *indication* has been *interpreted.* Evaluation leads to the decision as to whether the part must be rejected, salvaged or may be accepted for use.

40. REMOVER. A material which, when added to rinse water, assists in removing penetrant from test surfaces.

Chapter 4

NATURE AND PROPERTIES OF PENETRANTS

1. What is a Penetrant? The key material in Penetrant Nondestructive Testing is of course the penetrant itself. The name "Penetrant" comes from the most essential property of the material —namely, its ability to penetrate or get into fine openings such as cracks. Fortunately, the same properties which cause it to penetrate also act to facilitate its re-emergence from the defect after the surface has been freed of excess penetrant. Some liquids are notorious for their ability to "creep" over a surface and such materials usually make good penetrants.

But for inspection purposes much more is required of a penetrant than the mere ability to creep and spread over a surface and get into tight places. It must have stability—to heat and cold—it must have a distinctive color, it must not evaporate readily, it must be non-toxic; in short, it must have many special properties and these are not all found in a single substance. A penetrant must, therefore, be compounded of a number of materials to secure all the desired properties. So we speak quite properly of "designing" or "building" a penetrant. And it is the knowledge and care that go into present penetrant design that make these materials so far ahead of the old "oil and whiting" type penetrants—and the same comment applies equally to all the other associated materials necessary for successful penetrant testing today.

So we may ask ourselves "What makes a good penetrant?"; or, "What do we expect of the ideal penetrant?" At the outset we may as well agree that all penetrants as used commercially are less than ideal, since they are each in some degree a compromise in order to secure to a reasonable extent as many of the necessary properties required as possible; or to secure some special property to a high degree.

2. The Ideal Penetrant. In considering the desirable properties of an ideal penetrant we can write down quite an extensive list. Following are some of these "ideal" properties; and in comparing these with the properties of commercial penetrants it is surprising how successful the designers and compounders of such products have been.

A good penetrant must:

(a) be able readily to penetrate very fine openings.

(b) be able to remain in relatively coarse openings.

(c) not evaporate or dry up too rapidly.

(d) clean easily off the surface on which it has been applied.

(e) resist cleaning out of openings, even shallow and open ones.

(f) in a short time, come back out of openings, even very fine ones.

(g) have ability to spread out in very thin films, as from the edges of a fine opening.

(h) have great brilliance of color or fluorescence even when spread in very thin films.

(i) have permanence of color or fluorescence in exposure to heat, light and/or black light

(j) be inert with respect to the material being tested and to containers.

(k) be odorless.

(l) be non-flammable.

(m) be stable under conditions of storage and use.

(n) be non-toxic.

(o) be low in cost.

This list is compiled from the point of view of what the penetrant is expected to be and do. In searching for materials to meet these performance requirements, we must translate them into physical characteristics, and this is a far from simple step of translation or transition.

3. PHYSICAL PROPERTIES OF PENETRANTS. When we start to think of the physical properties in a material that will give us the above enumerated performance characteristics we become quickly aware that, first, no one material is likely to possess all of the necessary physical properties and second, that some of the properties that we feel should determine whether a material will be a good penetrant, do not necessarily do so.

We must realize that there is no one physical property, which more than any other, determines what makes a material a good penetrant, even from the point of view of its ability to penetrate fine openings. One thinks of viscosity, surface tension and wetting ability as being important and they undoubtedly as a group are of first importance, but no one of them is a complete guide to a good penetrant.

Listed below are various properties which *all* have a bearing on the selection of a material suitable for use in penetrant inspection:

- Viscosity
- Surface Tension
- Wetting Ability
- Density—specific gravity
- Volatility—boiling range, vapor pressure
- Flash Point
- Chemical Inertness
- Solubility
- Solvent Ability
- Emulsifiability
- Ability to "spread" or "creep"
- Tolerance for contaminants
- Toxicity
- Odor
- Freedom from skin irritation tendencies
- Availability
- Cost

There are other properties of a compounded penetrant which affect its performance which are not included in the above list. Some of these are color, brilliance, permanence, etc., and these will be discussed later.

4. VISCOSITY. This property in itself has very little to do with making a material a good penetrant. (When using the terms "good" and "poor" in the following discussions we are referring to the *ability to penetrate*, *"penetrability"* rather than to any other performance characteristic). Water, naturally a poor penetrant, has a low viscosity whereas some of the petroleum distillates of much higher viscosity are good penetrants.

Table I gives for comparison purposes, the viscosity of a number of common liquids.

Viscosity does have considerable effect on some of the practical aspects of the use of a penetrant. In the first place, viscosity is an important factor in the *speed* with which a penetrant will enter a defect, if not in the actual ability to penetrate. A viscous penetrant will move more slowly than a more fluid one, and offer more resistance to the forces drawing the penetrant into the defect.

TABLE I

VISCOSITY, SPECIFIC GRAVITY AND SURFACE TENSION OF VARIOUS LIQUIDS

Material	Temp. ° C.	Sp. G.	Viscosity (Centistokes)	Surface Tension Dynes/cm
Water	20	.9992	1.004	72.8
Ether	20	.736	.3161	17.01
Ethyl Alcohol	20	.789	1.521	23
Naphtha	20	.665	.61	21.8
Kerosene	20	.79	1.65	23.0
Ethylene Glycol	20	1.115	17.85	47.7
SAE No. 10 Lub. Oil	20	.89	112.3	31.0
Per-chlor Ethylene	20	1.62	.988	31.74

In the second place a viscous penetrant will drain more slowly from the surface of a dipped or sprayed part than a more fluid one. Drain time must be longer else excessive loss of penetrant due to "drag-out" will result. This will slow the process in cases where penetrating time could be short. Heavy drag-out of a viscous penetrant when the post-emulsification process is being used, results in rapid contamination of the emulsifier bath, and increases cost.

On the other hand, too *thin* a penetrant—one of low viscosity—would drain too fast. If the penetrant drains away rapidly, an insufficient "reservoir" of penetrant in the form of a surface film remains to provide material for penetration during a penetrating time which may be lengthy. In such a case, the part would have to remain immersed in the penetrant during the entire period for penetration, a serious limitation in most production operations. Drag-out in this case would be low, however, resulting in minimum loss of penetrant per square foot of area inspected, and this is of economic importance.

TABLE II

EFFECT OF VISCOSITY ON DRAG-OUT LOSSES OF VARIOUS LIQUIDS

Liquid	Density at 100° F.	Viscosity Centistokes at 100° F.	Drag-out Loss Gal./1000 sq. ft.
Water	.9930	.50	0.266
Kerosene	.7876	1.45	0.186
Ethylene Glycol.	1.1019	9.38	0.630
Neutral Oil	.9040	22.82	0.478
SAE 10-W Oil	.9193	50.3	0.827
SAE 40-W Oil	.8798	171.2	1.505
Water-wash Penetrant	.8414	5.00	0.295
Color Contrast Penetrant A	.9312	4.85	0.229
Post-emulsification Penetrant A	.8877	9.29	0.322
Color Contrast Penetrant B	.9638	8.90	0.281
Post-emulsification Penetrant B	.9889	9.47	0.319
Emulsifier A	.9239	50.8	0.785
Emulsifier B	.9409	118.9	1.255

Table II lists the density, viscosity and drag-out losses for a number of liquids and commercial penetrants. Density and viscosity are given for 100°F., a temperature perhaps more in line with usual operating temperatures than the 20°C temperature often used for these measurements.

It is evident from these figures that the relationship between viscosity and drag-out is not a very close one, especially among the liquids and penetrants of low viscosity. However, when viscosity increases by significant amounts, drag-out rises rapidly also.

Another effect of viscosity on performance is that thinner liquids in a crack are more susceptible to mechanical removal from the crack by the liquid—such as water—used to clean the excess penetrant from the surface. This fact favors the use of more viscous penetrant liquids.

So it appears that a desirable viscosity lies in the medium range —neither too thick nor too thin. Fortunately viscosity can to some degree be controlled by formulation.

5. SURFACE TENSION. Surface tension is one of the two most important properties which determine whether a liquid will have high penetrating ability or not, but is not of itself controlling. Generally speaking a high surface tension is desirable but water, for example, with a very high surface tension is not, in pure form, a good penetrant.

6. WETTING ABILITY—CONTACT ANGLE. The second important property required in a liquid if it is to have good penetrating power is the ability to wet the surface of the metal or other solid material to be tested. Ability to wet a surface is measured by the contact angle—i.e. the angle between the liquid and the surface at the point of contact as the liquid advances along the surface. The smaller this angle the better the wetting ability. Good penetrants have a *very* small contact angle.

Water, with its high surface tension has also a large contact angle with metal surfaces, and is therefore a poor penetrant. But by adding a wetting agent the contact angle is drastically reduced so that, even though the surface tension is also reduced, the resulting combination can make a very good penetrant.

Ability to penetrate, then may be said to be determined by a high value for the product of the surface tension and the cosine of the contact angle for a liquid and a given solid surface. It must be clearly understood, however, that this is not a property determined by the liquid *alone* and cannot therefore be used as a *general measure* of penetrability. The contact angle between a liquid and a surface varies widely with the material, surface roughness, cleanliness, etc., of the surface under test. There is no question that good wetting ability is a paramount requirement for good penetrating ability, but this means good wetting power for the *actual surface* involved. A carefully cleaned smooth aluminum surface might behave in a satisfactory manner with a given liquid, but the same metal if rough and carrying a film of oil or some other material might be highly unsatisfactory for penetration by the same liquid.

Penetrability, then, is influenced by surface tension and wetting ability, but at best it can be measured in terms of these properties only with respect to a specific surface.

7. DENSITY—SPECIFIC GRAVITY. This is a characteristic which has no direct influence on the penetrating properties of a liquid. Most commercial penetrants do have a specific gravity of less than one. This is because the principal constituents of penetrants are organic liquids of naturally low specific gravity, but these liquids are selected for other properties than their density. Only one of the commonly used fluorescent penetrants has a specific gravity of one or over. Some of the non-flammable color-contrast type penetrants have a relatively high specific gravity.

One advantage of a specific gravity of less than one is that water which may get into a tank of penetrant during use will drop to the bottom of the tank and not tend to interfere with the proper functioning of the penetrant. Water contamination is a problem which will be discussed more in detail. (Section 15 and Chapters 7 and 8).

Another practical advantage of low specific gravity lies in lower freight rates due to lower pounds per gallon of such materials.

Table III shows the specific gravity and pounds per gallon of some commercial penetrants.

8. VOLATILITY—BOILING RANGE OR VAPOR PRESSURE. As a general principle it may be stated that a penetrant should be non-volatile—which means a low vapor pressure, a boiling range as high as necessary to secure non-volatility. In the case of petroleum products however, viscosity increases as boiling range goes up, and in this group of materials the less viscous distillates are more desirable as penetrants if only because they penetrate more rapidly than the highly viscous oils. Still, for all practical purposes, high volatility disappears long before viscosity becomes a serious drawback from the standpoint of a penetrant.

The reason favoring non-volatile penetrants over volatile materials is mostly a practical one—avoidance of serious loss of material

TABLE III

SPECIFIC GRAVITY AND POUNDS PER GALLON OF SOME COMMERCIAL PENETRANTS

Penetrant Type	Specific Gravity 60° F.	Pounds per Gallon
Water-Wash Fluorescent	0.8550	7.119
Post Emulsification Fluorescent	0.9042	7.529
Post Emulsification Super-Bright Fluorescent	1.0000	8.328
Color-Contrast Low-Flash	0.8229	6.910
Color-Contrast High Flash	0.9371	7.804
Color-Contrast Non-Flammable	1.1241	9.361

by evaporation when the penetrant is used in open containers. Of more technical importance is the fact that a volatile penetrant will dry on the surface of a part during drain time, and may impose the requirement of complete immersion during the entire time of penetration. Also, it would tend to dry up inside a crack during drying and developing, and lose liquidity when it should remain fluid so that it can flow back out of the crack to form the indication.

A film of partially dried—and therefore less fluid—penetrant over the surface of the part is more difficult to clean off, whether by water wash or solvent, though the effect is more serious where water is used.

A fact requiring the incorporation of some high boiling liquids is the need for high dye solvency. The more volatile liquids are usually, but not in all cases, poor dye solvents.

When the liquids used are combustible, as is most often the case, the need to reduce the fire-hazard by keeping the flash point of the penetrant high is another and important reason for keeping the more highly volatile constituents at a minimum. When non-combustible constituents can be used this consideration does not apply, of course.

A proportion of volatile constituent is sometimes deliberately incorporated with an otherwise non-volatile penetrant. This is for the purpose of reducing viscosity to speed penetration. It also serves some purpose in reducing somewhat the tendency of the penetrants to spread away from the defect, as the volatile constituent evaporates on exudation.

9. FLASH POINT. A satisfactory commercial penetrant should have a high flash point. Flash point and fire point should not be confused. Flash point of a liquid is defined as that temperature at which sufficient combustible vapor, under standard conditions, is given off to form an explosive mixture with the air immediately over the liquid when a flame is present. Fire point—a higher temperature—is the point at which the liquid will take fire and continue to burn if a flame is introduced into the vapor cloud over the liquid surface.

Flash points of volatile liquids are usually measured in an apparatus called the "Tag" closed cup, or in a similar one called the Pensky-Martens closed cup. Closed cup flash points are lower than open cup flash points, since the former apparatus prevents stray air currents from blowing vapors away, and instead collects them in a closed chamber. See Chapter 17, Section 35.

A penetrant with a low flash point may give off enough vapor when it gets warm, to "flash" over the surface with explosive force if a flame is brought near it; and penetrants do get warm, from mere ambient heat in the shop, or from immersion of hot parts fresh from a vapor degreaser. Low flash point liquids almost invariably have a low fire or ignition point and so constitute a definite fire hazard.

The flash point of a liquid affects the conditions under which it may be shipped in interstate commerce. Liquids with flash points lower than 80° F open cup (which corresponds usually to 60° F to 70° F closed cup) are classed as "flammable", require a special red label, and must be shipped in small quantities by railway express or air freight. If the flash point is lower the restrictions are stiffer.

Table IV gives the flash points of some typical volatile liquids. Table V shows the flash points of some commercial penetrants

TABLE IV

FLASH POINTS OF VARIOUS LIQUIDS

Material	Flash Point °F—Closed Cup
Ethyl Ether	– 49°
Carbon Disulphide	– 22°
Acetone	0°
Ethyl Acetate	24°
Naphtha	30°
Toluene	40°
Methyl Alcohol	54°
Ethyl Alcohol	57°
Turpentine	95°
Stoddard Solvent	100°
Cellosolve	104°
Cyclohexanol	154°
Creosote Oil	165°
Ethylene Glycol	232°
Di-butyl Phthalate	315°
Glycerine	320°
SAE-10-Lub-Oil	450° (open cup)
Chloroform	Non-flammable

Many industrial and government specifications now limit the flash point of a desirable penetrant. It is considered that, under the average conditions of industrial use a penetrant with a closed cup flash of 130° F or over is not a very serious fire hazard.

10. CHEMICAL INERTNESS. It is obvious that a penetrant should be as inert and non-corrosive as possible toward the materials being inspected and the containers in which it is shipped and used. Oil-base and similar penetrant materials meet this requirement admirably in most instances, although in the formulation of water-wash penetrants the emulsifiers incorporated may be quite alkaline. If water gets into such a penetrant in a container, an alkaline

Chapter 4

NATURE AND PROPERTIES OF PENETRANTS

Table V

Flash Points of Some Commercially Available Penetrants

Type of Penetrant		Flash Point °F—Closed Cup
Water-Wash	A.	130°
Water-Wash	B.	105°
Post-Emulsification	A.	175°
Post-Emulsification	B.	185°
Post-Emulsification	C.	121°
Color-Contrast	A.	48°
Color-Contrast	B.	185°
Color-Contrast	C.	148°
Color-Contrast	D.	Non-flammable

mixture may be formed. Such a mixture may corrode aluminum, or may act on the paint or other protective coating of the container. This situation must be recognized and understood, and thereby guarded against.

Since penetrant remains on the surface of parts for a relatively short time in the ordinary course of inspection, there is little or no danger that corrosion of aluminum or other parts can result, especially since water must also be present if corrosion is to occur. This is one of the reasons why penetrants should be protected as much as possible from contamination with water. If penetrants containing emulsifiers are not completely cleaned from the surface (as they *should* be during a properly conducted inspection) but are allowed to remain on the surface of aluminum or magnesium parts for long periods, some pitting may occur.

Some nickel alloys are liable to damage if certain elements are in contact with their surface at high temperatures. Because of the possibility of incomplete removal, due, for example, to complex configuration of the part, a special penetrant low in content of those elements, may be required for the inspection of these alloys.

In liquid-fuel rocket or other systems for liquid oxygen, the penetrants used for tests must be practically inert to liquid oxygen

—that is, they must not react under a specified impact in a controlled test. Special penetrant families are compounded for this important use.

Attack by penetrants on the parts being inspected is more likely to be a factor when rubber or plastic parts are involved. Often special penetrants must be devised—and several are regularly available—to meet this condition.

11. SOLUBILITY. It must be possible to remove the penetrant easily from the surface of the part being inspected. Solvents are used for this purpose in many instances and it is important that the pentrant be easily removed with such solvents. Solubility is also desirable when cleaning tanks and containers and the equipment used to manufacture the penetrant.

12. SOLVENT ABILITY. Since all penetrants incorporate a dye or fluoragent, whether fluorescent or color-contrast in type, it is necessary that the penetrant *must* be a good solvent for these dyes. This tends to be a troublesome requirement, since the concentration of dye—especially in color-contrast types of penetrant—is very high. Dyes otherwise suitable are not numerous and the choice of dyes from the standpoint of their solubility is quite limited.

Not only must the penetrant dissolve the necesary high concentration of dye at ambient or elevated temperatures, it must be able to hold the dye in solution at very low temperatures. Penetrants may be shipped or stored at temperatures well below freezing, and if dye separates out it will usually settle to the bottom of the container. Even if the dye readily re-dissolves when the penetrant is brought back up to shop temperature, this will not take place satisfactorily unless the user is aware of the importance of mixing the material and making sure that re-solution is complete and uniform.

In some compounded penetrants the components are held in homogeneous solution by mutual solvents. Freezing of such a mixture may cause, in addition to the separation of dye, a separation of other components which may be re-combined only with great difficulty. Mutual solubility of constitutents as well as ability to dissolve and hold dyes in solution is therefore a most important characteristic from a practical point of view.

13. EMULSIFIABILITY. In the vast majority of penetrants, the cleaning is accomplished with water instead of a solvent. It is important that such penetrant be readily removed with water, which implies that it be readily emulsified with the aid of suitable emulsifiers. These are incorporated directly in the penetrant itself in the case of most water-washable penetrants, making them "self-emulsifying"—or the emulsifier may be applied separately, as in the post-emulsification process. In either case the oily or other material of the penetrant must respond to the emulsifier so that a clean surface results.

14. ABILITY TO SPREAD OR CREEP. This property is important, as on it depends the degree to which small amounts of penetrant retained in surface discontinuities will tend to come back out to form "seeable" indications. Many good penetrants inherently possess this property, but it is in most cases not alone sufficient to produce good indications. To help penetrants achieve the necessary amount and speed of spread, developers are used.

15. TOLERANCE FOR CONTAMINANTS. In use, a penetrant may become contaminated with foreign substances and these may affect unfavorably the action of the penetrant. If the penetrant is compounded of several ingredients nicely balanced into a homogeneous whole, a little water or degreaser solvent may upset the balance and cause the penetrant to separate into its several components. Actually, this does happen with some penetrants when the amount of contaminants becomes large enough—the aim being to make the formulation of the penetrant such that balance is not lost when the amounts of the contaminants are small. Modern penetrants have a high tolerance for water—the most common contaminant—as well as for oil, grease, and degreasing solvent.

16. TOXICITY, ODOR, SKIN IRRITATION. The health hazard involved for the operator is a matter of major consideration in designing a penetrant. It is true that it may be—as it actually is—impossible to build a penetrant free of *all* hazards. To do so would mean sacrificing properties essential to its performance as a penetrant. Still, no rank poison or corrosive, or highly malodorous material is permissible. Operators must work with it with minimum discomfort or hazard. Most modern penetrants are quite safe and satisfactory from this standpoint and possess no major health hazards.

Government and industrial users should require assurance as to the safety of their operators, and extensive toxicity tests should be made by competent biological laboratories before giving such assurance, and many commercially available penetrants have been so tested. However, certain fluoragents that have been proposed and that have actually been incorporated into penetrants are open to some question as to their harmlessness. (See Section 48, this chapter.) These should be used only with full appreciation of the hazard involved unless competent tests have shown that no hazard exists. With this exception, experience has demonstrated that, beyond occasional skin irritation and allergies, most penetrants now in use are relatively odorless and harmless when used in the prescribed processes and techniques. Even accidental swallowing of some of the material would not be expected to be fatal or produce permanent damage though severely unpleasant reactions might be expected.

The health aspect of penetrants will be further discussed in the chapters dealing with their actual use.

17. AVAILABILITY AND COST. These are practical considerations which must of necessity enter into the formulation of a good penetrant. Since penetrant testing is now an essential process in the manufacture of a wide variety of important materials and components, the composition of the penetrants used must not involve ingredients not commercially available or any which increase the cost of the penetrant—and therefore of the inspection—to an unreasonably high level. This is not to say that a special penetrant for a particularly important application may not be high in cost if the application is such that the added cost can be tolerated. But in the ordinary course of inspection operations cost should be kept as low as possible.

18. PENETRABILITY. It is evident by now that a good penetrant for the purposes of penetrant nondestructive testing is not a simple material—either to define, to produce, or to evaluate. Even the ability to penetrate well into very fine cracks or openings—which is what the term "penetrability" means—is not clear-cut in that no single physical property is determining. And, of course, penetrability of a high order does not in itself make a good commercial penetrant. Still, from the point of view of detecting the presence of very fine cracks, the maximum of penetrability is obviously desirable, and so the need to measure or evaluate this property of a penetrant has received much attention.

19. MECHANICS OF PENETRATION. How and why does a good penetrant find—or force—its way into fine openings? This question has been the subject of considerable discussion and investigation in the last few years, and some fairly satisfactory explanations have been offered.

The forces generated by capillary attraction seem to be basically involved in the entry of a liquid into a crack. These are the forces that cause a liquid to rise spontaneously in a small diameter (capillary) tube. The capillary pressure generated by a given liquid in a tube of given diameter and material, is a function of the surface tension of the liquid and its ability to wet the interior surface of the tube.

The height to which the liquid will rise depends also on the diameter of the capillary tube—the smaller the tube the higher the rise. It follows that a liquid with high surface tension and good wetting ability with respect to the surface of the tube will rise in a narrow tube, but the upper end of the tube must be open.

If the upper end of the tube is closed, however, the rise of the liquid is much less. Figure 15 shows the rise of water to which a

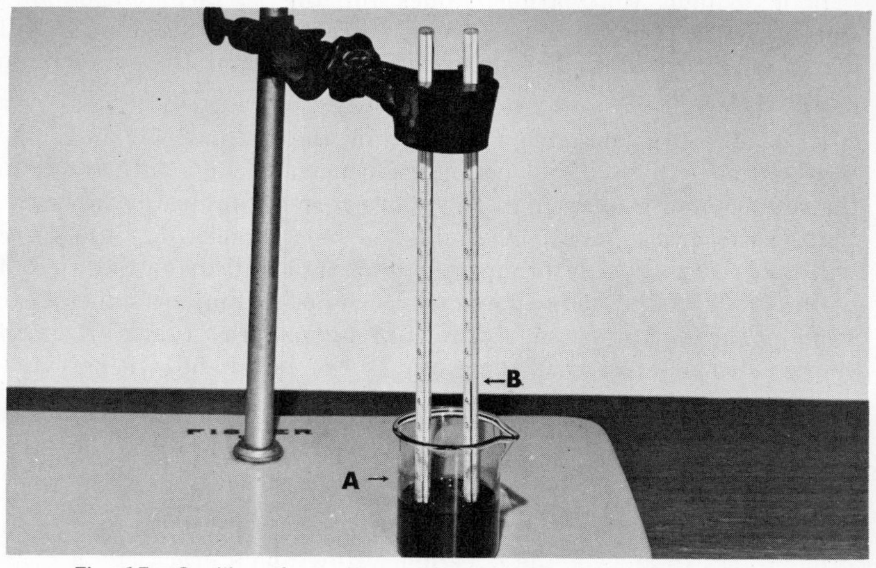

Fig. 15—Capillary force. Water plus wetting agent. a) Sealed tube. b) Open tube.

wetting agent has been added, in both an open and closed capillary. It would seem that the case of the closed tube is more nearly similar to that of a fine short crack, than is the open tube, because of the presence of the trapped air.

Even though the liquid does not rise appreciably in the sealed tube, because of the air which is trapped in the tube, very decided pressures are generated by the capillary forces. These pressures may be as great as one atmosphere or more—enough to raise a column of water over 30 ft. Forces are similarly exerted on the air trapped in a fine short crack. The tendency of a liquid penetrant to enter a defect is definitely related to this pressure. For a given penetrant and crack-like defect, the pressure developed may be expressed by the formula:

$$P = \frac{2S \cos.\theta}{W} \qquad \text{where}$$

P = capillary pressure.
S = surface tension of the liquid.
θ = equilibrium contact angle of the liquid and the surfaces of the crack.
W = width of the crack.

It is evident that larger values for the surface tension and smaller contact angles (which means greater wetting ability) will increase the pressure. The pressure is also greater the smaller the width of the crack.

It is of course possible that in time the trapped air in a fine short crack will be dissolved in the penetrant, and diffuse out to the surface and thus escape. The above formula indicates, however, that if the crack varies in width—as most cracks do—the force will be greater in the thinner portions, and will drive the air out of the crack at the wider portions. Such action may be sufficient to explain the entry of penetrant into almost any crack. It is of course also possible that some cracks are never fully penetrated.

Whatever the proper explanation of how penetrants get into cracks, it is an observed fact that, with good penetrants, penetration does take place into exceedingly fine openings.

20. Attempts to Determine Limits of Penetrability. In order to try to answer the question, "How fine a crack can a penetrant enter?", many attempts have been made to set values for penetrability. If one could produce a very fine crack of given size—or a graduated series of such cracks, one might find the limit of penetrability. Actually, no such limit has ever been measured although penetrants have been shown to enter cracks or spaces as small as 5 microinches (.000005 inch), or even smaller. Fig. 25

(P. 64) is a picture of cracks in chromium plate, taken with the electron microscope. One of these cracks is as small as 4 microinches.

21. THE GLASS PLATE EXPERIMENT. In 1951, in a paper presented before the Society for Nondestructive Testing, A. L. Walters and R. C. McMaster reported on some work previously done at Battelle Memorial Institute, on the subject of how fine a crack a

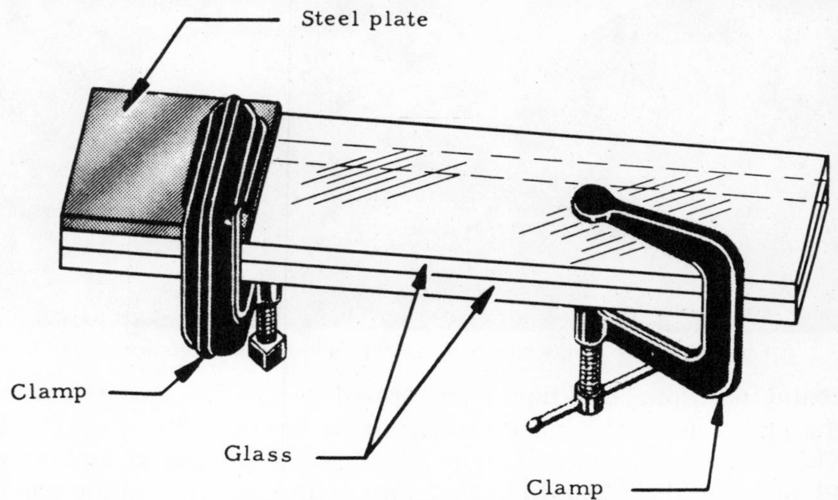

Fig. 16—Glass plate experiment.

penetrant can enter. To produce cracks of known width, two pieces of heavy plate glass were clamped together. Each plate was 10 inches long by 1½ inches wide by ⅜ inch thick, and was transparent. The extent of penetration could thus be determined by observation through the glass. When clamps were sufficiently tight and specimens were viewed under sodium light (5896Å) dark areas indicating plate contact appeared between the plates under and adjacent to the clamps. Interference fringes extended outward from these areas, making a convenient measure of the small opening between the plates. The distance between any two consecutive fringes represents a change in separation equal to one-half the wave length of the light used to produce the fringes. Under sodium light, the separation at the last fringe before the black contact area would be 13 microinches. Figure 17 is a photograph of the apparatus showing these interference fringes.

Fluorescent penetrant was swabbed onto the exposed edge of the interface between the glass plates, with the specimen in a hori-

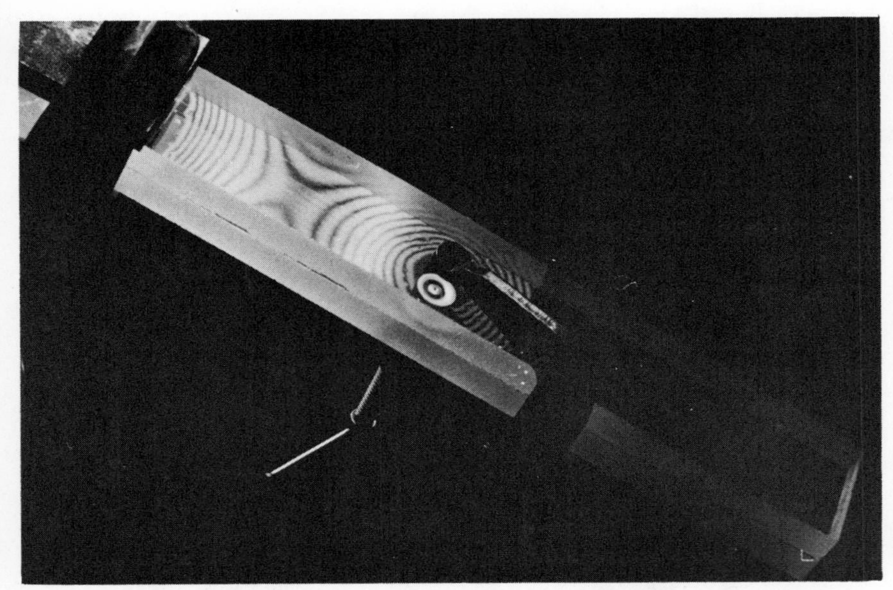

Fig. 17—Glass plates clamped together showing interference rings.

zontal position. The liquid penetrated the entire space between the plates up to the black contact area, where it "feathered" out. This demonstrates penetration into a space at least as narrow as 13 microinches (.000013 inch), and estimated at a minimum of 5 microinches. (It has since been shown that modern "super-bright" penetrants can be seen to a point well within this last interference ring.)

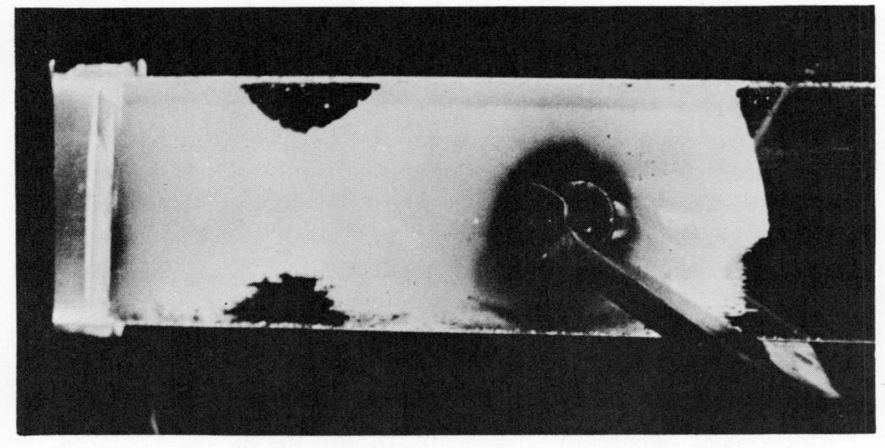

Fig. 18—Fluorescent penetrant entering space between plates to last interference ring.

CHAPTER 4

NATURE AND PROPERTIES OF PENETRANTS

Since glass is not a typical material inspected frequently with penetrants, and may present different penetrating conditions from those obtaining in a crack in metal, the experiment was repeated with metal for one face of the clamped pair, glass being retained for the other to make observation possible. Polished brass, and blocks of slightly oxidized (by heating for ½ hour to 1000-1100° F) copper, brass, aluminum, and stainless steel were used. In each case, penetration of fluorescent penetrant extended into the black area around the point of contact. It appeared to go farther into this area in the case of the heated, slightly oxidized surfaces, suggesting the possibilty that a thin oxidized coating may promote penetration, so long as it does not fill the crack.

Many other penetrants were tried on these glass plate specimens and it was found that most organic liquids of relatively low viscosity penetrated to the limit of the opening between the two plates —i.e., 13 microinches or less. Even water without wetting agent went this far, and water is known not to be a good penetrant for metallic cracks. Water on glass is a special case, however, because of the slight solubility of glass in water.

In another experiment with very fine cracks produced in brittle nickel plate on a steel strip, it was found that super-bright fluo-

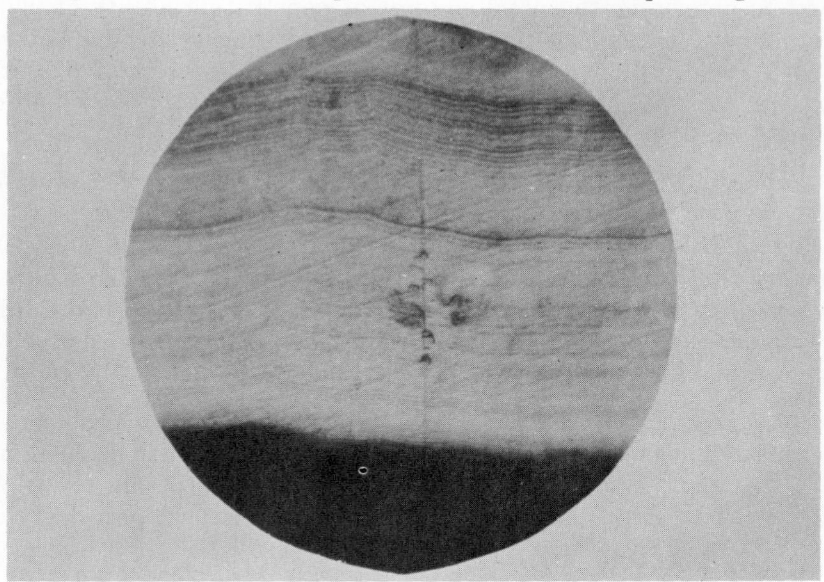

Fig. 19—Crack in brittle nickel plate—.000010 inches wide and .004 inches deep.

rescent penetrant detected cracks only 10 microinches (.000010 inch) wide and .004 inch deep. Figure 19 is a micrograph of such a crack at 580X magnification.

It has also been proposed to use brittle magnesium strips bent over a fairly small radius (½ inch) and then straightened before testing.* An analysis of the merit of this type of test strip is lacking, however.

22. METALLIC CRACKS. Some work was also done in this same investigation to try to measure fine cracks in metallic objects. Cracks were examined which had first been located with fluorescent penetrant. Fatigue cracks in steel bars were located with penetrant and measured microscopically and found to be 40 microinches wide at the surface. The finest crack found with fluorescent penetrant in this investigation was a forging lap in a small aluminum forging. This was measured at 16 microinches (.000016 inch)—a width approaching the greatest penetration observed on the glass plate specimen. The latter was less than ½ the wave length of sodium light, which is 13 microinches.**

23. OTHER ATTEMPTS. Various devices have been used to produce artificial cracks in metal. The purpose has been twofold—first to determine the possible limit of penetrating ability of penetrants; and second, to produce a series of cracks varying both in depth and width, including fine cracks at the lower limit of penetrating ability, for the purpose of comparing the crack-finding effectiveness of different penetrants.

Some of these cracked specimens have proven very useful for the purpose of evaluating penetrants though none so far has been altogether satisfactory or successful in providing a definitive means for measuring the crack-finding effectiveness of different penetrants. Unfortunately, no one has yet been able to make fully reproducible "natural" cracks—so necessary as a yardstick of penetrant effectiveness.

24. WHAT SHOULD WE MEASURE? Actually the problem in evaluating penetrants is a very complex one. In this problem we are not alone concerned with how *fine* a crack we can show but also with how *well* can we show a given fine crack with different

*See Govt. Spec. Mil-I-25135C (ASG)

**Paper presented October, 1951, to Society of Nondestructive Testing by A. L. Walters and R. C. McMaster.

penetrants. This is not to say that the minimum width of crack that can be shown by a given penetrant is not of great interest, but for evaluation purposes the excellence of the indication is of equal interest. In addition we are exceedingly interested in the performance of a penetrant on other than marginal cracks, since the *preponderance of defects found with penetrants are not of marginal dimensions.*

25. SENSITIVITY. This is a term most often used in comparing penetrants, but it is not always used in the same sense or even in reference to the same thing. What is meant by the statement that "penetrant A is more sensitive than penetrant B"? Actually such a statement has little meaning unless qualified by further information.

Sensitivity is not in any sense a single definite property of a penetrant to which a numerical value can be assigned. Fundamentally, the most sensitive penetrant—*for any given purpose*—is the one that most effectively finds defects *of the type sought and under the circumstances* involved. Thus the most sensitive penetrant for one type of defect may be very unsatisfactory for detecting some other type of defect.

Sensitivity therefore must be evaluated in terms of its ability to locate defects *of the particular type sought,* and *in the particular material involved.* Thus we speak of sensitivity for fine cracks or for open cracks—for deep cracks or shallow cracks. Sensitivity even varies for *fine* shallow cracks as against *wide open* shallow cracks. Different penetrants and different techniques are required to achieve optimum sensitivity under varying circumstances.

It is important therefore when we use the term "sensitivity" in relation to a penetrant, that we understand and define exactly what we mean by the term, since the word certainly does not have a single applicable meaning in relation to penetrant inspection.

26. FACTORS CONTRIBUTING TO SENSITIVITY. In order for a penetrant to fulfill its destiny and find cracks it must produce indications of cracks and other defects that *can be seen.* To produce an indication that can be seen the penetrant must:

1. Penetrate into the defect.
2. Be removed from the surface but not from the defect—so it must resist all the relatively vigorous washing and drying operations.

3. Have the ability to come back out of the defect and with the help of the developer form an indication.
4. Have the ability to be seen when present in very minute amounts, which requires the ability to produce indications having good contrast with the background of the surface of the material or part.

To get into the crack or defect, sufficient penetrability is required for the type of defect being sought. This requirement seems to be quite easily met, at least in the majority of cases.

In order to have a clean background against which to observe indications, the excess penetrant must be easily and quickly removed. This implies that the penetrant must be subject to removal by wiping, or by washing with water or a solvent. There are two prime requirements governing this cleaning operation. Removal of the surface penetrant should not remove *any* penetrant that has entered the crack or defect, and there must be a minimum of residual penetrant remaining on the surface that would reduce contrast of indications against background.

To produce a strong indication a maximum of penetrant must come back out of the crack. This calls for sufficient retained fluidity at this stage—penetrant must not have dried up in the crack—plus an ability to creep or spread. It also calls for a maximum of response to the blotting action of the developer. This means that the penetrant must be able to wet the developer so that it can take full advantage of the capillary network the developer presents, and then be dispersed over as much surface area as possible.

The fourth requirement is that the inspector must see the indication, and perhaps this is the most vital requirement of all. If the indication is there but not seen, the inspection fails. Thus a major factor in the ability to find cracks—which is sensitivity as we have defined it—is the ease and certainty with which small amounts of penetrant can be seen.

In color-contrast types of penetrant visibility is achieved by the addition of a colored dye to the penetrant. Developer is applied in a coat heavy enough to produce a white background. Minute amounts of colored penetrant come from the crack, are absorbed and spread by the developer, and form a colored line or spot in sharp contrast against this white background. The denser the color the sharper the contrast, so usually large amounts of dye must be dissolved in the penetrant, as this is the only way in which the color can be intensified. Fortunately, red dyes are available with high solubility in the desirable penetrant liquids so that intense color can be achieved—and red is one of the best of all the colors for contrast against white.

In fluorescent penetrants visibility is achieved by the addition of light-emitting fluorescent materials or dyes, and contrast obtained by inspection under black light. Intense fluorescence can be produced with a generally lower percentage of dye in solution than must be used in the case of color-contrast dyes. Contrast is increased by increasing the *amount* of dye and by selecting dyes of higher fluorescent ability and better fluorescent color. Increasing intensity of the black light used for inspection also increases brilliance of the fluorescent indication, and maximum visibility is attained by exclusion of most or all white light.

In both systems the developer plays a similar part in acting to draw the penetrant from the crack and in spreading the thin film of penetrant. It is equally important, in the fluorescent as in the color-contrast type, that the developer and penetrant interact in this manner, although with the fluorescent type the developer need not provide the white opaque background for contrast as is required for the color-contrast type penetrant.*

27. SENSITIVITY MEASUREMENT ATTEMPTS. Many attempts have been made to devise a method to measure sensitivity of penetrants. Since sensitivity is regarded as being a performance characteristic which may vary under varying test conditions, and not an independent property of a penetrant, most measurement attempts have involved the use of cracked test pieces of various types. One test (the meniscus test) has been proposed which seeks to measure sensitivity by measuring a single property of a penetrant and correlating or equating it with sensitivity. This test will be discussed later though its validity *as a measure of sensitivity* cannot be accepted. (See Section 34, this chapter.)

28. TEST SPECIMENS USED FOR PENETRANT COMPARISON. Various approaches have been tried and some test specimens are now being used in various efforts to compare the crack-finding ability of different penetrants.

29. U. S. NAVY TEST BLOCK. The U. S. Navy Engineering

*See discussion of developer action in Appendix II.

Experiment Laboratory at Annapolis has developed a test block, designed to be reusable, to produce cracks or crack-like discontinuities of controlled width and depth for comparison of penetrants.* Here, two hardened surfaces are ground and lapped to mate perfectly and are forced together as sleeves on a shaft by screwing down a nut with a specified torque. By varying the torque (pressure) the size of the opening between the two surfaces can be varied. After applying penetrant and making an observation, the test block can be disassembled, cleaned and re-used.

Such a test piece solves the problem of reproducibility quite well, but the "crack' so produced is not a typical "natural" crack and the faces of the lapped surfaces are different in texture from any conceivable natural discontinuity. This leaves considerable doubt as to the reliability of comparisons of penetrants made on it. The

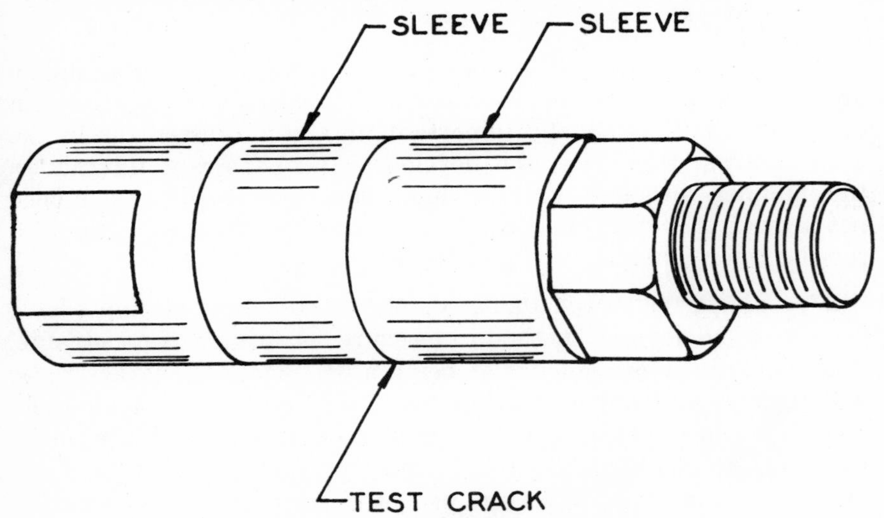

Fig. 20—United States Navy test block.

turned and polished surface on which the indication is produced favors the use of solvent developers, since dry developers work less well on such a surface. Thus the important effect of developers on crack-finding sensitivity is not controlled. (See discussion of this point, Chapter 5, Section 28 and Appendix II.) Figure 20 is a drawing of this test block.

A similar test piece was developed in England by the Aeronautical Directorate of the Ministry of Supply at Harefield. In this

*R. W. Miller, Welding Journal, Jan., 1958, p. 30.

assembly small relief segments are lapped at four points on the circumference of one of the mating surfaces, to the extent of .0001″, .0002″, .0003″ and .0004″ respectively. The surfaces are then clamped together with an intervening layer of .0007″ lead foil using a torque measured pressure on the nut to secure reproducibility. Excess foil is trimmed off with a razor blade.

This is a quite useful piece of equipment also, but it is open to much the same objections as the Navy version. It has the advantage that some knowledge of the width of a series of cracks is possible, and some variation in the behavior of different penetrants over the range provided may be observed. It should be noted, however, that the finest opening is 100 microinches, whereas other tests have indicated that widths down to 10 to 16 microinches or less must be reached to be able to differentiate penetrating abilities among good penetrants.

30. FATIGUE-CRACKED BAR. In an attempt to produce a specimen containing true "natural" cracks of varying dimensions, the idea of producing fatigue cracks in a test bar was tried. A ⅜ inch round cold rolled steel bar was heavily overloaded in a rotating-beam type fatigue testing device, and run until failure occurred. Under such conditions, in a short time, the bar develops a whole series of fatigue cracks, from fine to large, very shallow to deep, in addition to the crack at which failure occurs. Widths of the

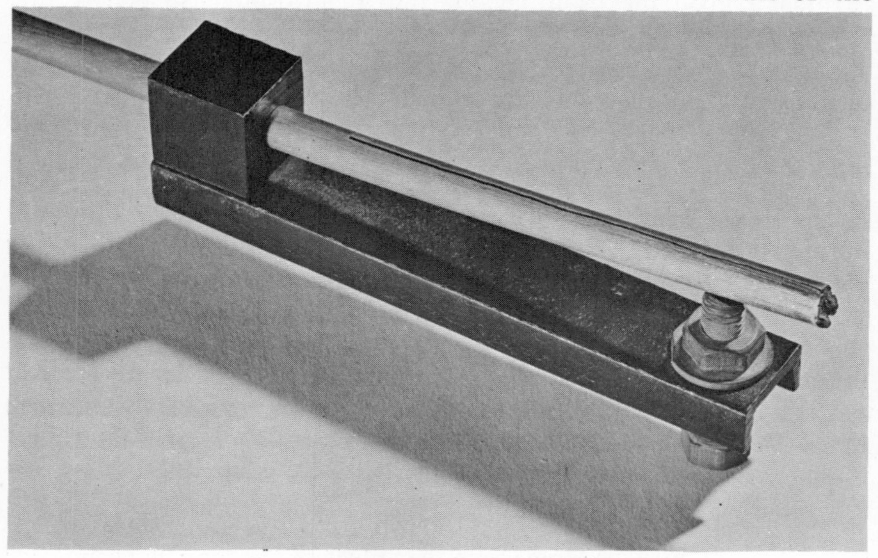

Fig. 21—Fatigue test-bar specimen.

cracks can be further varied by clamping one end of the bar and loading it as a cantilever, which opens the cracks on the tension side and forces them closed on the compression side.

Such a specimen is useful in comparing the performance of two penetrants on a whole series of cracks of a wide range of width and depth, though it gives no *measure* of either width or depth of the minimum crack shown by each. By slicing the bar lengthwise two substantially similarly-cracked specimens are produced which can be used side by side with the two penetrants being compared. The principal objection to these test pieces is the difficulty of preparing them in quantity. It is desirable that a fresh test piece be used each time since complete cleaning of penetrant out of fine cracks cannot be assumed.

31. ALUMINUM TEST BLOCKS. One of the best and most popular evaluation test specimens so far devised and one quite cheap and easy to reproduce, is the quenched aluminum block which was developed by Magnaflux Corporation; but as in all of the test specimens intended to compare penetrants, these, too, have their limitations.

These test blocks are non-uniform and the depth and width of cracks are uncontrolled. However, in a properly prepared block, a wide range of cracks, both in width and depth, are present. They furnish a good means of evaluating general-purpose penetrants, but again they represent only a single material and type of crack. They should be used for *comparisons only,* and not for absolute evaluations. Because the size and depth of the cracks are uncontrolled, these blocks are not particularly effective for comparing *high sensitivity* penetrant systems.

The blocks are prepared from 3/8″ by 2″ bars of 2024-T-3 aluminum, about 3″ long. They are heated to 525° C and quenched in cold water, which produces an over-all crack pattern. (See Chapter 17 Section 15 for details of preparing and using these blocks.) A slot is cut down the center of the face of each block, so that a different penetrant can be applied to each half for a direct comparison. If properly prepared, the blocks present a fairly uniform crack pattern on both sides of the center cut and both sides have both coarse and fine cracks.

The blocks *can* be reused, though for important comparisons tests should always be made on a new block. They may be "renewed"

NATURE AND PROPERTIES OF PENETRANTS

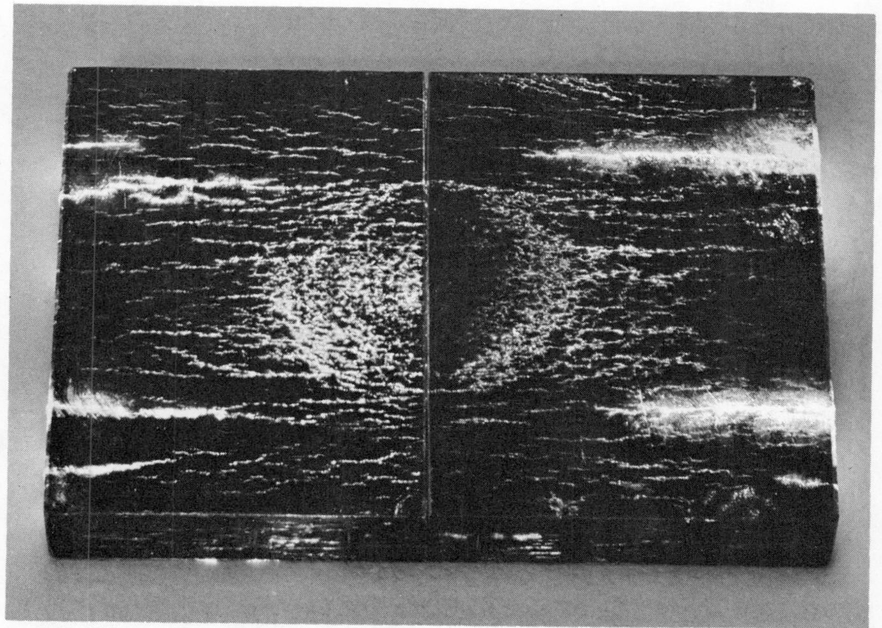

Fig. 22—Comparison of two fluorescent penetrants on aluminum test block.

by careful cleaning and reheating in all cases. Generally only two or three renewals are possible.

Figure 22 shows a comparison of two good penetrants which perform similarly, but which nevertheless show some differences in this test. Figure 23 shows a comparison in which there is no doubt as to which is the better. In making such comparisons some experi-

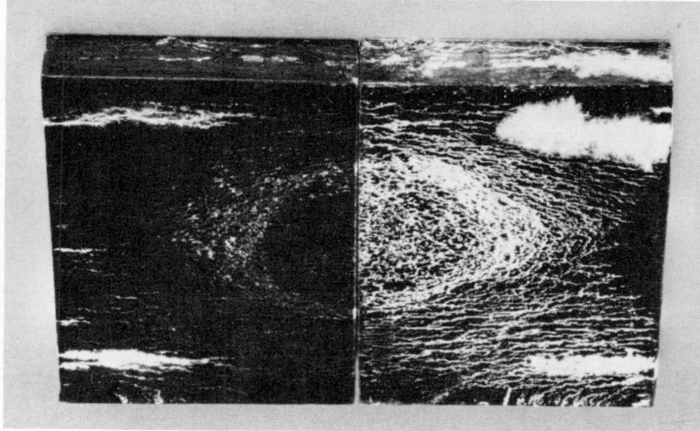

Fig. 23—Comparison of very poor and very good penetrants on aluminum test block.

ence and judgment is needed to make a fair evaluation. Photographic comparisons are not satisfactory except for recording special cases. This is because the technique of photography with black light is difficult and results vary with light intensity, exposure time, lens systems, type of film and other factors, all of which are not easy to control or to standardize. The human eye has so far proven to be the only suitable device for evaluating the results of these comparisons even though it, too, has serious deficiencies for this purpose.

32. PLATED STRIPS. The use of brittle electroplated coatings has long been looked on favorably as a means of producing cracks of known and controlled depth for use in comparison of penetrants. In 1952 a method was devised for plating a layer of brittle iron on a ductile iron base.* The test strips are 3″ x 1½″ and are cut from hot rolled steel sheet. By careful control of the plating process coatings of known thickness and fairly reproducible brittle characteristics can be consistently produced. Families of cracks are

Fig. 24—Comparison of very good and very poor penetrants on plated iron test strips.

*Developed by L. M. Taussig in the Magnaflux Corporation laboratories. The test pieces are sometimes referred to as "Taussig Strips."

then formed by bending the plated strip on a die of such radius or shape that the cracks extend completely through the brittle coating but do not penetrate the ductile base. By using dies of uniform radius a crack pattern quite uniformly spaced is produced. A non-uniform bending die produces a pattern varying in frequency.

The cracks on the convex surface of the bent strip will be fairly wide open. By replacing the strip on the bending die, and bending in the opposite direction, the cracks on the first surface will be tightly closed. Thus either open or tight cracks are obtained depending on which surface is examined. Usually, for evaluation or comparison tests, the closed cracks on the concave surface are used, since they are more difficult to locate.

The penetrants may of course be applied on either surface of the bent specimens. If the concave surface is used, cracks will be very tight—possibly of the order of 10 to 15 microinches or less. If the convex surface is tested, cracks will be open, depending on the radius of bend. By using the cantilever bending die the cracks may have a range of widths on the convex side depending on the curvature used, say from 100 or more microinches at the fixed end down to 20 microinches at the end of minimum bend. By sawing a slot down the middle of the strip (after bending) two identically cracked portions are available for comparing two penetrants.

These test specimens have numerous advantages. Crack depths are known and may be up to 2500 microinches or more (.0025″) depending on the thickness of the brittle plated layer. Crack width can be controlled, but not readily measured. The cracks are known to be clean and unfilled with any material, especially if the bending to produce the cracks is done just before testing. See Chapter 17, Sections 18-20, for a further discussion of these test pieces.

It is desirable to use both the aluminum test blocks and the plated strips on the same comparisons, to evaluate the behavior of the penetrant on the two different types of cracks, and on two different materials.

33. CHROME PLATED TEST SPECIMENS. A different type of plated specimen has recently been proposed.* This consists of a chrome plate over nickel on sheet steel. The chrome plating is conducted under conditions to produce cracks in the chromium

*Roy B. McCauley and Quentin Van Winkle at Ohio State University. Technical Documentary Report No. WADD-TR-60-520 Part I. March, 1962.

layer, many of which, though not always all, extend through the chrome to the nickel base.

The number of cracks per lineal inch in both X and Y axes are determined by direct count under the microscope, and by electrographic printing, the latter being intended to reveal only those cracks or discontinuities that extend to the nickel base. Thickness of plate can be controlled, as can frequency per lineal inch of cracks. Studies indicate that specimens with the higher crack frequencies

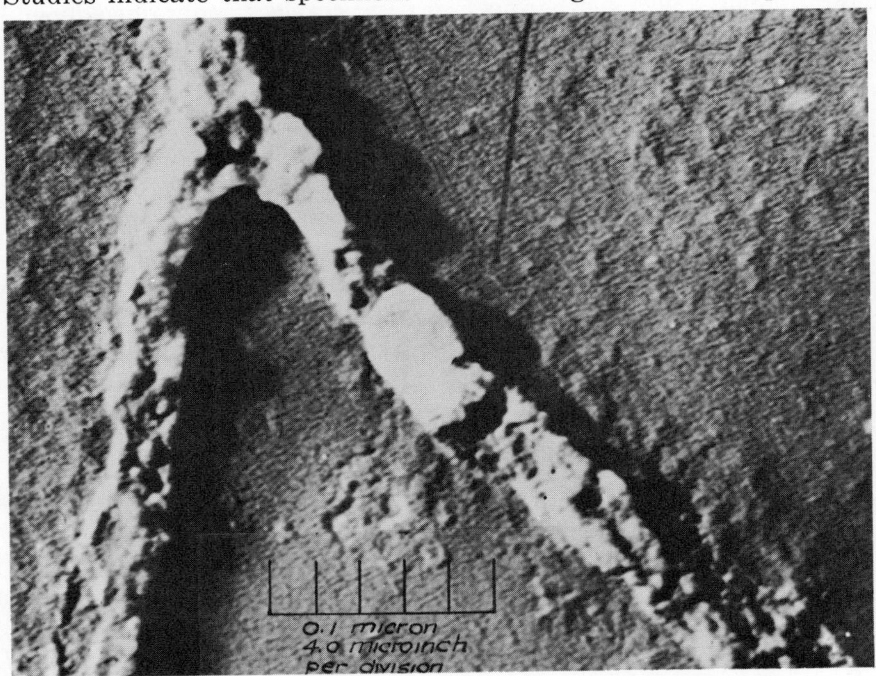

Fig. 25—Electron microscope photograph of crack pattern in chrome plate specimen, showing residue in cracks (using replica technique).

tend to have cracks of smaller width. The preferred crack depth (chrome plate thickness) is about 140 microinches (.000140″) although it may vary between 30 and 250 microinches. Crack widths varied from 200 microinches down to below 50, and in some cases have been found to be as low as 4 microinches (.000200″ to .000004″). See Fig. 25.

In making evaluation tests the penetrants are applied and the excess removed in the usual manner. Indications are counted per lineal inch and the ratio of indications to the original crack count, expressed as a percentage, is taken as a measure of the "crack detection efficiency" of the penetrant. The method thus attempts to make the comparison quantitative and thereby provide a numerical rating for evaluating various penetrants.

Such a quantitative rating is certainly desirable. Here, however, it is obviously valid only on the particular types of cracks which occur in this type of test piece. Because these cracks are deliberately created *during* plating, they are likely to be more or less filled with the by-products of electrolysis and dried residual chemicals. Also, the surface of the chromium plate is very smooth and it is an established fact that the character of the surface affects the performance of any given penetrant system. The cracks are marginal in both width and depth and undoubtedly require penetrants of special properties to find them most reliably. It does not follow logically, however, that the best penetrant to locate these cracks is also the best for the wide range of defects found in commercial parts and materials. In other words, sensitivity toward such very fine plating cracks is a special case and is not sensitivity to the same degree toward all other cracks and discontinuities. Use of the term "crack detection efficiency" applied to various penetrants should therefore be qualified and limited to the particular type of cracks used for the evaluation.

Chromium plated strips cracked by bending *after* plating have also been proposed, though they have not as yet been satisfactorily evaluated. Such test pieces would present clean cracks, and may prove to have value to supplement other means of comparing penetrant systems.**

34. THE SPOT OR MENISCUS TEST. This test was originally proposed as a method of directly determining penetrant effectiveness by measuring its "thin film fluorescence" value.* The method employs a plano-convex lens of 1.06 meter radius, placed upon an optical flat. A drop or two of penetrant is introduced under the lens so that it fills the space for some distance out from the point of contact.

When viewed with black light, a dark spot appears around the point of contact of the lens and the flat, where the thickness of penetrant film approaches zero. The diameter of the dark spot is a measure of the minimum film thickness at which the penetrant in question will produce sufficient fluorescence to be detected by

*"Theory and Applications of Liquid Tracers." James R. Alberger, SNT Journal Vol. XX No. 2, 1962.

**Here see Appendix III for further discussion of this type of test specimen.

the viewing means and under the black light excitation employed. The spot diameter of a given penetrant will change depending on whether the eye with or without the aid of magnification, or whether photography or photometry is the viewing means. It will also change with different black light intensities, and with different operators.

Within limits, the diameter of the spot by any given viewing means varies inversely with the amount of fluoragent present in the penetrant involved. The largest factor in producing high thin film fluorescence is the presence of a high proportion of fluorescent dye or material in the penetrant. The principal factor limiting this effect is the fact that the penetrant liquid itself (including the dye in solution) filters out some of the fluorescent light emerging through it. This effect is very pronounced with some liquids and dye solutions and may therefore sometimes be a considerable factor affecting the spot diameter. The *thinner the film* of penetrant—as at a fine indication—the less does this factor enter into "seeability." But in the case of the meniscus spot where film thickness varies widely, it can be important.

The meniscus test, then, is a possible method of measuring the relative ability of penetrants to fluoresce in thin films—but this is only one of the properties involved in the term *sensitivity* as we have defined it. It can be a useful test for the information it gives but is not by itself a measure of sensitivity and much work remains to be done defining and standardizing the steps in its performance before it can yield dependable and reproducible results. (See also Chapter 17, Section 13, for further discussion of this test.)

35. SENSITIVITY TO FINE, CLEAN, DEEP CRACKS. The characteristics of a penetrant which influence sensitivity come into play with different emphases when we consider the detection of different types of discontinuities.

If the crack to be indicated is clean, and very fine and relatively deep, emphasis will be on maximum penetrability of the penetrant, to insure penetration of the crack with the greatest possible volume of liquid. Fortunately, as has already been shown, good penetrability is not difficult to achieve and a penetrant of high penetrability to fine cracks is not too difficult to formulate.

Since the amount of penetrant in a very fine crack is at best very minute, maximum sensitivity in this case requires that *no* penetrant be removed from the crack by the washing operation. Both the character of the penetrant and the manner of washing are factors here, and must be considered when setting out to find this type of defect. Maintenance of fluidity of the penetrant is also important. Good penetrating materials are available, both of high and of low volatility. It is necessary to be sure that volatility in this case be not too high, so that the penetrant does not dry up in the crack. If the penetrant that has entered the crack remains fluid it will later tend to come out, since the ability to penetrate is allied to the ability to creep and spread.

The developer chosen can seriously affect sensitivity at this stage, and selection of the proper developer for the conditions involved is here of great importance. (See Chapter 5.)

Visibility or "seeability" is the most critical factor in sensitivity for very fine defects—and it is the most difficult to achieve. The reasons for this are:

1. Only a very small amount of penetrant can appear at a very fine crack. As it lies in the crack it is a very thin film, on edge, so to speak.
2. As it comes from the crack and spreads, with the help of developer, it is possibly an even thinner film, but spread flat to the viewer.

It is self-evident that if such a small amount of penetrant is to be seen it must possess great contrast with its background, and the finer the discontinuity the more critical this requirement becomes. Color-contrast dyes cannot compete in these marginal areas of crack size. Even with highly fluorescent dyes, highly energized with black light, such an indication is difficult to see, and where cracks of this sort are being looked for the very maximum in sensitivity must be secured.

36. CONTRAST AND SEEABILITY. Whether or not an indication will be seen involves two major factors:

1. The *relative* amount of light reflected and/or emitted as between an indication and its background. This relationship is called the *contrast ratio* and is subject to measurement with instruments designed to measure light reflection or light emission.

2. The *actual* amount of light reflected or emitted by an indication. This relationship is in this discussion referred to by the coined word "seeability", though the complete concept of "seeability" also involves factors of color, ambient light level and contrast.

37. CONTRAST RATIO. Measurements have shown that the maximum of light that will be reflected from a pure white matte surface is about 98% of the incident white light. In the same way a minimum of 3% of the incident white light will be reflected from the best black matte surface. This means that the maximum contrast ratio that can be achieved by colored pigments is about 33 to 1. As a practical matter, however, such values will not be reached in practice, and a ratio of 90% to 10%, or 9 to 1 is probably the best that could be expected as between a black dye indication and a white developer background. Using a red colorant instead of black this is reduced to about 9 to 1.5, or 6 to 1.

When fluorescent surfaces are considered, however, such a numerical value cannot be assigned as readily to the contrast ratio, since the two conditions being contrasted are not two values of light, but rather the contrast of light with darkness. This ratio, even with some ambient white light present can reach 300 to 1 (or 1000 to 1), and in complete darkness approaches infinity.*

38. "SEEABILITY". "Seeability" involves the receiving end of the indication-viewing combination, and in penetrant inspection, in practically all cases, the viewing device today is the human eye.

The eye is a peculiar and complex mechanism which has the power to change its ability to perceive objects and differences in light and colors depending on the general level of illumination that exists when the observation is made. In strong white light the sensitivity of the eye to small differences in light intensity is not particularly great, though its ability to differentiate colors and degrees of contrast is at a maximum. When the illumination falls to a low level an entirely different perceptive mechanism comes into use. In dim light the ability to distinguish differences in color and contrasts of color is poor, but the ability to see dimly lighted

*For a study and measurement of contrast thresholds for the human eye the reader is referred to the following: "Contrast Thresholds of the Human Eye" by H. Richard Blackwell, Journal of the Optical Society of America, Vol. 36 No. 11, Nov. 1946; and "Studies of Psychophysical Methods for Measuring Visual Threholds," also by Blackwell in the same Journal, Vol. 42 No. 9, Sept. 1952.

objects and small light sources is tremendously increased. Figure 26 is an attempt to show these two ranges of perceptive ability of the human eye in graphic form. No scale is conveniently applicable in such a representation since the two areas of vision are entirely different and operate by entirely different mechanisms. Everyone has experienced the sensation of "not being able to see a thing" when passing from a brightly lighted room to a dark one, but

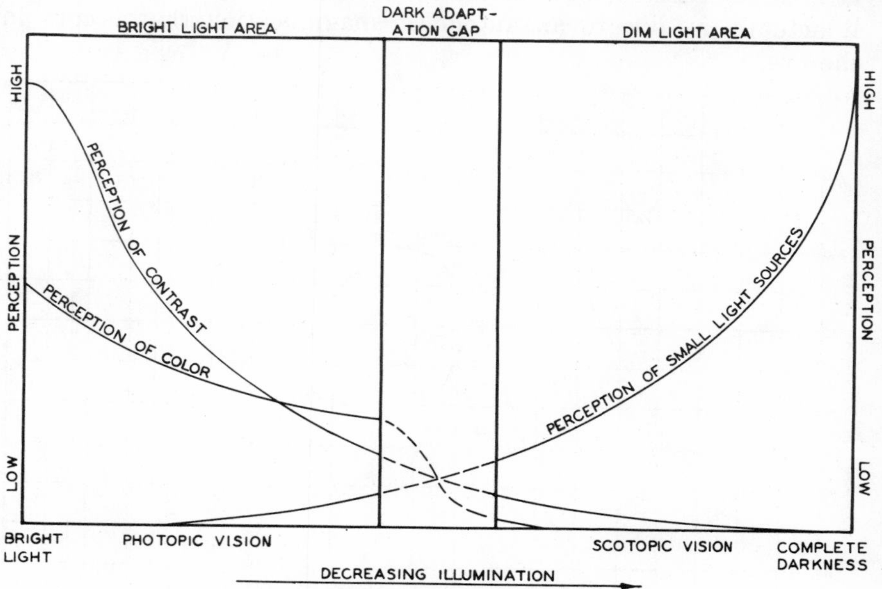

Fig. 26—Chart of perception by the human eye.

finding after a short time that objects in the dark room become quite readily visible. When returning to the bright room one is first blinded until the eyes readjust to this high light level.

This is a most important phenomenon in connection with penetrant testing. Color-contrast indications *must* be viewed in bright white light in order to have maximum use of the eye's ability to distinguish contrasts and colors. Seeability is improved to some extent by the red color of the indication against the white background, since the color attracts the eye, because red is "out of context."

Fluorescent indications are viewed in darkness or in dim light at a level where the more sensitive eye mechanism is in action. The effect is called "dark adaptation" and requires a period of 5 to 20 minutes in the dim light before it is fully attained. Once the eyes are dark adapted, minute light sources, too small even to be seen in a bright light environment, appear relatively brilliant and easily seen. Seeability of small light sources such as fluorescent indications is increased by two factors. One is the fact that the eye is drawn to any source of light in a dark background. The other factor is the phenomenon of halation. When the eye looks directly at a small source of light the size of the source apears larger than it actually is, due to an automatic magnification that occurs in the eye.

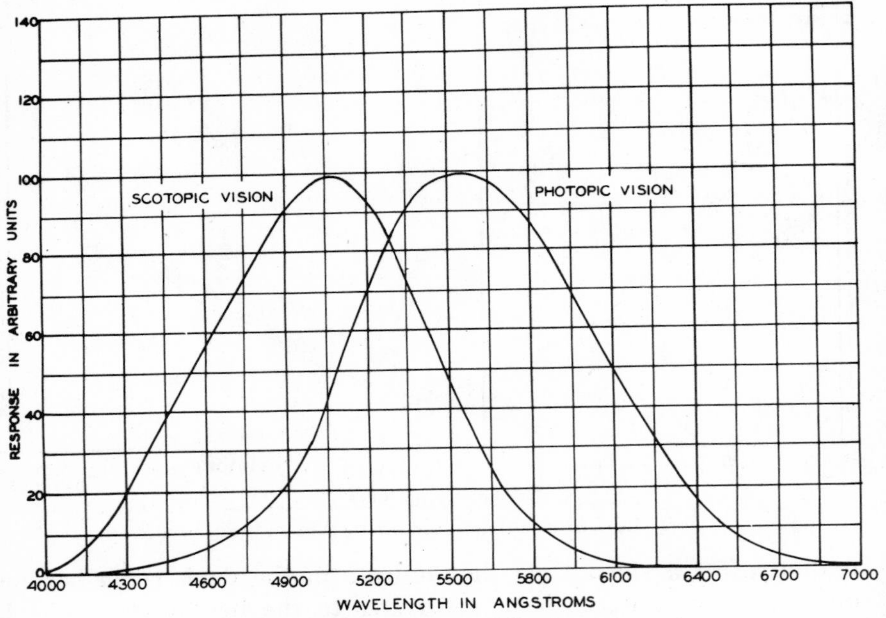

Fig. 27—Color-response of the human eye.

The color of the fluorescent light from the better penetrants is a yellow green, and this color is selected in preference to other possible ones because of another characteristic of vision with the human eye. The eye is not equally sensitive to all colors of the spectrum, but varies quite widely, reaching a maximum in the yellow-green area. Figure 27 shows the curve of eye response to the various colors. Use of penetrant emitting yellow-green light, therefore, adds one more plus factor to the seeability of indications. Yellow-green light has the added advantage of being "out of context" as to color, compared to the white to blue-white fluorescence of oils and greases which may be encountered on machine parts if not properly pre-cleaned.

Thus the seeability of fluorescent indications is by their nature and by the environment in which they are viewed of a distinctly higher order than those of color-contrast penetrants.

39. MEASUREMENT OF "SEEABILITY". Attempts have been made to assign quantitative values to seeability but this has not seemed practical because of the many variable factors that enter into the problem, which are difficult or impossible to evaluate or control. The idea is of some interest however—not for the purpose of evaluating different penetrants—but rather to determine some approximate parameters of effectiveness of different types of penetrant when their indications are viewed with the human eye.

One such experimental method* seems worth including in this discussion. Though not an absolute measurement, the tests give a general idea of the relative seeability of some different types of penetrant when viewed by the eye under conditions of illumination that attempt to approximate those encountered in actual inspection operations.

For the purpose of the tests a Klett visual comparison colorimeter was used as a light extinction apparatus. A water solution of Black Nigrosine dye (.05 gm per liter) was used for the light absorption fluid. Fine indications were simulated by using a white absorbent thread approximately .008″ in diameter which had been dipped in the penetrants diluted 4 to 1 with methylene chloride and dried at room temperature. The threads were mounted between two microscope slides, using a non-glossy white paper background for the color-contrast penetrants.

Each penetrant specimen was viewed at two light levels. For color contrast penetrants, 50 and 10 foot candles were used with an incandescent light bulb as the source. For fluorescent penetrants, 250 and 50 foot candles were the selected levels using a 100 watt spot type mercury arc bulb with black light filter. These are light levels comparable with high and low level illuminations met with in practice. Each viewer adjusted the instrument himself to the position where he could first see the penetrant-coated thread. Average of a number of measurements was taken for each viewer.

Seventy-five persons selected at random, ranging in age from 17 to 72 years, both male and female, were used for the tests. The

*J. T. Schmidt, working in the Research Laboratory of Magnaflux Corporation, Chicago, 1961.

group did include several experienced inspectors. Each observer was tested on each of six penetrants—two color contrast and four fluorescent, and at each of two illumination levels. Results are expressed as the reciprocal of the decimal fraction of the total reflected (or emitted) light necessary to give threshold visibility. Table VI gives the comparative values obtained in each of the penetrants. The figures are given as Relative Visibility Units in the first column for each light level. A penetrant requiring 2% of the available light for visibility would have a numerical value of 50 in this column. For purposes of comparison the relative seeability by this method is given in the second column in terms of multiples of the least seeable.

TABLE VI

SEEABILITY TESTS

Penetrant	High Light Level		Low Light Level	
	R. V. U.	Relative Seeability	R. V. U.	Relative Seeability
A	37	1.0	13	1.1
B	40	1.1	12	1.0
C	97	2.6	30	2.5
D	207	5.6	75	6.2
E	264	7.1	90	7.5
F	378	10.2	119	9.8

Types of penetrants tested:

A. Color Contrast—Solvent Clean
B. Color Contrast—Solvent Clean
C. Fluorescent—Water Wash
D. Fluorescent—Water Wash
E. Fluorescent—Post Emulsification
F. Fluorescent—Post Emulsification—Super Bright

NOTE: R.V.U. = Relative Visibility Units. These values are the reciprocal of the decimal fraction of the total reflected or emitted light necessary to give threshold visibility. If 2% of total available light is required, the R.V.U.'s in this instance would be 1/.02 or 50.

As has been stated these results should not be used as a means of rating penetrants for sensitivity or crack-finding ability. They give information regarding only one of the elements of sensitivity.

They do correlate fairly well with the experience in the field with these penetrants as to their ability to produce indications that can be seen. They are more realistic as to the relative effectiveness of color-contrast and fluorescent types than are the numerical values obtained from contrast measurements. They also point up the known sizable differences in seeability among various fluorescent penetrants.

40. SENSITIVITY TO CONTAMINANT-FILLED CRACKS. If the crack is filled with some foreign material such as oil, oxides or corrosion products, the difficulty of the penetrant getting into the crack in the first place may be the controlling factor. Of course, once penetration is accomplished, all the requirements applying to clean cracks become of the same relative importance brought out in the preceding sections.

The ability of a penetrant to get into a filled crack may not be a question of penetrability alone. A penetrant having a solvent action on the contaminant may be superior in this instance to a better penetrant not possessing such solvent ability. Mechanical vibration or heat are sometimes used to break the contaminant away from the sides of the crack as a preliminary to penetration. If this can be done and the contaminant is inert to the penetrant, the problem may be no more difficult than in the case of the clean crack.

Some contaminants react with a penetrant to change its color or, in the case of some fluorescent penetrants, actually to kill the fluorescence entirely. If this condition exists it obviously would be controlling, and if penetrants are to give an indication at all, they must be inert to such a contaminant. Acids or chromates which may remain in cracks from some previous process or operation are examples of such possible contamination.

Therefore, unless conditions are exactly defined, it is not possible to specify the properties of the most sensitive penetrant for contaminant-filled cracks.

41. SENSITIVITY TO WIDE OPEN AND SHALLOW DEFECTS. In a good many instances it is important to be able to locate surface discontinuities which are shallow and open and which may in fact be no more than nicks or scratches. For this purpose the factors determining sensitivity are again different. Penetrability is of little or no importance, but the cleaning or washing characteristics are of critical importance. The penetrant must resist removal or washing from the shallow open defect, which requirement eliminates almost completely the use of water-wash type penetrants for this purpose. Solvent-type cleaners are even less applicable. The post-emulsification penetrant and process were devised primarily to secure sensitivity to this class of defect. Seeability is of course of equal importance as for fine cracks but is more easily attained because more penetrant is usually available to form the indication.

Other advantages of the post-emulsification process will be discussed in detail in Chapter 8.

42. SENSITIVITY TO VERY FINE AND VERY SHALLOW CRACKS. If a crack is very fine — say of the order of 10 microinches (.000010″)—and at the same time very shallow—let us say of the order of 100 microinches (.000100″)—a special sensitivity is required. For cracks of such size, a degree of fluorescing ability beyond that required for most defects is demanded. Although the width-depth ratio (1 to 10) classifies these cracks as "deep", the actual amount of pentrant available for an indication is infinitesimal.

If cracks of this size are sought, penetrating ability should be at a maximum; but even more important, seeability must be amplified as highly as possible. In order to obtain fluorescent intensity in such small amounts of penetrant, the fluorescent dye content must be increased drastically. Washing techniques should be applied with great care, both to produce surfaces free of background and false indications, and to insure that no penetrant is removed from these relatively shallow cracks.

43. DYES FOR COLOR-CONTRAST PENETRANTS. Selection of dyes for penetrants is dictated by the properties the dyes are expected to contribute to the formula. In the case of color-contrast dyes solubility and color are the properties of first importance. In color-contrast penetrants, maximum sensitivity is achieved by very high dye concentration, so that minute quantities of re-emergent penetrant will have the maximum staining effect on the white developer background. Red dyes are almost universally used since the deep red color of these dyes presents excellent contrast—and the red dyes have a high degree of solubility in many penetrant liquids. Much higher levels of dye content are necessary than in the case of the fluorescent penetrants.

Solubility at low temperatures is also a factor in selecting dyes for color contrast penetrants, since separation of dye during low temperature shipment or storage should not occur. If dye does separate, re-solution is important but often most difficult to bring about. Particles of separated dyes can cause clogging and malfunctioning of spraying devices used for applying penetrants.

Presumably dyes of other colors, such as black, blue, green or orange, would have some value for special applications, provided solubility of such dyes were high enough to give sufficiently intense colors. As a practical matter, however, no fully satisfactory dye of color other than red appears to have been found. It is therefore fortuitous that highly soluble red dyes are available, since dark red against white provides one of the highest possible color contrasts.

44. FLUORESCENT DYES. As usually interpreted in penetrant work fluorescence is the property of a substance to receive radiant energy of a wave length below the visible spectrum—i.e., in the near-ultraviolet—and re-emit a portion of the energy in the form of light in the visible range. In order to be most efficient the dye must respond in maximum degree to the black light wave length with which it is energized. Conversely, the black light should "peak"—i.e., concentrate the maximum of its output—in the wave length range to which the dye is most responsive.

Black light used for penetrant inspection has long been standardized as peaking at 3650 Angstrom units, the wave length at which the black light filter transmission peaks. This wave length is just under the shortest visible violet light. Most fluorescent dyes react well to light of this wave length, although their *peak* receptivity may not always coincide with this same wave length.

In some cases a dye which does have a peak receptivity at 3650 Angstroms does not emit a light of desirable color or intensity. Another dye may be most receptive to the emitted wave length of the first dye and at the same time re-emit light of desirable wave length, say in the yellow-green range. A combination of two or more such dyes may produce a penetrant with more intense fluorescence and with a more desirable color value than any one of the multiple dyes could deliver alone. Such combinations in penetrants have been designated as "cascading" and are the subject of a patent issued Jan. 5, 1960.*

45. COLOR OF FLUORESCENT DYES. There are a number of dyes ranging in fluorescence all the way from blue to red. In order to

*U.S. Patent No. 2,920,203. Joseph L. Switzer and Donald W. Parker. Jan. 5, 1960.

achieve maximum seeability, a desirable color is one to which the human eye or other viewing device is most responsive. For the human eye this color is in the yellow-green to green-blue range, with preference for the yellow-green side. (See Section 38 and Figure 27.) For photo-multiplier tubes or other scanning devices, this optimum wave length may be quite different.

The yellow-green color is to be preferred over the bluer colors for a less theoretical reason. Most greases and petroleum oils have some natural fluorescence in the blue-white range. A yellow-green luminescence stands out as a distinctive penetrant indication if any casual fluorescence due to stray oil happens to appear on the surface of a part. The bluish color of some penetrants is less desirable for this reason.

46. SOLUBILITY OF DYES. Most dyes are not particularly soluble in the materials that make suitable penetrants, so that a factor in selecting a dye is its ability to go into and stay in solution. Fortunately fluorescent dyes are available today that do have satisfactory solubility. Sometimes a special solvent must be incorporated in the formula to insure that the dye-stuff does not come out of solution when the penetrant is exposed to low temperatures.

The brilliance with which a penetrant fluoresces is a direct function of the amount of dye in solution, and for a given dye continues to increase as the concentration of dye increases. Quenching action of the penetrant fluid tends to limit the increase at the higher concentrations. The limit of brilliance, therefore, becomes mainly a question (a) of solubility and (b) of cost. Some of the superbright penetrants become so costly that their use is not economically justified except in cases where the importance of the inspection outweighs the cost.

Since solubility is a function of temperature, the useful solubility of a dye is limited by the lowest temperature to which a penetrant may be subject, and this in turn may place a limitation on the brilliance attainable for any given penetrant formulation with any given dye.

Penetrant shipped and stored in northern climates may be subjected to temperatures of 0° F and below, for protracted periods. If under these conditions dye separates out of solution, and precautions are not taken to redissolve this dye before use of the penetrant, brilliance of the penetrant may be greatly reduced due to this loss of dye content. If separation of dye does take place, usually the penetrant must be warmed up to some reasonable temperature (70° or above) after which agitation of the liquid should, with a satisfactory formulation, effect re-solution of the dyes. Preferably, of course, penetrant formulation should be such that no dye separation occurs even after prolonged storage at sub-zero temperatures. In the case of color-contrast penetrants concentration of dye is very high and maintenance of true solution under all conditions is difficult. In the best commercial penetrants, however, this has been satisfactorily achieved.

47. PERMANENCE OF DYES. Dyes used for fluorescent penetrants must possess other important qualities in addition to brilliance and good solubility. A number of dyes which are available and relatively cheap, and which fluoresce quite brilliantly, lose their ability to fluoresce in solution after very short exposure to ultraviolet or black light. Permanence of fluorescent intensity is very important, since loss of fluorescent brilliance means loss of sensitivity to fine—or any—defects.

Penetrants are exposed to the ultraviolet radiation contained in ordinary light when kept in open tanks. They are again so exposed during the draining or penetration time after they have been applied to surfaces of parts. Black light is used during the step of washing or cleaning, so as to ensure satisfactory removal of penetrant. Black light is again applied during inspection and in many cases a part is examined more than once under black light before its disposition is decided. Progressive loss of fluorescent intensity during this process is obviously highly undesirable and could be critical, especially in the case of very fine cracks. Fortunately the best dyes which have been developed for penetrant uses, do have excellent resistance to fading under black light, though nearly all show some fading under such exposure. The poorer dyes, however, fade so rapidly that they are generally unsatisfactory for penetrant purposes for this reason.

Fluorescence of dyes may be impaired by other agents than exposure to black or ultraviolet light. Heat destroys or reduces fluorescence of most dyes. Since parts being tested by the fluorescent penetrant process are customarily dried with heat, at temperatures of 150° F to 225° F, it is imperative that these temperatures, at least, should not affect the intensity of fluorescence of the dyes. Resistance to heat is therefore of the greatest importance.*

*Here see Appendix I for further discussion of maximum operating temperatures for penetrants.

The fluorescence of most dyes is seriously affected by contact with acids, and no dye really resistant to acid is yet available. Alkalies on the other hand have little effect on the fluorescing ability of the dyes. It is important to understand this characteristic of dyes so that the environment in which the tests are conducted be such that acids do not come in contact with the penetrants, either before or during the inspection of parts. This prohibition applies not only to acid liquids, but also to acids or acid vapors in the atmosphere coming in contact with parts undergoing inspection. The precautions necessary in specific circumstances will be further discussed in Chapter 7.

48. TOXICITY OF DYES. One of the questions most often raised with regard to fluorescent dyes is "Are they a health hazard?". Specifically, there is a popular impression that fluorescent dyes are either poisonous or are likely to generate cancer when they come in contact with the skin.

Fluorescent dyes, in common with most dyes used for coloring fabrics or in paints and inks, are not non-poisonous. On the other hand, neither are they any more poisonous if taken into the system than are a host of other commercial dyes and pigments.

The impression that fluorescent materials may generate cancer is without doubt derived from the fact that some naturally fluorescent substances are known to be dangerous. The term used is "carcinogenic". This is notably true of certain crystalline hydrocarbons derived from the distillation of coal tar, and some of these substances have actually been used in some fluorescent penetrant processes. If used, extreme precautions must be taken to avoid continuing contact of this material with the skin.

But practically all of the synthetic fluorescent dyes (as contrasted to the fluorescent crystalline hydrocarbons) are quite harmless and free of any tendency to be carcinogenic. This has been proven repeatedly by elaborate tests carried out on rabbits or other animals. No reputable manufacturer of penetrants would risk offering a fluorescent product containing a dye which had not been cleared of suspicion of such a hazard by such careful tests. In the case of the above-mentioned fluorescent crystalline hydrocarbons, if these are used in penetrant systems, clear warning of the danger of repeated contact should be given to all users.

49. NON-FLUORESCENT COLOR INTENSITY. Many of the fluorescent dyes, including those green-yellow dyes commonly used in commercial fluorescent penetrants, possess very little color intensity when viewed in ordinary white light. This is of some practical importance, since such penetrants do not stain the skin or clothing of operators to any conspicuous degree, and their presence becomes apparent only when the dyes are activiated with black light. Some of the red fluorescent dyes do have a rather pronounced white-light color, although of nothing like the intensity of the dyes used in color-contrast penetrants. While this lack of strong color in the fluorescent dyes may have no importance from the point of view of effective inspection, it does mean that operators do not have to combat unsightly stains on hands and clothing.

50. TYPES OF FLUORESCENT PENETRANTS. A number of different penetrant types are in wide commercial use. In addition, a considerable list of special penetrants for relatively limited applications have been developed and are available.

51. WATER-WASH FLUORESCENT PENETRANTS. The first fluorescent penetrant to come into wide use was of the self-emulsifying or water-wash type. Improved penetrants of this type continue to be used for the majority of applications. The penetrant liquid incorporates a sufficient proportion of emulsifier to permit the excess penetrant to be cleaned from the surface of the part by means of a water spray. A number of formulations of this type are on the market, varying quite widely in ease of washing and in intensity of fluorescence. The effect of these variations will be discussed in detail in Chapter 7.

52. POST-EMULSIFIABLE FLUORESCENT PENETRANTS. This type of penetrant was developed to meet special operating and sensitivity requirements, and is the second most widely used in industry. It differs from the water wash type in that no emulsifier is incorporated in the penetrant itself, so that the latter is not water-washable alone. Emulsifier is applied as a separate step, after which washing the surface with water is satisfactorily accomplished. Extremely high brilliance and sensitivity are attained by this means. These penetrants will be more fully discussed in Chapter 8.

53. WATER-BASE FLUORESCENT PENETRANTS. For some applications a noncombustible penetrant is required, having brilliance and sensitivity comparable with the more commonly used organic-liquid penetrants. Such penetrants have been developed and are in use in certain cases where combustible or oxidizable liquids cannot be tolerated, as for instance in fuel containers and systems of missiles for handling liquid oxygen. Such materials are impact tested to evaluate their reaction to liquid oxygen.

54. SPECIAL PENETRANTS. In addition to some special formulations for the inspection of liquid oxygen systems, another group of special penetrants has been developed which are very low in sulphur, phosphorus and chlorine. These are required for the inspection of special alloys which are damaged by these elements at high temperatures. Such penetrants are specified to avoid all possibility of residual amounts of the objectionable elements remaining on the surface of such alloys when they are placed in their high temperature service environments.

55. OTHER SPECIAL LIMITED PURPOSE FLUORESCENT PENETRANTS. A few of these are listed below:

(a) Red fluorescent "leaker" penetrant—used for leak detection on welded tanks and systems. Red color makes differentiation easy as between the natural blue fluorescence of petroleum oils, or other substances which may be present, and a true indication of a leak.

(b) Yellow fluorescent, oil free penetrant—used when oils or petroleum distillates are incompatible with the material being tested—as some plastics, rubber, etc.

(c) Yellow fluorescent dry concentrate—for use with water as a penetrant liquid for leak detection where a large volume of liquid is needed—as in testing large tanks or utility condensers.

(d) Yellow fluorescent dry concentrate similar to "c," but with better wetting properties for leak detection under more critical conditions—such as oil well "Christmas Trees."

(e) Yellow fluorescent dry concentrate for use with oil as the penetrant liquid in testing oil fuel systems for leaks.

(f) Red fluorescent dry concentrate, for use with water or alcohol or similar water-miscible liquids combined as the penetrant liquid, where a red colored indication is preferred.

(g) Blue fluorescent dry concentrate for use with water as the penetrant. Provides a cheaper penetrant where large volumes are required and where clear-cut differentiation from the natural blue fluorescence of petroleum oils is not a problem.

(h) Yellow-green fluorescent oil penetrant. Incorporated in refrigerator oil for leak location in refrigeration systems.

(i) Penetrants using harmless dye compounds in edible oils, for use in testing food processing machinery.

(j) Special formulation to perform satisfactorily under exceptionally high temperature conditions. Used for detecting defects in welds while the welded metal is still at temperatures so high that none of the conventional penetrants can function. (See Appendix I.)

56. TYPES OF COLOR-CONTRAST PENETRANTS. By far the greatest amount of color-contrast penetrants used is of the solvent-wash type. In this case the excess penetrant is removed from the surface by means of a solvent which dissolves both penetrant and dye. Three variations are in common use.

(a) The low flash-point type in which the penetrant liquid is primarily a relatively volatile flammable oil.

(b) The high flash-point type, in which the penetrant consists of organic liquids which may be combustible but which are much less of a fire hazard than type "a."

(c) The non-combustible type in which the penetrant liquid consists of an organic liquid or a mixture of organic liquids which are essentially nonflammable and noncombustible.

In addition, color-contrast penetrants can be and have been formulated to parallel both the water-wash and the post-emulsification varieties of fluorescent penetrants. Extensive use of these latter two types has never developed for color-contrast penetrants, since there is little or no demonstrable advantage to offset the greater sensitivity and the lower cost of the fluorescent counterparts.*

57. OTHER APPROACHES. A considerable number of variants of the penetrant flaw-detection idea have been devised and offered to industry, and some have found a certain amount of use in some areas. Some of these will be briefly described here because of their general interest, and to round out this discussion of the subject. None has achieved any wide-spread acceptance in industry,

*At this point please read Appendix IV for a discussion of later developments in color-contrast penetrant systems.

and none is an appreciable factor today in the overall field of penetrant inspection.

58. DRY-FLUORESCING INDICATORS. The dyes used in conventional fluorescent penetrants fluoresce brilliantly when in solution, but do not fluoresce appreciably when the undissolved dye is exposed to black light. There is a group of substances—not dyes in the usual sense of the word—which fluoresce brilliantly when in dry crystalline form, but some of them lose this property to a considerable extent when dissolved. Notable among these materials are such coal tar hydrocarbons as anthracene and chrysene.

This property of these substances has been made the basis for a crack detection penetrant process in England, and is the subject of a British patent, of the early 1940's.* A solution of these materials in an organic volatile solvent acts as the penetrant. After immersion of the part in the solution it is withdrawn and the surface quickly flushed off with clean solvent. Penetrant in a crack comes back to the surface, the solvent evaporates, and a small quantity of the crystalline fluorescent material is deposited at the crack. Under black light a bright green fluorescent indication is seen. In one version the solution is contained in a vapor-degreaser, the part immersed in the hot liquid and cleaned in the vapor as it is withdrawn.

The method works satisfactorily on only certain types of defects. It is not reliable on most fine cracks, unless they are perfectly clean and of appreciable length and depth. It does not clearly delineate the extent of coarse defects and is of no value whatever on the shallow wide-open type. The solvent cleaning must be expertly done else penetrant in the cracks will be dissolved out, and this is especially true in the vapor-degreaser system. A further drawback is the fact that the fluorescent materials used sublime at rather low temperatures, resulting in relatively rapid fading and disappearance of indications. This occurs more rapidly in the vapor-degreaser version, since when the dry indications are formed the parts are warm from the hot solvent. The volatilization of the fluorescent substance is at the same time of some possible advantage, as the thin film of fluorescent material remaining over the surface if not completely removed by solvent, tends to disappear more rapidly than the indications and thereby reduces background fluorescence.

*British Patent—No. 566,652 July 23, 1943.

The solvents used as well as the fluorescent coal tar hydrocarbons bear a considerable stigma today from the point of view of industrial health hazards, though this might be minimized by proper handling precautions if the method were sufficiently attractive to make it worthwhile. However, the only really attractive feature is the one-dip procedure of the vapor-degreaser technique—but sensitivity and reliability are so far from camparable with present day conventional fluorescent penetrant methods as to make the dry-fluorescing system of little industrial value.

59. METHODS DEPENDENT ON PENETRANT-DEVELOPER INTERACTION. In conventional penetrant methods the penetrant itself contains the indicating dye and the developer serves merely to hasten or improve the appearance of the indication. A number of methods have been proposed and tried in which the developer carries the indicating material or in which the indication is produced by some physical or chemical interaction between developer and penetrant.

In one of these a soluble dye is mixed dry with the developer. The penetrant contains no indicator, but is a liquid which is a solvent for the dye. The liquid penetrant at a defect wets the developer when it is applied and in doing so dissolves and spreads some of the dye, producing a visible indication. Either color-contrast or fluorescent dyes can be used. The method can be quite sensitive even for fine defects, but so far has not come into industrial use.

In another version, the dye incorporated with the developer is one of the pH indicators, such as phenolphthalein. The penetrant—presumably water base—has a high pH, so that the color of the indicator is developed as the penetrant at the defect comes in contact with it. The method is probably not as sensitive for fine defects as the one just described and has found no acceptance for practical use.

A much better approach (and one which has a quite satisfactory sensitivity) is to use a non-volatile penetrant containing no indicator, and after cleaning and drying the surface, to dust on a special developer containing very finely divided pigment.* If the particle size of the pigment is of the order of 10 microns or less, some of the pigment will be caught by the liquid penetrant emerging from a crack. If the pigment is a fluorescent one, very few particles need be

*U.S. Patent 2,707,236—T. de Forest, and U.S. Patent 2,848,421—T. de Forest

trapped to produce a vivid indication under black light. By formulating the powder to include a considerable proportion of coarse light particles, a scrubbing action over the surface acts to carry away surplus fluorescent pigment, thus leaving a minimum of interfering background.

This method is quite practical, but actually offers little or no advantage over established penetrant techniques and materials; and has never achieved commercial importance.

60. REVERSED-FLUORESCENCE METHOD. Another ingenious method uses fluorescence but in a sort of photographic-negative manner. Color contrast penetrant is used to produce the indication in the normal manner up to the point of applying the developer. Developer is applied as a solvent suspension in much the same way as for the usual color contrast procedure. The developer has a low-intensity fluoragent incorporated in it, and carries only a relatively small amount of developer powder. When dry, and viewed under black light, the entire background of the surface glows with a low-intensity fluorescence, with the indication itself a dark line or spot, where the dye of the color contrast indication has killed the fluorescence of the developer.

The method is quite sensitive and offers some practical advantages.

61. ETCHING AND SIMILAR METHODS. Mild etching has long been a means for increasing the visibility of surface cracks by eating away the edges of a crack and making its surface width greater than the actual width of the crack itself. A number of devices have been proposed and used to increase the visibility of such etched cracks by means of reagents which stain or dye the edges by reacting with emergent etching liquid or with the retained product of the etching reaction.

One of these methods was developed by Sikorsky Aircraft Div. for use on magnesium castings*.

Although subject to certain restrictive limitations, it is reported to give quite satisfactory results when applicable. Successive dips in sulphuric acid, hydrofluoric acid and a chromic-nitric acid mixture, with intervening water rinses, results in production of a brown stain at cracks and surface openings caused by the bleeding

*"New Non-Destructive Test for Magnesium Alloy Castings"—G. R. Van Duzee, Materials and Methods, January 1956.

out of the chromic acid. A later improvement adds a methylene blue dye dip, which produces a blue color at the defects. Since the etching removes appreciable amounts (.010″) of surface metal, the method cannot be used on machined parts. It is also open to all the objections inherent in the use of acid baths in any industrial process.

Very similar to the above is the use of the anodizing process on aluminum for the detection of cracks. This process marks many surface openings with stains due to bleeding of the reagents used from such openings. Careful evaluations have shown that these indications cannot be depended upon to disclose the presence of all types of discontinuities, and the anodizing process is today seldom considered to be a satisfactory substitute for the more sensitive penetrant techniques.

A variation of the etching methods was developed for aluminum forgings and other aluminum articles by the Aluminum Company of America.* Here the clean article is dipped briefly in dilute hydrofluoric acid solution, rinsed, and then dipped in a hot dye solution. The aluminum compound formed in the crack by the acid acts to fix the dye, so that after further rinsing to remove excess dye solution, the defects are permanently colored. The method is open to the same objections as are all processes involving acids, and its sensitivity to very fine defects is open to considerable question. It has never achieved any important commercial acceptance.

62. USE OF POWDER AS PENETRANT. An interesting method has been made the subject of a patent by Raytheon Manufacturing Company for the detection of fissures in tungsten lead-in wires.**

After degreasing and chemical cleaning, the articles are shaken or tumbled in a fine powder consisting of a mixture of the fluorescent dye fluorescein with an extremely fine silica dust. This mixture sifts into or is deposited in surface openings such as fissures or cracks. Subsequently the articles are immersed in an oil bath, after which surplus oil and powder are washed from the surface with warm water, and then dried in an oven. The oil is absorbed by the powder in the fissures or openings in the articles at the same time dissolving the fluorescein dye. The oil-powder mixture is not removed during the washing, but some of the oil-dye solution seeps

*U.S. Patent 2,391,522—Chas. J. Slunder.
**U.S. Patent 2,470,341—Wm. C. Darrah.

out of the crack after the parts are dried. Black light is then used to locate the indications so produced. Since the powder mixture cannot equal the penetrating ability of a good penetrant liquid, the method gives satisfactory results only in certain favorable circumstances and has no general applicability.

63. BREAKING-FILM METHOD. This method was devised in an effort to magnify the indications of defects produced by a penetrant emerging from cracks.* It employs an oily penetrant in the conventional manner, and removes the excess by wiping or washing. Over the dry surface is flowed a solution of a dye in a volatile solvent having a different surface tension from the penetrant. The emerging oily penetrant at a surface opening acts to break this colored film which draws away from the vicinity of the defect. The evaporation of the dye solvent leaves the surface of the part colored except for an area immediately surrounding the defects. Such uncolored areas are observed by inspection of the surface in a good light, and remain as a permanent indication until the dye film is washed off. While of interest, the method has no advantage over conventional penetrant procedures and has found no commercial applications.

64. PETROLATUM TEST FOR INCIPIENT FATIGUE CRACKS. Prof. T. J. Dolan at the University of Illinois, in connection with his work on the fatigue failure of metals, has used a novel method for detecting the beginning of fatigue cracking in laboratory specimens undergoing fatigue testing. The method also was used for detecting fatigue cracking in aluminum specimen at General Motors Research Laboratories. The bright machined specimen is coated with white petrolatum at the start of the test. When a crack starts, "working" of the metal as the crack is opened and closed due to the applied stresses, permits some petrolatum to penetrate the crack. In a short time the wearing of one side of the crack against the other rubs a small amount of metal from the crack surfaces as these are smoothed to produce the typical smooth surfaces of a progressing fatigue crack. This removed metal acts to stain the petrolatum a dark to black color, visible at the surface of the test specimen as continued working of the crack squeezes petrolatum out of the crack.

The test is reported to give good indications, although it may be questioned whether the actual inception of a crack is indicated.

*U.S. Patent 2,340,940—T. de Forest.

Magnetic particle or fluorescent penetrant techniques would be expected to be more sensitive, provided the tests were applied at the proper time. It would seem that some error in the number of stress cycles at the start of cracking is permissible, and that the continuous "in test" nature of the petrolatum technique would be of great advantage if the results are within such a permissible error.

65. FUGITIVE DYE METHOD. One other approach, which, in contrast to most of those described above, has all the elements of a practical and very sensitive test for both fine and coarse surface flaws, has been given the name of "Fugitive Dye Method."* The penetrant in this process is formulated for maximum penetrability—that is, no modification to make the penetrant water-washable is necessary. The dyes used, either fluorescent or of the color-contrast type, are selected for their *instability* when exposed to intense short-wave ultra-violet light. The former insures maximum penetrability, the latter gives a means for quenching all surface background color by the fading technique.

In practice the penetrant is applied by any of the usual methods. Excess penetrant is removed by wiping, or by a water wash, but no effort is made to remove the surface film completely. The parts are then subject to heat to dry the surface to free it of both penetrant and/or water, and then exposed to intense short-wave ultraviolet light. The heating and exposure can be simultaneous and automatic operations. Time of exposure may vary from a few seconds to two or three minutes.

The ultraviolet light, during the exposure, destroys the thin surface film of dye completely, but does not penetrate to or destroy the dye in either the wide and shallow or the fine tight defects. Great flexibility is possible by varying the time of exposure, with respect to the sensitivity to the wide shallow type of defect. After this exposure, developer is applied in any of the usual ways, and inspection carried out under black light.

Lack of permanence of the fluorescent dyes, if exposed for any length of time to either black light or daylight, is a principal drawback of the method. Fading is of course much slower under these types of radiation than under the intense short-wave ultra-violet used in the processing. Advantages lie in speed and simplicity of

*U.S. Patent No. 2,774,886, Taber de Forest and D. W. Parker.

processing, and the possibilities for automation. Sensitivity is comparable to the post-emulsification penetrant process. The latter has secured commercial acceptance because it fits in well with the techniques and equipment long in use for the water-wash type of penetrants; whereas the fugitive dye method would require many changes in operations and equipment.

CHAPTER 5

NATURE AND PROPERTIES OF DEVELOPERS*

1. FUNCTION OF THE DEVELOPER. The term "developer" is aptly applied to this material and inherently describes its function in the penetrant inspection process. The dictionary defines the word as an agent that "discloses or reveals" or causes something "to become gradually visible or manifest." This is exactly what the developer does to a penetrant indication at a defect.

The minute amount of penetrant liquid which emerges from a small surface opening presents to the designers of this test method the problem of enhancing in any possible way the visible evidence of its presence. Penetrants themselves are made more brilliant and intense in color and this has done a great deal to make the indication more "seeable." However, the developer acts in a different way to increase "seeability." It uses the penetrant that is available at the defect and by spreading it increases the amount of light emitted or the contrast that makes it visible to the eye.

2. HOW THE DEVELOPER WORKS: The developer has several different actions, all of which tend to increase "seeability." Developers consist of fine powder applied over the surface of the part being inspected, after the penetrant has been applied and the excess removed. The developer powder then does the following things:

(a) It has a blotting action, which serves to draw more penetrant liquid from the surface opening.

(b) It provides a reflective base over which the penetrant can spread and disperse, thus increasing the amount of penetrant-covered surface exposed to the eye.

(c) It acts to cover up confusing background, and in some forms provides a complete background contrast layer over the surface.

(d) Solvent-type developers, in addition to the blotting action of the developer powder itself, act to bring more penetrant out of the crack through the solvent action of the suspending liquid on the penetrant.

(e) Through all the above actions the developer increases to a high degree the sensitivity of the method, and at the same

*Please refer also to Appendix II for additional discussion of developer action.

time shortens the time required for indications to become visible to the inspector.

The developer, then, may actually be a critical part of the inspection process, in that it may make visible borderline indications which might otherwise be missed. In all cases, however, it is a desirable step since it cuts inspection time significantly by hastening the appearance of indications.

In order to function properly to this end it should be emphasized that the developer must be designed to work with the penetrant with which it is to be used. A developer tuned to a specific penetrant should be used with that penetrant, and may be completely ineffective with another. The penetrant and developer must be consistent and compatible with each other. They must not repel each other.

3. PROPERTIES REQUIRED OF A DEVELOPER. To carry out its functions to the fullest possible extent, a developer must therefore have certain properties or characteristics, which can be clearly defined. Though all of these characteristics are usually not to be found to a maximum degree in any given material or formulation, still they must all be considered in designing a good developer.

(a) The material must be absorptive so as to secure a maximum of blotting action.

(b) It must be fine grained and have a particle shape that will disperse and expose the small amount of penetrant at a defect over as large a surface area as practical, while retaining strong indications and sharp definition of defects.

(c) It must be able to mask out to as large a degree as possible interfering background colors, and itself provide a contrast background for indications, particularly with color contrast penetrants.

(d) It must be easily, evenly and lightly applicable.

(e) It must form a thin or minimum coating uniformly over a surface.

(f) It must be easily wet by the penetrant at the defect and allow the liquid to spread over the particle surfaces.

(g) It must not be itself fluorescent if used with fluorescent penetrants.

(h) It must be easily removable after the inspection is completed.

(i) It must not contain ingredients harmful to parts being inspected or to the equipment used in the inspection operation.

(j) It must not contain ingredients harmful or toxic to the operator.

4. TYPES OF DEVELOPERS. Developers are of four types:

(a) Dry powders.

(b) Water suspensions of powders.

(c) Solutions in water.

(d) Solvent suspensions of powders.

5. DRY DEVELOPERS. Historically, dry powders were the type first to be used with fluorescent penetrants, though the alcohol-whiting suspensions had been used for many years previously with the old oil and whiting method. Today the dry powders are still very widely used in fluorescent methods, though they have little application with color-contrast penetrants.

The first powders used were simply chalk or talc and these gave reasonably good results under most circumstances. As the method became more widely used, and the action of developers better understood, however, shortcomings of these powders became more apparent. They were not reliable in many borderline cases. Later much lighter amorphous silica powders were used and these were in many ways superior.

Today the best dry powder developers are combinations of powders carefully selected to give all the characteristics needed in a developer.

6. CHARACTER OF POWDERS. Ideally, dry powder developers should be light and fluffy and should cling to dry metallic surfaces in a fine film of dust. The tendency to cling should not result in excessive adherence of powder over the surface since at fine defects the amount of penetrant is so small it cannot work through a heavy powder coating.

Ideally also, the powder should not float and fill the air with dust. Unfortunately the powders that make the best dry developers do float to a considerable extent so that dusty air at the developer station is unavoidable. Special consideration must therefore be given to the effect on the operator if the dust is breathed in. (See Section 7 below.)

The color of the powders is usually white. In some cases an identifying tinting color is added in very small amount, since the whiteness is only of real importance if used with color contrast penetrants. Fluorescent inspections are conducted in at most dim light, and color in the developer does not affect results. However, if any tinting color is added to a developer it must be very slight, and since many dyes tend to quench the luminescence of fluorescent dyes, this type should not be used at all. Even a *little* tendency to quench fluorescence at a marginal fine indication might be very serious. It is of more importance, in this case, that both the color and the composition of the powder be transparent to black light. Developer particles should not absorb the ultra-violet wave lengths used, since if they do, the amount of black light available to energize the fluorescent indication would tend to be reduced.

For purposes of storage and handling, as well as application, the powders should not be hygroscopic. If they tended to pick up moisture when stored in an area of high humidity, they might lose their ability to flow and dust easily, and might pack or lump up in containers or in the developer bins of the inspection equipment.

7. TOXICITY AND PRECAUTIONS. Dry developers made and sold by reputable manufacturers do not cause silicosis or other lung diseases if breathed by the operator. The fluffy, artificially produced silica powders which are used differ in this respect from siliceous rock dust which is notorious for this hazard.

Nevertheless, the powders are dry and absorbent by design, and they do therefore tend to dry the skin or other membranes. If breathed to any large or continuing extent, the linings of air passages may become dried and irritated as by any dust, and this can result in discomfort for the operator.

If an operator is working continually at a developer station rubber gloves to protect the hands, and respirators for the nose may be desirable. Modern equipment often embodies an exhaust system over the developer bin, which prevents dust from rising above the level of the bin. Powder recovery filters are a part of such an installation. Automatic application of developers also eliminates this difficulty.

NATURE AND PROPERTIES OF DEVELOPERS

Fig. 28—Exhaust and recovery equipment for dry developer bins.

8. METHODS OF APPLYING DRY DEVELOPERS. Hand processing equipment usually incorporates a developer station, and if dry developer is used, this consists of an open tank containing the developer powder. Parts are dipped into the powder, or powder is picked up with a scoop or the hands, and dropped on the surfaces of the part. Excess powder is removed by shaking and tapping the part. This is a simple and very effective method of application. Some of the powders are so light and fluffy that parts are dipped as easily as into a liquid, and excess freely comes away.

Other effective methods make use of rubber spray bulbs, or air-operated spray guns. An electrostatic-charged powder gun also has been developed for dry powders which gives an extremely even and adherent coating on metal parts. A simple applicator is a very soft bristle brush. The latter is useful if only a portion of the surface of a large part is being inspected.

Another method of application, using a low pressure air system, has been used very successfully. The dry developer powder is contained in a 15-gallon air agitated pressure tank. Powder is carried by the low pressure air from the tank through a 1-inch diameter soft rubber hose, which is manipulated by the operator to apply the powder over either baskets of small parts or individual large components. The system works very well and readily deposits a light layer of developer powder where it is needed. A dust collecting system is necessary at the station where it is used to draw away the excess powder emitted by the hose.

A fully automatic applicator has proven quite successful in a number of applications. This consists of a dust-cabinet in which, by means of air nozzles, developer powder is blown into the air space of the cabinet to form a dense cloud. Parts are passed through this cloud and become coated with powder. In one version a bin contains the powder with the air nozzles to blow up the dust cloud, and parts or baskets of parts are set onto a grill over the bin. Special design precautions must be taken to assure even coating on the

Fig. 29—Automatic dry powder developer application unit.

bottom as well as on the top of parts. To prevent escape of dust into the room the cabinet should not be opened until the powder has time to settle after shutting off the air blast. In some installations an exhaust and powder recovery filter is used.

9. REMOVAL OF POWDER AFTER INSPECTION. In many cases the amount of powder adhering to the surface is so small that removal is not necessary. This is especially true in connection with castings or other unfinished parts. Sometimes the presence of the light film of developer powder makes it obvious at a glance that the parts have been inspected, thus serving a useful purpose.

In many cases, however, removal of the powder is essential. Cleaning with an air blast sometimes suffices, or a water or solvent spray can be used. The most effective method is to put the parts through a mechanical washer.

10. CONTAMINATION PROBLEMS. It is worth while to take precautions to keep the developer bin clean and to avoid foreign material of any sort getting into it. Droplets of penetrant falling into the developer bin may cause false indications when such developer is applied to a part. Water and oil similarly will cause the developer to function poorly and to stick to surfaces, and thus interfere with a proper developer action.

11. WET DEVELOPERS. Wet developers are of three types. The first and most widely used is a suspension of developer powder in water. The second consists of solutions in water of suitable salts. The third is a suspension of powder in some volatile solvent. Each has certain advantages and disadvantages, which will be discussed below.

12. WATER SUSPENDIBLE DEVELOPERS. The idea of suspending the developer powder in water was an obvious answer to the problem of speeding up developer application in the mass inspection of small to medium size parts by the fluorescent inspection process. A basket of small, irregularly shaped parts that has gone through the steps of penetration and washing can be coated with developer in one quick dip in a water suspension. Not only is it quick but coverage is thorough and complete over all surfaces. No dry powder application method has all these advantages to the same degree.

The application of wet developer is made just after washing and before drying, and the parts are then put through the drier. The dried surfaces are thus uniformly coated with a thin film of developer. Developing time is cut down materially, since the heat of the drier helps to bring penetrant back out of surface openings and with the developer film already in place, developing action proceeds at once. Since parts are ready for inspection in a shorter period of time, before excessive bleed-out from large openings takes place, better definition of defect indications is often obtained.

It is easy to see the advantage of the use of wet developer with automatic inspection equipment, since baskets of parts, or individual parts, can be coated thoroughly with developer merely by a quick dip in a bath or by passing through a developer spray or shower station on a conveyor.

13. SENSITIVITY OF WET DEVELOPERS. There has been a great deal of discussion and considerable difference of opinion as to the relative sensitivity of the wet and dry developers. As a matter of fact, each type has advantages in sensitivity under certain conditions. (See Section 28 below.) Careful comparisons in the laboratory seem to indicate that in most circumstances the wet is slightly less sensitive than the dry in showing up borderline indications. Sensitivity of the wet developer can be seriously impaired if the thickness of coating applied becomes too heavy, and very careful maintenance of the suspensions at the proper concentration is of importance. Some operators consider that the advantages of the wet system of developer application over the dry out-weigh some reduction in sensitivity, and this may be a matter for individual decision.

14. COMPOSITION OF WATER SUSPENSIONS: The material for wet developer is furnished as a dry powder which is added before use to water in recommended proportions—usually from one third to one pound per gallon. After drying on the surface of the part, the film of developer must in general possess the same characteristics as the dry developer powders; that is, it must have the same ability to absorb and disperse the penetrant emerging from the defect.

However, formulation of the wet developer material is more complicated than the dry. It must contain various agents to make a good working suspension. Dispersing agents, and agents to help retard settling out and caking are necessary, as well as inhibitors to prevent or retard corrosion of parts and of equipment. Agents must also be added to assist or make easy, removal of the developer coating from the surface of parts after inspection. To insure complete and even coverage over surfaces which may retain a trace of oil, wetting agents are also required. In addition to all this, the dry material as furnished must stand shipping and storing without hardening or caking in the container. Thus the formulation of a suitable wet developer is a far more complex problem than is the case with the powders which are applied dry.

The dried coating of developer must not itself fluoresce, nor may it absorb or filter out the black light used for inspection. Furthermore, none of the ingredients can have any deleterious reaction with the fluorescent dyes or in any way act to reduce their brilliance. (This requirement does not apply to the same degree if the developer is used with color-contrast penetrants.) Usually, therefore, the water suspension has a pH on the alkaline side, since acids tend to impair the fluorescent brilliance of the dyes. This alkalinity, though not high, does impose the need to protect the hands of the operator from prolonged or continual contact with the suspension, and wearing of rubber gloves is recommended.

15. APPLICATION OF WET DEVELOPERS. The simplicity of applying wet developers is their outstanding advantage. Hand application by dipping or flowing-on from a nozzle are common methods. In automatic units flowing or spraying are usual, though automatic dipping into tanks is also sometimes employed. Care must be taken that the suspension is well agitated so that all particles are in suspension. If this is not done, control of the thickness of applied coating—which is of great importance to secure uniform inspections—is impossible. Special pump agitators are essential in automatic units to maintain a uniform suspension, and are desirable in *all* types of equipment.

Spray application in automatic units sometimes introduces problems due to foaming of the suspensions. Design of spray equipment must be such as to minimize air-entrapment, or otherwise combat the tendency of the developer suspension to foam.

16. TEMPERATURE LIMITATIONS. Since the suspending liquid is water, operation of equipment at temperatures below freezing becomes difficult. If *parts* are not at freezing temperatures, heating units in the developer tank will prevent the suspension from freezing in the tank, but this will not go very far in preventing freezing on the surface of exceeding cold parts. Fortunately in most cases the inspections can be carried out in warm shops. Castings, or other parts which may have been stored outside in near-zero weather, can be brought in and allowed to warm up before inspecting.

At the other end of the scale, no serious limitation exists at temperatures moderately above ambient, except that loss of water by evaporation is more rapid, the higher the temperature. To avoid having the bath concentration climb beyond safe limits at such elevated temperatures, more frequent checks are necessary, with addition of make up water as required.

17. REMOVAL AFTER INSPECTION. As in the case of dry developer, removal of the coating of developer is not always necessary, depending on what subsequent processing the parts are to receive. However, cleaning of *finished* parts is usually necessary. The coating of developer applied by the wet method can best be removed by a water wash. This can be done by hand with a water spray—preferably with warm water—or better by putting the parts through a mechanical washer using a detergent.

If allowed to remain indefinitely on the surface of some aluminum alloys, some surface corrosion or even pitting can occur, although this is by no means true with all metals or alloys.

18. CONCENTRATION OF SUSPENSIONS. In using the water suspended developers, the amount of powder in suspension must be carefully maintained at the optimum point. Too much or too little developer on the surface of a part—within fairly narrow limits—means loss of sensitivity. Methods for control of bath concentration have been devised and they should be constantly used for frequent checks.

Too heavy a bath leads to difficulties other than overall loss of sensitivity. A heavy bath tends to stick more in fillets and pockets, and to accumulate along the lower edge of parts, and not drain clean. This not only interferes with proper inspection in these areas, but makes cleaning after inspection more difficult. Details of maintaining bath strength are given in Chapter 7, Section 14, and in Chapter 17, Section 47.

19. WATER-SOLUBLE DEVELOPERS. By using a material soluble in water to produce, after drying, a coating of suitable characteristics for a developer, many of the problems inherent in the suspension type wet developers are eliminated. Unfortunately most water soluble materials do not make good developers, and although some fairly successful formulations have been devised, it does not appear probable that this type of developer will ever fully replace the suspension type.

Wetting, corrosion and foaming considerations must be met in the solution just as in the suspension type; but the problems of maintaining a uniform suspension of proper concentration are of course absent. Concentration changes due to evaporation must however, be controlled. Problems of even distribution over the surface and of removal after inspection are much simplified. Further improvements in this type of material are to be expected and the use of soluble developers may well become increasingly important.*

20. SOLVENT SUSPENDABLE DEVELOPERS. The prototype of modern solvent suspendible developers is the whiting-alcohol mixture of the old oil and whiting method. The solvent technique is a very effective means for getting a smooth coating of developer over the surface. Since the solvents used are moderately quick-drying, there is very little running of developer even on vertical surfaces, and a uniform coat is not difficult to obtain. The solvent may or may not also be a solvent for the penetrant. It is sometimes a partial solvent, at least, for the dye of the penetrant.

With fluorescent penetrants this type of developer is used primarily in portable kits, with spray cans, but is seldom used in connection with large lot inspection for reasons which will be discussed in the following section (21). It is almost universally used with color contrast penetrants and serves some different and important functions in the latter process.

21. FUNCTION OF THE SOLVENT. In the old oil and whiting method it would seem probable that alcohol was originally chosen as the solvent because it was easily available, quick drying, and would "cut" the remnants of oil or grease on the surface of parts, to give a good smooth coat. It had little tendency to dissolve oil out of the defects, allowing the dirty oil to come out in due course without assistance, to stain the developer layer

The solvent in present day developers still serves the same purposes, but has the additional function of helping to bring the penetrant out of the defect by tending to dissolve the penetrant as a whole, and giving it greater mobility on emergence to produce a

*Here see Appendix II for further information on water soluble developers.

stain on the developer. Actually there is some question as to whether this is an altogether good effect. To the extent that the developer dissolves penetrant from the defect it does so prematurely and spreads the penetrant and dye before the developer coat is dry. At very fine defects this hinders the formation of very fine indications.

Whether this is actually seriously harmful or not, the solvent developers do seem to help produce indications in the color-contrast method, and are almost universally used. Since the color-contrast method inherently has difficulty revealing the finest of cracks, perhaps the limit of sensitivity is reached before the harmful effect of the solvent action of the developer makes itself felt. There is no reason why solvent developers should not be used on fluorescent penetrants provided the above limitations are accepted. They actually are used with some portable field testing outfits.

On a rough surface the solvent developer sometimes has an unfavorable effect in a different way, with the very brilliant fluorescent penetrants. It draws out any small trace of fluorescent material remaining in rough spots and causes an undesirable over-all background glow. A sensitive dry developer is best used on such rough surfaces.

As stated before, the matter of the effect of solvents on sensitivity is somewhat controversial. It seems reasonable, however, that a solvent like alcohol or selected chlorinated solvents which are of high volatility would be less harmful than kerosene or other liquids which remain to spread and blur the indications. As a matter of fact it has been found that solvent spray developers employing *volatile* solvents can be very effective in showing up very fine cracks if the spray is passed lightly and rapidly over the surface. In this way the surface is wetted for only a very short period of time. Penetrant is drawn out of the cracks but spreading is minimized due to quick evaporation of the solvent. The technique can also be used very effectively with fluorescent penetrants.

22. OTHER TYPES OF SOLVENTS. Chlorinated solvents have been used quite extensively for this type of developer. They have the advantage of being non-flammable, which of course alcohol is not. But some objection is raised against their use because of the health hazard involved. Some of the newer types of chlorinated solvents have been approved as being no more hazardous to health than gasoline or oil vapors, and are considered safe to use for this purpose in the quantities usually involved in color-contrast applications. Certainly the fire-safe aspect is very important, as alcohol-base materials are extremely flammable.

23. FUNCTION OF THE SUSPENDED POWDER. The powder must possess the usual properties of a developer—ability to absorb and disperse penetrant. In addition, in the color-contrast system, it has an important—in fact essential—part to play in the inspection. It must form the uniform, dead white layer which serves as an opaque background for the colored dye indications. Chalk is commonly used for the purpose—or a mixture of chalk and other white powders—to improve the color and texture of the background. It is important that the powder be easily suspendible, and that it not cake hard in the container. It must be readily re-suspended after it has stood for some time, in storage or between uses.* **

24. APPLICATION OF SOLVENT TYPE DEVELOPERS. The simplest method of applying is with a paint brush, and this method is commonly used and gives a satisfactory developer coat. In recent years pressure spray cans have been very successful and have rapidly become the preferred method of application. In large installations air-pressure spray guns have been used.

In applying, excessive deposits are to be avoided, as too heavy a powder coat greatly reduces sensitivity for fine defects. However, a minimum coat is limited by the need for an even, fairly opaque covering of the surface, as without the white background the color-contrast process will not give satisfactory indications.*

25. REMOVAL AFTER INSPECTION. Because of the dense white coat left by the developer, removal is almost always required. The powder washes off easily with water or with solvents. Vapor degreasing also is a satisfactory way to clean, except that the powder will accumulate in the degreaser and will necessitate rather frequent cleaning of the equipment if many parts are so treated.

26. CONCENTRATION OF THE SUSPENSION. This type of developer is almost always pre-mixed by the manufacturer to the optimum concentration. The exact ratio of powder to solvent is actually not very critical, but cans of mixed developer must be kept tightly

*Here see Appendix IV for further discussion of color-contrast penetrants, developers and techniques.

**Here also see Appendix II for full discussion of the functions of developer coatings.

closed to avoid loss of solvent, resulting in too heavy a mixture. Too thin a mixture, on the other hand, will not give an opaque coat in one brushed-on application, and this is a practical limit for a minimum ratio of powder to solvent.

27. EFFECT OF SULPHUR. The presence of sulphur and certain other elements in any developer is considered objectionable when inspecting certain types of alloy steels. Such metals will absorb these elements and become brittle if they are heated to high temperatures with developer containing such elements remaining on the surface, either during fabrication, heat treatment, or in the course of operation in service. If the developer were *completely* removed after inspection no embrittlement problem would exist. But on highly critical components it cannot be assumed that all developer is always cleaned out of fillets and holes difficult of access.

For this reason developers are formulated to avoid insofar as possible the presence of such elements. However, some of the materials needed in the formulation of certain developers inherently contain sulphur, so that if these critical alloys are being inspected it is well to verify the content of such objectionable elements in the developer being used.

28. SELECTION OF PROPER DEVELOPER. Since developers play such an important part in securing successful results in penetrant inspection, it is important that the right one be used for a given job.

It has been found, for instance, that on very smooth or polished surfaces, the dry powder does not adhere sufficiently, but slips off of the smooth surface. Here wet developer or even solvent developers do a better job. On the other hand, on very rough surfaces dry powder gives far better results than wet.

A few general rules regarding the choice of developers can be set down:

(a) Use wet developer (water suspendible or solvent base) in preference to dry on very smooth surfaces.

(b) Use dry developer on very rough surfaces.

(c) Wet developers are best adapted to high production inspection of small parts due to greater ease and speed of application.

(d) Wet developers cannot be used reliably where sharp fillets unavoidably accumulate developer so as to mask indications.

(e) Solvent developers are good on cracks, but are not satisfactory for finding wide shallow defects.

(f) Reprocessing rough surfaces is difficult when wet developers or solvent developers have been used.

Table VII shows some of these preferences in tabular form.

In all cases it should be remembered that the developer does not in itself produce indications. It simply absorbs the penetrant indication already present in or at the defect and amplifies its visibility and makes it easier for the inspector to see it. Developers and application methods must be such that they do not smear, reduce or otherwise interfere with the function of the indications in locating and delineating the defect.

TABLE VII

CHOICE OF DEVELOPERS BASED ON SURFACE CONDITIONS

For Fluorescent Penetrants In Order of Preference		
Very Smooth Surfaces	Very Rough Surfaces	All Other Surfaces
1. Wet	Dry-Fluffy	Water soluble
2. Solvent	Water soluble	Dry-Fluffy or Wet
3. Dry-Fluffy	Wet	
4. Water soluble	Solvent	Solvent
For Color Contrast Penetrants All Types of Surfaces		
	1. Solvent	
	2. Wet	

For a further discussion of developer function and its action in increasing the "seeability of indications" please turn to Appendix II.

CHAPTER 6

THE PENETRANT METHOD—FACTORS AFFECTING ITS OPERATION

1. THE FIVE ESSENTIAL STEPS. In Chapter 2 the five essential steps of the penetrant inspection process were enumerated. We are ready now to look at these steps in greater detail and examine the factors that are involved in their successful performance—without at this time going into details of techniques when using specific penetrants. The five steps are:

(a) Cleaning and preparation of parts.

(b) Application of penetrant. Fig. 30 shows this step diagramatically, the penetrant filling the crack and extending in a film over the surface.

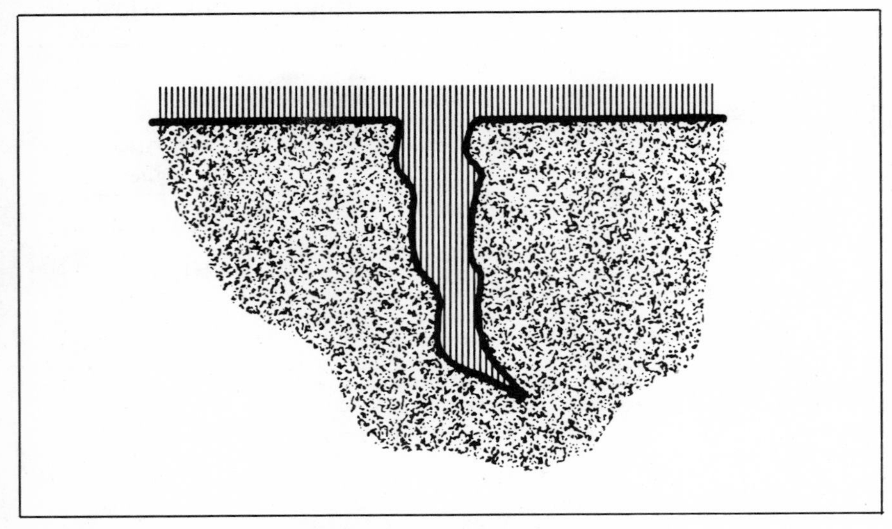

Fig. 30—Penetration.

(c) Removal of excess penetrant from the surface. Fig. 31 shows this removal by means of a wash or spray, though other means will be discussed later.

(d) Development. It has been pointed out that a drying step is involved between removal of excess penetrant and development, if water has been used to wash. If wet developer

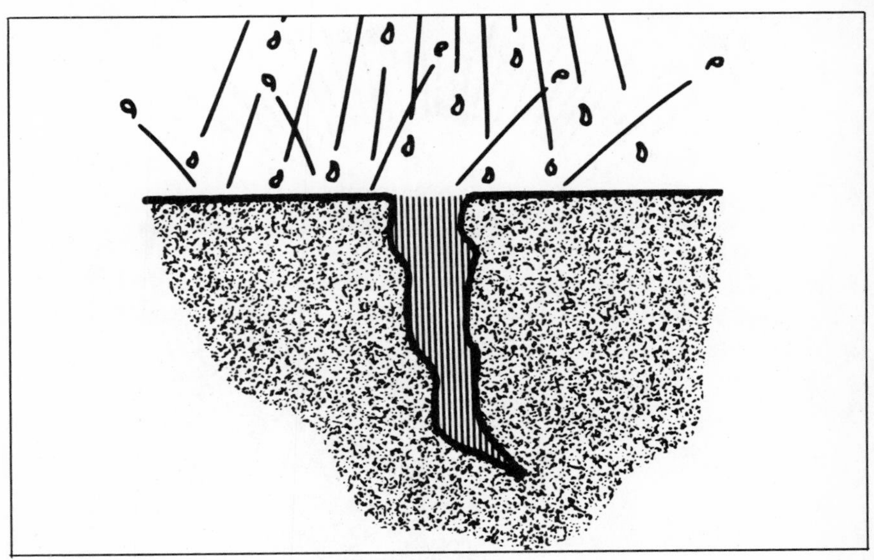

Fig. 31—Wash.

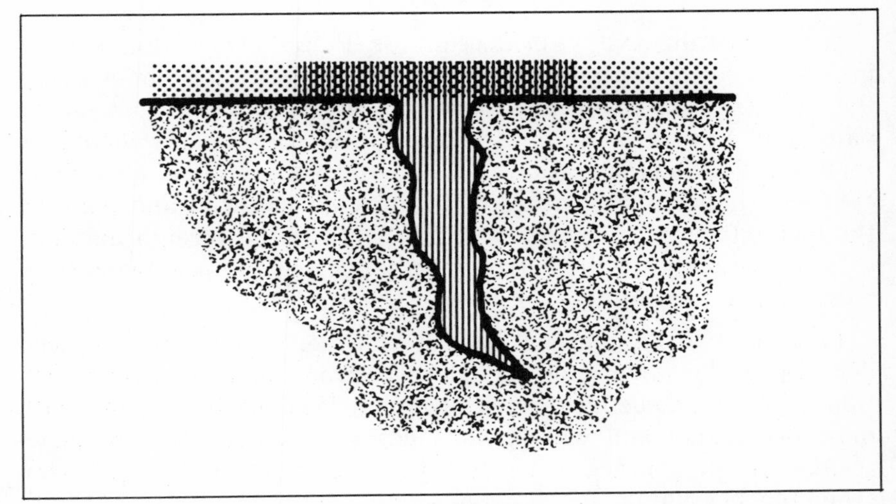

Fig. 32—Develop.

is used it is applied before the drying. Fig. 32 shows the action of the developer.

(e) Inspection. This is carried out under black light or white light depending on the type of penetrant used. Fig. 33 illustrates the viewing of the indication.

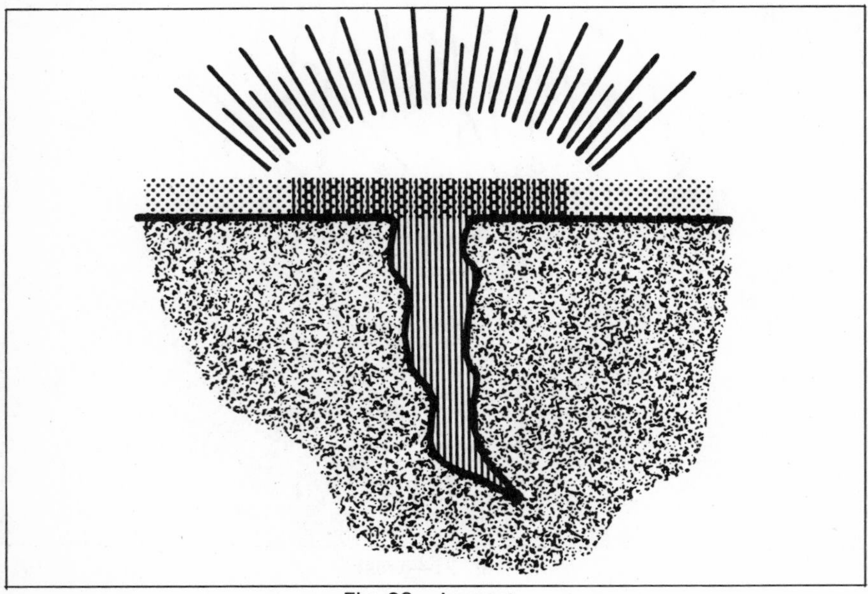

Fig. 33—Inspect.

2. Cleaning and Preparation of Parts. This step is most important since anything that hinders the penetrant from entering the defects will defeat the inspection entirely. Dirt, rust, scale, paint and any form of foreign matter on the surface should be removed. Previous operations, such as drawing, buffing, anodizing, etc., may indicate the nature of the foreign material and point to the method for satisfactory cleaning. Even if the foreign material does not actually fill the defect, it may prevent the penetrant from wetting and spreading evenly over the surface.

Especially to be guarded against is water, which may be accidentally on the surface, or may be there from some previous operation, such as anodizing or etch cleaning. Water will not mix with most penetrants and will in most cases absolutely prevent penetrant entering a crack. Therefore the part must be dry and clean from the beginning.

Cleaning of the surface may be done with a stiff brush to remove loose dirt, and with a solvent to remove oil or grease. Not only may these prevent penetration, if present, but they will contaminate the penetrant in the tank and reduce its life and its effectiveness.

By far the most satisfactory cleaning process is vapor-degreasing. This process cleans out the cracks and other surface openings better than any hand process; and, because the parts come from it hot, all solvent is driven out of the defects. Any water which may have been in them is also driven off by the heat. There is no way to insure that cracks are dry and free of water except by heating. For these reasons, vapor degreasing as a step preparatory to any form of penetrant inspection is recommended and should always be used if practicable.

3. APPLICATION OF PENETRANT. Basically all that is necessary is to cover the surface of the part with penetrant, and leave it there long enough for it to get into the defects. Actually it is not as simple as this, for there are numerous things to consider under different circumstances.

4. METHODS OF APPLYING. If the penetrant is in a tank of sufficient depth, the obvious, simple, method is to dip the part into it and lay the part on a rack to drain. The principal thing to watch for here is that there are no pockets of trapped air due to openings in the part, which will prevent the penetrant from covering all surfaces.

If parts are hot from the degreaser they should be allowed to cool to room temperature before dipping; or, if dipped hot, they should remain in the penetrant bath until they have cooled down. If removed from the penetrant while still hot, the heat will tend to dry the penetrant on the surface and prevent proper penetration. (See Section 6b below.)

If parts are too large to dip, penetrant tanks are often equipped with a pump and hose, so that the liquid can be flowed over the surface, again making sure all cavities have been covered with penetrant.

With automatic equipment spray nozzles are used to impinge penetrant on the part from all directions. If shape of the part permits, hosing or flooding may be used. Sometimes automatic dipping devices have been incorporated, instead of sprays.

For field application, penetrant, both color-contrast and fluorescent, is available in small pressurized cans which makes application for local or spot inspections easy. For larger areas—as for instance the blading of a steam turbine—air-pressure operated spray guns are used. In these circumstances no effort is made to recover excess penetrant. However, control of the spray is such that only that amount of penetrant necessary to cover thoroughly is put on, and no excessive waste results. Color-contrast penetrants are often applied with a small brush—especially when they are used for the inspection of local or restricted areas.

5. Penetration or Drain Time. When parts have been dipped, or coated with penetrant by hosing, flooding or spraying, they are usually set aside on a rack to drain. Excess penetrant is returned to the tank and recovered. The length of time during which parts are allowed to drain is an important factor in successful operation. Recovery of the penetrant is of economic importance but otherwise incidental.

Different types of discontinuities in various materials require different times to become fully penetrated. Fine, tight cracks require the longer times—as do cracks which contain oxide, carbon or some other material not possible to remove by cleaning. Penetration times vary from a fraction of a minute to many minutes and even hours. Table VIII gives some examples of typical times for penetration in various types of materials and parts. Actual

(Courtesy Pan American World Airways)

Fig. 34—Steps in the penetrant process. Parts in foreground have been dipped in penetrant and are draining. Washing station followed by drying oven are in background.

recommended times will also be given in discussing inspection of certain specific parts. (See Chapters 7, 8 & 10.)

TABLE VIII

TYPICAL PENETRATION TIMES FOR VARIOUS MATERIALS

Material	Type of Defect	Penetration Time Minutes
Aluminum		
Castings	Porosity—Cold Shuts	5-15
Magnesium		
Forgings	Laps	10-30
Welds	Porosity—Lack of Bond	10-30
Stainless Steel		
Forgings	Laps	10-60
Stainless Steel	Fatigue Cracks	20-30
Glass	Cracks	5-30
Carbide Tipped		
Tools	Grinding Cracks	10-20
Plastics	Cracks	2-30

It is usually necessary only that the surfaces be covered with penetrant, since the surface film of penetrant provides a sufficient supply for penetration of most discontinuities. Parts ordinarily need not be held submerged in the bath during penetration time. If more than half an hour is required, however, the penetrant may dry to the point where it will no longer be fluid enough to penetrate. In this case a second application or dip is needed to renew the film of penetrant.

Some specifications for the inspection of parts having defects known to require long penetration time, call for the parts to be completely immersed during the entire time. Not only does this insure maximum opportunity to penetrate, but if the time involved is several hours, it will avoid the need for reapplying penetrant every half hour. In any case, if parts are hot when dipped, they should remain in the penetrant until they have cooled completely, to avoid the accelerated drying of penetrant from a hot surface.

The above considerations apply equally to fluorescent and to color-contrast type penetrants, though the latter are seldom applied by dipping. However, if they dry during penetration time reapplication is necessary.

6. AIDS TO PENETRATION. Various procedures have been suggested and tried, and some are in actual use, for the purpose of increasing the penetrating ability of the penetrant, or more often, to speed up the penetration process. Actually experience has not shown any significant gain from these special techniques except in very special conditions or for specific purposes.

(a) HEATING OF THE PENETRANT. This has been tried and is in use in a few locations, but it is difficult to demonstrate any significant gain from the practice. A definite disadvantage is that penetrant—or some of its constituents—will evaporate from the tank even at ambient temperatures, and this evaporation is increased as temperature goes up. This can result in imbalance of the penetrant, requiring frequent renewals of the penetrant bath. It is not a recommended procedure.

(b) HEATING OF PARTS. If heat is to be employed it is much better to heat the parts, and this *does* sometimes improve penetration. Expansion of parts due to heat may open up fine cracks or may tend to loosen contaminants inside of cracks. Heating of parts also insures that all volatile materials, including water, are driven out of surface openings This is one of the advantages of degreaser cleaning.

It should be pointed out, however, that if hot parts in volume are continually being placed in penetrant tanks and allowed to cool there—as they should—the temperature of the penetrant will rise, and cooling coils may be necessary to keep the penetrant near room temperature. Also, parts should not be heated too hot, a safe limit being the maximum degreaser temperature, about 240° F.

(c) PENETRATION UNDER PRESSURE. This device is of no value whatever, since penetrant cannot be thus forced into openings closed at one end. Capillary forces available are usually far in excess of any practical pressure possible. Pressure *is* a help and is used, in testing for leaks in closed systems with penetrant. (See Chapter 14.)

(d) PENETRATION UNDER VACUUM. This is a much more logical procedure though in the majority of cases it does not show improvement at all commensurate with its cost. But it has been used in a few instances where parts are quite small and penetration time lengthy. In one case, penetration time was reported cut from 16 hours to 1 hour. The parts are submerged in penetrant in a suitable chamber and the air over the penetrant evacuated. Another procedure—probably more effective—is to exhaust the air over the parts in a suitable container, and then without releasing the vacuum, admit penetrant to cover the parts. On large parts this is not a very practical procedure.

(e) USE OF VACUUM AND PRESSURE. Theoretically, after drawing all the air out of a crack, penetrant under pressure can then be forced in. However, no improvement over the straight vacuum technique has been reported, and the increase in complexity of the equipment and cost of the process certainly do not justify its use.

(f) VIBRATION. Vibrating of parts has long been used in an effort to speed or facilitate penetration, and in some instances has been of considerable help. Vibration can be anything from hitting a part with a hammer, through mechanical vibration as with an air hammer, to sonic and ultrasonic vibration from suitable sources. Vibration, through mechanical "working" of the sides of a discontinuity, may hasten penetration. Also, vibration may loosen contaminants in cracks and allow penetrant to enter.

Ultrasonic "pumping" of the penetrant and sonic vibration of the part have been tried and found to be useful in certain critical cases though no commercial application has yet been made of these findings.*

None of the above methods will make a good penetrant out of a poor one—and if a penetrant is good to start with these "aids" are of little real help except in special instances. For example, one commercial color-contrast penetrant was found to be useless below 55° F. Pounding the part being tested with a hammer gave some test results down to 45° F. Another penetrant, however, worked perfectly well down to 20° F without pounding or vibration. Vibration might sometimes help in a different way: namely, to *shorten* penetration time or help loosen contaminants in cracks.

*U. S. Patents #2,883,549, C. E. Betz; and 2,856,538, R. C. Switzer.

The most useful "aid" is preheating the part to insure it is perfectly dry before penetration is attempted.

7. ABILITY TO PENETRATE. The ability to penetrate has already been discussed (Chapter 4, Section 18 and following), and it is necessary here only to repeat that the ability to get into cracks is a property of many if not most liquids, and that good penetrating liquids are not difficult to find. On the other hand penetrants that will successfully find defects involve more than good penetrability. The liquid with the best or fastest penetrating ability is not necessarily the best for forming indications of defects.

8. ABILITY TO PENETRATE ALSO A FUNCTION OF THE DEFECT. Defects which are clean and open at the surface are easy to penetrate even when very fine. But if the edges of the defects are forced together at the surface by high stresses, such defects may be difficult to penetrate even by the best penetrants. Such conditions are produced during rolling or forging or by shot peening of finished surfaces. If the defect is filled by some contaminant penetration may be impossible.

The character of the material under test, kind of defects expected and the processes the part has been through all may give advance warning of penetration difficulties that may be encountered.

9. REMOVAL OF EXCESS PENETRANT FROM SURFACE. Whether this step is conducted properly or not may make a great deal of difference in the success of the inspection. It is desirable to remove

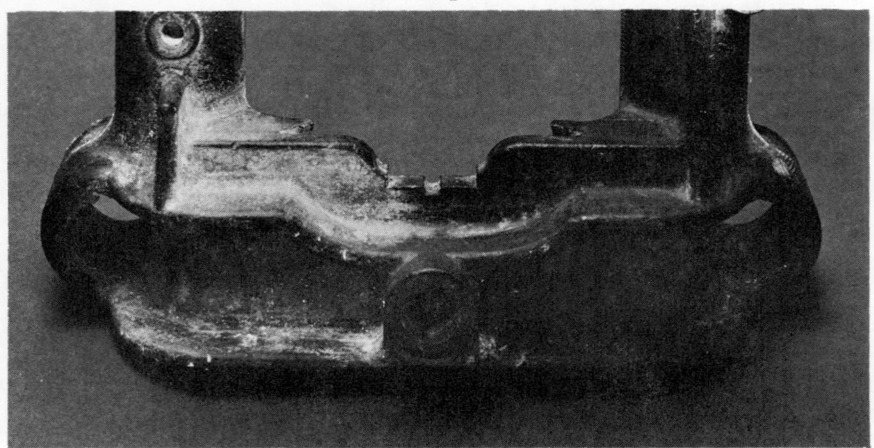

Fig. 35—Effect of poor washing—black light photograph. Left—poorly washed area. Right—properly washed area.

all excess and leave no confusing background to interfere with the indications of defects. At the same time, the cleaning operation must not remove penetrant from defects themselves. So the method of removing the surface excess is important.

10. WIPING THE SURFACE. Wiping with a dry, absorbent cloth or even paper towels is sometimes done, though it is slow, "messy" and does not leave a very clean surface. It has the single advantage that it will remove *no* penetrant from defects, except from very wide open, shallow ones. It works fairly well on smooth or polished surfaces, but very poorly on rough surfaces.

Use of a cloth moistened with solvent is a common method of cleaning, especially with color-contrast penetrants. The method is a good one if carefully done, using minimum amounts of solvent and removing the solvent quickly from the surface. If excess solvent is used the tendency to dissolve penetrant out of discontinuities is considerable. The method is too slow for quantity inspections but reasonably satisfactory for spot checking.

11. SOLVENT CLEANING. Cleaning by spraying with solvents gives a very good clean surface but is dangerous from the point of view of washing penetrant out of defects. If solvent is used it should be controlled by using a cloth to wipe the surface promptly.

Brief exposure in a vapor degreaser has been employed and in some cases it has been reported to be quite successful. It will certainly give a perfectly clean surface in a minimum of time, but the danger of removing penetrant from defects is very great. In the hands of a very careful inspector the results can be quite satisfactory on certain types of parts.

The great problem in vapor-degreaser cleaning of surface penetrant from parts is that thick metal sections have greater heat-absorbing capacity and condense more liquid on the surface than do thin or web sections. Therefore, controlled uniform surface cleaning, even with extreme care, is possible only on parts of uniform section. This condition is seldom encountered in practice.

Since excessive exposure of the surface of parts to solvents after penetration is to be avoided, use of the vapor-degreaser method of cleaning cannot be recommended for general use.

12. CLEANING WITH WATER—SINGLE STEP. To clean successfully with water requires penetrants formulated so as to be emulsifiable with water—i.e., water-wash penetrants (Chapter 7). Emulsifier might be incorporated in the wash water instead of the penetrant but this has never been successful commercially. Water is an excellent washing medium since it does not dissolve penetrant as the solvents do, and is itself a poorer penetrant than oil. Thus the tendency to remove penetrant from defects is minimized.

However, prolonged washing with water does tend to remove some penetrant from defects when the emulsifier is incorporated either in the penetrant or the wash water. The hotter the water the more this tendency increases. For this reason washing with hot water is not recommended although there is a temptation to

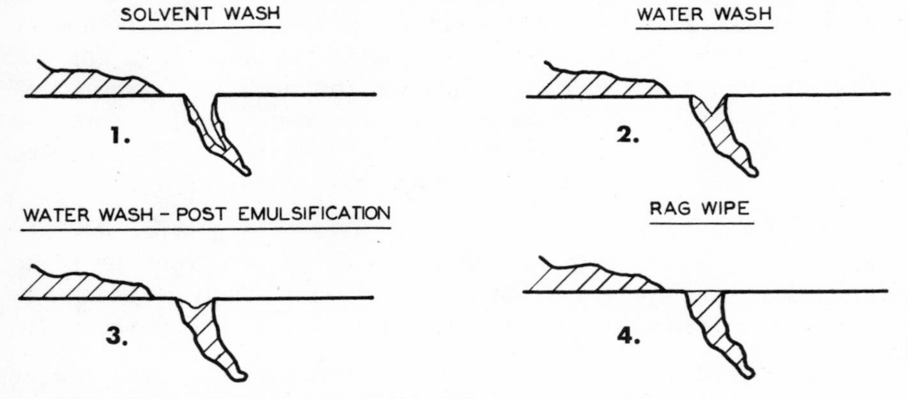

Fig. 36—Removal techniques, rated by tendency to remove penetrant from defects in order of severity. 1. Solvent-wash. 2. Water-wash with emulsifier incorporated in penetrant. 3. Water-wash with separate emulsifier. 4. Dry rag wipe.

use hot water since it makes it easier to get a clean background surface. A good compromise is to use water at ambient temperatures, but not over 110° F. Use of water under high pressure is to be discouraged, since it tends to remove penetrant from defects —especially open ones—by the force of the stream alone.

13. METHODS OF WATER WASHING. The use of a wet rag with a bucket of water is not a very good procedure even though it is sometimes used. There is little danger of over-washing, but the bucket gets contaminated with penetrant and the rag cannot be rinsed clean. If fresh water is freely available a good clean surface can be produced by repeatedly rinsing the rag in clean water.

Washing the part directly under running water from a tap is a better method, but still is not very satisfactory and often does not give a clean surface. Hot water gives cleaner surfaces than cold, but the danger of washing penetrant from cracks is considerable. The character of the emulsifier in, or used with, the penetrant is a factor in determining the optimum wash-water temperature.

The best method of washing is by use of a hose and nozzle. The character of the spray is important. It should be strong and forceful, but composed of rather coarse droplets. Such a spray

Fig. 37—Proper spray for water-washing.

seems to cut through the film of penetrant by impact, and then get under it and "roll" it off the surface. Proper spray technique removes most of the advantage of hot water in washing, although water at 75° to 110° F is still preferable to water at 45° to 50° F. It is the physical scrubbing action of high velocity large water droplets at an angle along the surface, which is most important in this best water-wash procedure.

In some applications a combination of air and water, or even of steam and water, has been tried, to hasten or make easier the washing operation. These methods cannot be broadly recommended, especially the use of steam which heats the water. Too much force with an air-water spray will increase the tendency to over-wash, though, properly used, an air-water spray gives good results. A high-water, low-air volume mixture, with fairly high air pressure in the washing gun gives best results. This gives high velocity to large water droplets and large amounts of water to sluice away penetrant, once it has been separated from the surface. High-air low-water mixtures will give poor results. The air-water gun is also a way to get *enough* force in the spray if water pressure is low.

14. WASHING BY IMMERSION. Immersing the part in water has been frequently tried as a method of washing, and under proper conditions can give quite satisfactory results. There are however a number of factors that must be considered in this technique. The self-emulsifying penetrant must be such that simple immersion in water brings about complete emulsification without much—or any—motion. All water-wash type penetrants do not meet this requirement. If the water bath is vigorously agitated with air or the part kept moving in the water, results are considerably improved, and both of these things are done where the process is in use.

The tank should be so constructed that there is a constant overflow of water at the surface, so that any penetrant that may rise to the surface will be carried away, and the bath be continually renewed with fresh water. Also, in this case hot water is generally used. Absence of force or vigorous motion minimizes the tendency of hot water to over-wash, although over-washing can still occur if immersion is unduly prolonged. Temperatures of water used are from 140° F to as high as 185° F. The hotter the water the cleaner the surface produced, but the greater the danger of washing penetrant out of defects.

15. WATER-WASHING—TWO STEP PROCESS. This is the post-emulsification technique. In this case the penetrant does not incorporate an emulsifier. Instead, when penetration is complete, a coating of emulsifier is applied over the surface as a separate step. Time is allowed for the emulsifier to mix with the surface film of penetrant, after which washing with a water spray readily gives a clean surface. Again, water at temperatures up to 110° F gives best results.

In this case the wash water removes only that penetrant which has become impregnated with emulsifier, and prolonged washing will not remove penetrant in either the fine or the open defects

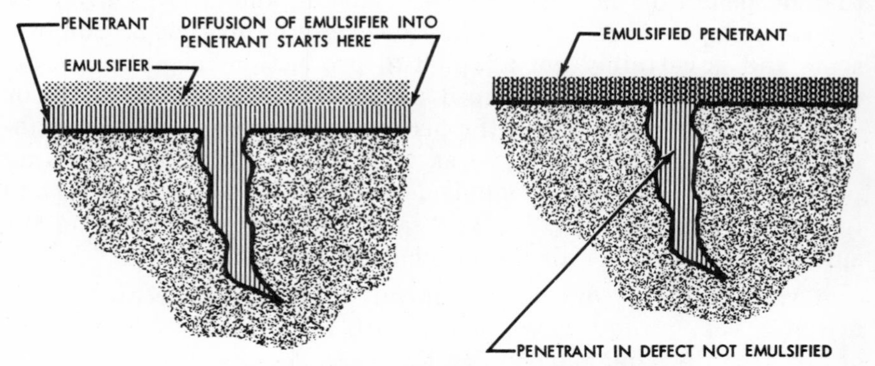

Fig. 38—Action of emulsifier in P.E. method.

into which *emulsifier* has not entered. The technique is especially sensitive for wide shallow discontinuities.

With very large parts, washing with water spray after applying the emulsifier cannot always be accomplished without giving the emulsifier too much time to act on some portions of the surface. Here a dip into a water bath is sometimes employed to stop emulsifier action over the entire surface at just the right time, after which washing is completed with a suitable water spray. The dip bath is usually hot—165° F—and the immersion time should be brief, so that all emulsifier penetrant mixture is not removed from the surface. Some remaining emulsifier after the dip is necessary to help the spray wash produce a clean surface. Although used in a few cases, this procedure has not been altogether satisfactory. See Chapter 8 for a full discussion of the post-emulsification process.

16. CHECKING THE WASHING PROCESS. The cleaning from the surface of excess fluorescent penetrant should be checked with the black light to make sure all areas and openings receive a thorough washing. When hand water-washing is used a black light is usually placed over the washing station and the progress of cleaning can be observed as it is being carried out. After automatic washing, if the process is working properly, this may not be necessary, though checking is still desirable.

17. OTHER CLEANING METHODS. Some other methods of removing excess penetrant from the surface have been tried but none has found widespread applications. In a few cases, where water or solvents have not been available or not conveniently used, a dry cleaning with a mild sand blast or blast with other solid material has been fairly satisfactory. Dry blasting has the advantage that no penetrant is removed from defects, and if carefully done a good clean surface can result. However, the method is cumbersome and is certainly not adapted to production inspection, especially of small irregular shaped parts. However, if the sand- or shot-blast is already part of the production process, as in the cleaning of castings, it can serve as a no-cost method of removing penetrant, if penetrant is applied before this cleaning step; and it does an excellent job. In fact, sand particles remaining on the surface may serve as all the developer needed, as well.

A variant of the dry-blast removal of surface penetrant is the use of a very strong water blast—with or without the admixture of air—for the same purpose. In this case cleaning is a mechanical action, when used to remove non-emulsifiable penetrant. The method has been used successfully, especially on color-contrast type penetrants. The procedure is not recommended when emulsifiers are used, since the vigorous blast tends to increase removal of penetrant from defects.

Chemical "quenching" of fluorescent dyes, with acids or other chemicals which destroy the dye has been proposed and tried. It has never been found to be very effective and has numerous disadvantages.

A better "quenching" method is the destruction of surplus fluorescent dye on the surface with short-wave ultraviolet light—the "Fugitive Dye" method. (See Chapter 4, Section 65.) This process gives a background almost completely free of fluorescent dye, and has the great advantage that no dye is removed from cracks or other surface openings into which the ultra-violet rays cannot penetrate.*

18. DRYING. Although drying was not listed separately (Section 1 above) as one of the five essential steps of the penetrant process, it is certainly a sub-step of the highest importance and can have a critical effect on the results of the inspection. In order for penetrant to come back out of surface openings and give clean-cut indications with the help of developers, the surface around the discontinuity must be clean and dry. Drying also aids the formation of indications in many instances, as will be shown.

*Here see Appendix V for further information on cleaning methods.

If removal of excess penetrant has been by dry wiping or with a volatile solvent, the surface is at once dry and ready for developer. If any water-wash method has been used, water must be dried from the surface. (If wet developer is to be used it is applied *before* drying (See Section 26, this chapter).) If the surface is not completely dry before dry developer is applied, the dry powder will stick to the surface unevenly and excessively. Small amounts of water getting into the developer bin will cause the powder to ball up and again lead to unsatisfactory distribution of the developer over the surface.

19. DRYING METHODS WITHOUT HEAT. Simplest method of drying is to wipe with a dry cloth, but this is slow and not applicable either to large parts or to mass inspection of small parts. The surface is seldom rendered dry enough for the immediate use of dry developer, and a short air-dry period must be allowed.

Compressed air can be used to blow off most of the surface moisture and if followed by a short air-dry period can work quite well. It is, however, slow and time consuming and rarely has any advantage over the more rapid heating methods, and does not contribute to the formation of indications as the latter methods do. In some applications an air blast is used to remove gross amounts of water from the surface, especially from cavities, before the part enters the hot air drier. This has the advantage of shortening drying time. (See Section 22 below.)

Drying by simply allowing the part to lie in the air until the water evaporates is very slow and has no advantage to offer. Water will dry unevenly, and too much time will elapse to give clean-cut indications after developer can be applied. The penetrant will bleed from large openings and spread unduly, and interpretation of the indications is made more difficult. Nevertheless, with very large parts that cannot be dried with heat, natural evaporation may be the only possible way to get them dry. In such cases use of cloths or an air blast to remove much of the water from surface and pockets will speed the operation somewhat. If a warm air blast can be made available, this also will help, but still is not equal to a heated drier.

20. DRYING WITH HEAT. The use of heat is by far the best procedure for drying, for reasons that will be apparent. But the function of hot-air drying must be understood if its full effectiveness is to be realized. The fundamental concept is that the *part* *itself* must reach a minimum temperature in addition to the mere removal of water from the surface. If the part becomes warm, penetrant tends to come out of surface openings more rapidly. Furthermore, as the penetrant emerges onto the warm surface, the volatile constituents will evaporate. The non-volatile, more viscous components do not then bleed and spread over the surface nearly so badly particularly from the larger openings which provide considerable amounts of penetrant. These effects combine to give sharp indications in a minimum of time, and they are not brought about unless the part itself becomes heated. Similarly, indications of very fine cracks are made more distinct in a shorter period and developing time is decreased.

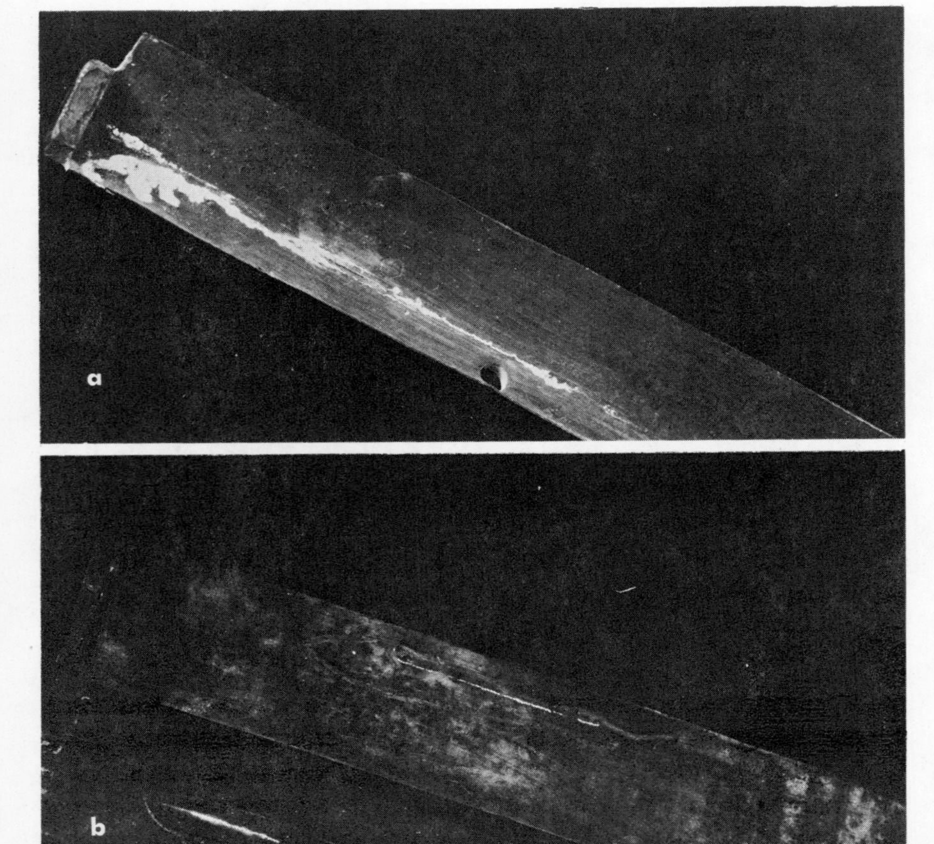

Fig. 39—Effect of bleeding on indications on bronze turbine blades. a) Bad bleeding—poor delineation. b) Little bleeding—clean cut indications.

21. WARM AIR DRYING. For the reasons just given, warm air blasts are not very satisfactory drying means. A "hair drier" type of warm air blast has often been tried. The heat available is not sufficient to warm the parts in a reasonably short period, and evaporation of water from a cool surface does not proceed very rapidly, since much of the heated air is wasted.

Heating parts under infra-red lamps is equally ineffective. The radiant heat from the lamps is not easily controlled, and is absorbed by the metal parts unevenly depending on size of the sections. Also, the radiant heat reaches only the surfaces exposed to it, and moisture in pockets or openings not directly so exposed has little tendency to dry off.

22. HOT AIR DRYING. The criterion for a good drier, or a good drying operation, is only partly its ability to dry the surfaces quickly and thoroughly. Of equal importance is the ability to heat the part to an optimum temperature in a minimum of time, so that the part is both dry and warm as promptly as possible, since this definitely increases sensitivity.

Experience has shown that these results can only be satisfactorily acomplished in an enclosed drier in which the air is moving, and to which heat is supplied at an adequate rate. With heaters of ample capacity and good recirculation of air a thermostatically controlled oven or tunnel type drier accomplishes this excellently. The amount of heat input required depends on the load of parts in the drier and even more on the efficiency of the engineered design of the drier itself, to minimize heat loss while providing adequate and efficient air circulation over the surfaces of the parts. By recirculating the air and maintaining it thermostatically at the proper temperature this is readily done. The moving air reaches all surfaces of the parts and heats them from all sides.

The proper temperature for drying has been carefully defined by long experience and careful experimentation. It should for most parts be somewhat in excess of the boiling point of water, to insure complete water removal. At the upper limit it should not be so high as to cause excessive evaporation of penetrant, so that the upper limit may vary somewhat with different penetrants. The maximum should be below any temperature that could in any way injure the part being dried. Usually 200° F is considered a good optimum temperature at which to operate the re-circulating hot air dryer, with 225° F as a pretty rigid maximum.

Parts should not be left in the drier longer than necessary to be dried and heated, since developer should be applied promptly, before too much penetrant has come out of a defect and become partially dried. With most parts, proper temperature for the parts is reached in about the same time required to dry off all moisture. Actually the part itself should not reach the full 225° F of the drying air current. For parts of thin section—say ¼″ thick—heating of the part may be too rapid, and in such cases operation of the drier at lower temperatures may be advisable—possibly as low as 150° to 175° F. Parts should not exceed 140° F.

If air blast is used, as on some automatic equipment, to blow off excess water and to lighten the drying load and shorten the time, it must be remembered that there is no merit in shortening the time below that needed to heat the parts to 150° to 175° F.

When wet developer is used, this *time* is perhaps less critical, since heating and developing take place simultaneously after the developer film has become dry.

On the other hand it should again be pointed out that drying time should not be so short that the parts themselves *fail* to reach a temperature of 140° F.

23. DRYING AFTER WET DEVELOPER. In spite of what has just been said, this is actually a somewhat more critical operation than drying before applying dry developer. Wiping and air blast drying methods are obviously inapplicable. Slow drying at ambient or slightly above ambient temperatures is very likely to produce an uneven coat of developer. Rapid drying and heating in the controlled heat of an efficiently designed recirculating hot air drier gives an even coat of developer and makes maximum use of the effect of heat on forming of indications, since the developer is fixed in place early in the heating cycle.

24. DEVELOPMENT. If the surface of the part is clean and dry it is ready for dry developer. The dry powder should be applied lightly and evenly over the entire surface. Not much powder adheres, but the amount that does is sufficient to act to bring up indications when a correctly engineered developing powder is used. Dipping, blowing or any other method of accomplishing this is satisfactory. Air-borne clouds of dust in a cabinet are used on some automatic equipment, but the method is not usable on all sizes or shapes of parts. Excess powder should be removed by shaking or tapping the part or basket of parts, or by blowing it off with a current (not a blast) of air. An air blast can easily remove too much of the powder.

25. DEVELOPMENT TIME. A minimum of time for development is a requirement for all types of inspection, in order that indications reach their maximum intensity. The actual time varies from a few minutes to an hour or more, depending on the character of the material and the defects sought. A good rule of thumb is that development time for any given material or type of defect is about one half that considered proper for penetration time. See Chapters 7, 8 and 10 for further discussion of this factor. (Also Section 32, this chapter and Appendix II on developers.)

26. WET DEVELOPMENT. As has been said, if water-suspended wet developer is used it is applied immediately after water-washing and before drying. Wet developer is seldom used on a wipe-cleaned or a solvent-cleaned surface. On such surfaces solvent-suspended wet developers are often used, however, in connection with portable kits. They are then usually applied with pressure spray cans. Wet developer (water-suspended) kept in an agitated tank, is applied by dipping, flowing or spraying over the surface. The part is then dried in a controlled heat recirculating air drier, care being taken that pools of developer are not trapped in fillets or other irregularities in the part. It is important that drying time be not prolonged, for although with the film of developer in place, developing action begins in the drier, nevertheless too much heating at this stage tends to thicken the penetrant and retards its flow out of the defect before a maximum indication is produced. As a rule parts should come out of the drier as soon as the developer has dried to a smooth white film, to allow further development to occur as the part cools. The only exception to this rule would be the case of parts of large mass, requiring additional time to warm the part itself. Time for development following drying may be equally as important with dry developer. See further discussion in Section 32 below and in Chapters 7 and 8, and Appendix II.

27. STRENGTH OF DEVELOPER BATH. The concentration of wet developer in the bath is of great importance. Too dense a bath gives too heavy a coat and may mask fine indications. Too light a bath may fail to develop fine indications at all. Bath strengths have been carefully worked out for optimum results, and means are available to make frequent checking of the bath possible, and control of bath concentration thereby easy. See Chapter 17, Section 47, for details of these controls.

28. BASIS OF CHOICE BETWEEN WET AND DRY DEVELOPERS. This subject has already been broadly discussed (Chapter 5, Section 28). Aside from the technical reasons there given for this choice, other considerations may sometimes play a part or even be controlling in making this decision. Some of these considerations are the following:

(a) Dry developer may be quicker and easier where only a few parts are involved.

(b) Dry developer is usually easier to apply to very large parts.

(c) Where cleaning has been by wiping, or with solvent, and no hot air drier is available, dry developer is usually more convenient.

(d) Wet developer is easier to apply to large numbers of small parts, using basket handling.

(e) Wet developer is easier to apply in automatic equipment by spraying or flowing.

(f) Completeness of coverage is better assured when wet developer is used than with most methods of dry developer application.

(g) Foaming of wet developer must be considered as a problem (though usually solvable) in many automatic applications.

(h) Use of dry developer may simplify removal problem after inspection, on some materials or parts, though in most cases wet developer may be very easily and completely removed with proper washing equipment.

(i) On a basis of sensitivity both are about equal with balance in favor of dry developer in some critical instances. Here method of application plays a part, as well as the character —smooth or rough—of the surfaces involved.

(j) Wet developer tends to give a sharper definition for most defects. Dry may be better on defects where heavy bleed-out of penetrant occurs.

(k) Economics may be a controlling factor. Handling of parts and application of developer may affect cost of equipment, and overshadow any questions of sensitivity or of other technical preferences. Very low-cost materials and techniques are available if maximum sensitivity is not the major factor—and if low cost is vital for the use of the penetrant test, as on industrial products of relatively low unit value.

29. SOLVENT DEVELOPER. This type of developer is used almost exclusively for color-contrast penetrants with which the dead white opaque background is essential. Usually rather heavier coats of developer are required to produce a satisfactory background than are necessary or desirable when fluorescent penetrants are used. Application by spraying or brushing onto surfaces which have been (usually) cleaned with solvents presents no particular problem.

For field or portable kit use, the solvent developers are often used with super-bright fluorescent penetrant. In this case solvent cleaning has also been used and techniques are the same as with color-contrast penetrants, except that somewhat lighter developer applications are desirable; or dry developer may be preferred on rough surfaces. (See here also Appendix V.)

30. INSPECTION. *The inspector is the key to the successful location of defects with penetrants.* If we assume that all processes up to this point have been correctly applied for optimum results, the actual seeing and appraisal of indications is up to the inspector.

The good inspector must have certain physical abilities and natural competencies. He must have good eyesight and should not be color-blind. He must be alert, intelligent and conscientious, and must be fully aware of, and willing to accept the responsibilities of the job he has to do. Given a good inspector, there are a number of things that should be done to aid him and to minimize the chances of his missing indications. Some of these things are:

(a) A good white light should be provided for color-contrast penetrant inspection.

(b) Suitable darkened booths should be provided for fluorescent penetrant inspection. Complete darkness is the desirable optimum, but reasonable exclusion of white light is often sufficient for all but the most critical inspections. Such booths or rooms should be well ventilated (even air conditioned) for comfort, since comfort is highly important to insure maximum alertness at all times. A white light should also be provided in the booth for use when needed.

(c) Black light of sufficient intensity must be provided. This is a critical requirement. See Chapter 9 for a full discussion of black light requirements.

(d) An inspector should not be expected to give continuously excellent inspections over a long period of time. Eye fatigue results in loss of efficiency. In many installations inspectors are relieved every two hours, or oftener. Sometimes operators and inspectors change off at intervals.

(e) Eye fatigue can be minimized by so placing black lights that no reflection reaches the inspector's eyes. Wearing of yellow sunglasses is recommended, since these filter all black light and most visible violet light, but permit the yellow-green light of the fluorescent indications to pass. (See Chapter 9, Section 21.)

31. DARK ADAPTION. The inspector should not walk into the booth from a normally lighted shop and immediately start to inspect fluorescent penetrant treated parts. The pupils of the eyes are contracted in bright white light, but expand greatly in dim light or in the dark, and the actual mechanism of seeing is different under the two conditions. Ability to see fine fluorescent indications is absolutely dependent on full dark adaption of the inspector's eyes. This may be accomplished simply by entering the darkened inspection area, and waiting from 5 to 10 minutes for the pupils of the eyes to dilate. Wearing of red glasses for 10 to 15 minutes before entering the booth hastens the process considerably.

Dark adaption is rapidly lost in brighter light, so the inspector should not leave the booth more often than necessary, as he must go through the process of dark adaption each time he returns. Neither should he turn on the white light in the booth unless he subsequently again allows time for dark adaptation to take place after he turns it off.

It should be remembered that absolute darkness is best for maximum sensitivity, and anything less than that is a compromise. Care should be taken that the inspection table not become spattered with stray penetrant, since this produces unwanted fluorescent light. Painting the floor of curtained inspection booths black is a good procedure, as it reduces the amount of white light reflected up into the booth from lighted shop areas.

CHAPTER 6

THE PENETRANT METHOD

32. TIMING OF INSPECTION. Inspection should be made only after proper development time has elapsed, but should not be unduly delayed thereafter. If the inspection is made too soon, maximum intensity of indications has not been achieved, and some fine indications may not yet be visible. If too long a time elapses indications may bleed excessively and a distorted picture of the defect may be given.

Proper development times are determined by experience only. Table IX gives some examples of development times for various types of materials. These may be varied in specific instances, and

TABLE IX

EXAMPLES OF DEVELOPMENT TIMES FOR VARIOUS MATERIALS AND DEFECTS

Material	Type of Defect	Development Time Minutes
Aluminum Castings	Porosity—Cold Shuts	2-10
Magnesium Forgings	Laps	5-15
Stainless Steel Forgings	Laps	5-30
All Metals	Fatigue Cracks	5-15
Glass	Cracks	2-15
Plastics	All	1-15

more exact times recommended for certain circumstances will be given when discussing the inspection of specific parts (Chapter 13). Color-contrast penetrants usually require longer development times than fluorescent for the same type of defect.

Development time assumes added importance when inspecting under certain specifications. Rejection of a part may be based on the intensity of the indication on the assumption that it indicates the degree of severity of the defect. Such practice is valid only when inspecting many identical parts and correlation of indication with defect has been established. But since development time plays a significant part in the intensity of a given indication, under such circumstances inspection must be carried out at the stated time after developer has been applied.

33. USE OF FLUORESCENT PENETRANTS IN DAYLIGHT. The super-bright fluorescent penetrants are so brilliant that they may in some cases be used with a strong black light in dim daylight. Field applications sometimes make this desirable, and although sensitivity can never approach that obtainable in darkness, in many cases sensitivity exceeding that obtainable with color-contrast penetrants has been reported.

34. REPROCESSING OF PARTS. Sometimes it is felt necessary to reinspect parts on which indications have been found—for purposes of checking, interpretation, evaluation or salvage. It should be realized that a second time through may not produce exactly comparable results to the first inspection. This is for the reason that once the penetrant has entered a very fine opening, it is not easy to get it all out again so that the process may be repeated. Penetrant remaining in the defect may have dried and will then prevent new fluid penetrant from getting in. This restriction applies especially to the water-wash type penetrants which incorporate an emulsifier. The latter, once dried in the crack, does not yield readily to cleaning by solvent.

Fairly satisfactory results can usually be obtained if the parts are given a thorough cleaning in the vapor degreaser and nearly all indications can then be expected to reappear. The same type of penetrant should be used on the re-test as was used originally. If heating of parts to 325° F is possible without damage to structure or dimensions, this also helps to drive out residual penetrant. But it should always be borne in mind that indications of exceedingly fine cracks may not be produced on a second inspection.

Reprocessing to check indications may not always be necessary. Original indications will persist for a long time, especially if high quality permanent fluorescent dyes have been used, which do not fade rapidly when exposed to daylight—assuming that, in addition, the indications have not been smeared by handling.

Any attempts at additional reprocessing after the first retest are very likely to be increasingly unsatisfactory. However, post-emulsification type penetrants are much more thoroughly removed from cracks by de-greasing, so that reprocessing when this type of penetrant is used is much more apt to be successful.

A fluorescent test following a color-contrast test will invariably have sensitivity reduced. If optional, color-contrast re-test should follow fluorescent. See Chapter 10, Section 39.

CHAPTER 7

WATER-WASHABLE FLUORESCENT PENETRANTS MATERIALS AND TECHNIQUES

1. HISTORICAL. The first penetrant inspection method to be used widely industrially, after the "oil and whiting" method, was offered as a complete technique in 1942, and employed fluorescent penetrant with an emulsifier integrally incorporated in it. This was the "water-washable" penetrant, so called because, by virtue of the emulsifier in the penetrant, water could be used to clean the excess penetrant from surfaces of parts being inspected. All the steps of the method as practiced today were used in the initial applications, except that at first only dry developer was used, wet developer being conceived somewhat later.

The method came into existence and was developed commercially under war-time pressure. It has stood the test of over 25 years of use and although other types of penetrants and techniques have come along, the water-wash technique is still the most widely used production penetrant testing method. Improvements in formulation of the penetrant—as for instance the use of the principle of "cascading" dyes—of materials, and improvements in processes and equipment have been made continually over the years. The method is much more effective today than it was at first—yet there has been no actual fundamental change.

2. STRONG AND WEAK POINTS. The water-wash fluorescent method has, of course, all the advantages and disadvantages of penetrant methods in general which were discussed in Chapter 2. However, within the penetrant family of methods, each type has its own reason for existence, therefore each possesses certain advantages and disadvantages which distinguish it from the others. For this water-wash process these good points may be listed as follows:

(a) It is a fluorescent process and has all the advantages contributed by the extreme brilliance and seeability of indications.

(b) It is a single-step process—coating with penetrant is followed directly by washing. This makes for ease and economy in operating the process.

(c) It is rapid, especially on small parts in production. Many parts can be handled as a unit (in baskets) and individual handling is required only on inspection.

(d) It is simple to use and is economical as to cost of materials.

(e) It is applicable on a wide variety of parts—size, shape, material—and for locating a wide variety of defects.

(f) It is good on rough surfaces and for finding defects in fillets, keyways and threads.

As to its limitations, especially in comparison with other penetrant processes, these are listed below:

(a) It will not reliably find open or shallow defects.

(b) There is danger of "over-washing"—removing penetrant from defects by prolonged or over-vigorous washing.

(c) Complicated formulation makes the penetrant susceptible to deterioration by contaminants, especially water.

(d) Sensitivity is affected by presence of acids, especially chromic acid, and chromates.

(e) Reprocessing of parts after the first inspection is not very reliable, as all indications may not be reproduced on the second run.

(f) If for any reason water is not available or cannot be used (as for instance in inspecting a portion of an assembled engine or machine), the method is not always usable.

(g) In common with all fluorescent processes, the inspection requires a black light and must usually be carried out in a darkened area.

3. PENETRANTS FOR THIS PROCESS. The penetrants for use in the water-wash process are not simple dye solutions but rather complicated formulations of a number of ingredients. These include penetrating oils, dyes, emulsifying agents and stabilizing agents. The goal here is a single liquid that combines good penetrating ability and dye solubility with easy water-washing properties, into a stable material that will not "come apart" under wide variations in temperature and other operating conditions.

Such a formulation necessarily involves certain compromises. For example, in order to be easily washed from the surface of parts and leave a minimum of fluorescent background, a high emulsifier content is desirable. However, the more readily water mixes with and washes away the oils of the penetrant, the more readily, too, does it wash penetrant and dye from the defects. If emulsifier content is dropped to minimize this difficulty, clean washing is hindered and fluorescent blotches will be left on the surface to confuse the operator. Thus, either way, loss of sensitivity for fine defects may result, and a close balance between those two conflicting tendencies must be maintained.

In the modern penetrants, ways have been found to increase simultaneously both sensitivity and ease of washing, but the improvement, though considerable, is still a matter of degree and over-washing can still occur. Nevertheless, the improvement in washability without loss of sensitivity is significant, since it has made possible substantial shortening of the over-all inspection time over that required with earlier penetrants of this type.

Another compromise is with respect to dye content. A high dye content, although it may add materially to cost, is desirable to give high brilliance to indications. However, high dye content may lead to instability under temperature variations—dye may separate out at low temperatures—and also makes clean washing more difficult, thus requiring higher emulsifier content. Low dye content avoids the latter two difficulties but at a sacrifice of the desirable high brilliance at defects. Again, a close control of factors is necessary, and the modern penetrants embody optimum properties in these respects.

4. THE PENETRATING LIQUIDS. Preferably, the penetrating liquid should be non-volatile, so that losses by evaporation in dip tanks or other open storage containers will not occur. Also, if non-volatile, drying of the penetrant film on parts during the penetrating period, or in defects during drying, would not be a problem. But the addition of the emulsifying agent thickens the liquid, and it is also important that the viscosity of the penetrant be relatively low, so that drag-out losses are not too great and drainage during penetration be fast enough to return most of the penetrant to the tank.

So here another compromise dictates the use of a proportion of thin, light liquid which while not so volatile that the flash point of the penetrant is objectionably low, nevertheless is volatile enough that evaporation does occur slowly. There is, however, a compensating advantage in the presence of this more volatile constituent.

When the penetrant comes back out of the defect, the volatile liquid tends to evaporate, especially when the part is warm from the drier. The heavier and more viscous portions do not spread as rapidly, and the tendency of penetrant bleeding from larger openings to spread widely and possibly mask finer indications, is reduced. Also, this concentration due to evaporation of part of the liquid makes for greater brilliance and delineation of indications.

5. THE DYES. The fluorescent dyes are selected for high fluorescence and for permanence under ultraviolet light. Also of great importance is the color (dominant wave length) of the fluorescent light emitted. See Chapter 4, Section 38 for a full discussion of this factor.

6. OTHER IMPORTANT CONSIDERATIONS. As has already been pointed out (Chapter 4, Section 46) penetrants are frequently shipped and stored at temperatures which are well below 32° F and sometimes may be lower than 0° F. It is, therefore, important that no significant change in the penetrant take place under possibly prolonged exposure to such conditions. The low temperatures should not cause separation of any of the components, including the dye. The penetrant should always be ready for use, when withdrawn from stock, although it should not be actually used at temperatures below 40° to 50° F.

In addition, the penetrant should not contain any foul-smelling ingredients nor should there be any components which are likely to be injurious to the operator.

7. TOXICITY AND SKIN IRRITATION. (See also Chapter 4, Section 16.) Reputable manufacturers of modern penetrants have toxicity tests on animals run by competent biological laboratories to assure users that there is no specific hazard to the health of the operator involved in the use of such penetrants. These tests are run on the penetrant as a whole and on the separate ingredients.

The only hazard against which special precautions are advised in using most water-washable penetrants is that of irritation of the operator's skin if continually exposed to the penetrant. The nature of emulsifying agents is such that they, in common with most strong detergents, will tend to dry and crack the skin. This may result in discomfort and may leave the skin open to secondary infection. In using penetrants of this type, therefore, the operator should not handle parts or baskets of parts in and out of the penetrant bath with bare hands and arms, and penetrant should not be allowed to splash on or saturate clothing. Instead, oil-resistant gloves and aprons should be worn. *Occasional* exposure of the skin to the penetrant should have no effect—the liquid is not corrosive like an acid is—but repeated exposure may have a cumulative effect.

Remedy for the condition is to stop the exposure, and the skin irritation should clear up in a short time. Use of soothing skin creams is a help. In the case of those few persons who possess a real alergy to oils—or to any of the other ingredients of penetrants—the use of extra care to avoid contact may be all that is required. If not, the only remedy for such rare cases is to transfer to another job not involving contact with the penetrant.

8. NEED FOR UNIFORMITY IN PENETRANTS. Since penetrant inspection is an important link in assuring failure-free performance of critical parts, users of the inspection process should in turn be assured that optimum results are being obtained with it at all times. This places a high emphasis on unfailing uniformity in the penetrant and other materials of the process. The inspector's judgment as to the nature and severity of defects is based on experience, and such experience assumes consistent indications. Penetrants should, therefore, not vary in any essential characteristic from batch to batch, and a reputable manufacturer should establish rigid controls to assure uniformity. Since water-wash penetrants are a rather complex combination of many ingredients, manufacturers of this type of product should exercise especial care to avoid variations which might affect defect-detection performance.

Present penetrants of the water-wash type are a vast improvement over the original formulation. They have increased stability, better washability, greater brilliance and sensitivity, etc. Such progressive improvement of penetrant is highly desirable but manufacturers have the responsibility of informing users when changes which affect sensitivity are made, so that necessary adjustments in the significance assigned to an observed indication can be made by the inspector.

9. DETERIORATION OF PENETRANTS WITH USE. It is obvious that a penetrant, carefully formulated for definite properties, may be affected or altered if it becomes contaminated with foreign substances or liquids. This is actually the case. although the effect of contaminants on the usability of the penetrant varies, both with the contaminant and the type of penetrant.

Water-wash penetrants, which are balanced mixtures of a number of ingredients, are particularly susceptible to certain contaminants. Deterioration of the penetrant bath is usually not too serious a problem where inspection rates are rapid and the process is in more or less continuous use. Carry-out of penetrant by parts dipped in the bath requires constant replacement with new penetrant and this tends to minimize all forms of deterioration. Where penetrant baths are not in continuous use or are used infrequently, deterioration from various causes may be more of a problem.

10. KINDS OF DETERIORATION.

(a) LOSS BY EVAPORATION.

Penetrants are sometimes used in open tank containers, which permit evaporation of some of the more volatile constituents. This effect is increased if the bath is allowed to become heated from any cause, or even when ambient temperatures become excessively high. Also, if the bath is used only occasionally, evaporation will gradually occur. Loss of the more volatile materials changes the character of the penetrant and may result in failure to get normal results. Such loss by evaporation cannot be corrected by the addition of volatile liquids, since these will not become properly incorporated to restore the penetrant to its original condition.

Penetrant containers should be tightly covered when not in use, to minimize loss by evaporation, and any steps possible should be taken to prevent the penetrant bath from becoming unduly heated. Where open containers are used, even though covered when not in use, penetrants with flash points above 130° F are recommended. Flash points are a rough guide to volatility where petroleum distillates or other combustible liquids are used in the penetrant formulation.

(b) CONTAMINATION WITH WATER.

Water as a contaminant is the most frequent source of difficulty and produces, when present beyond a critical percentage, serious changes in the bath, rendering the penetrant useless. It should be borne in mind that water-wash penetrants may contain small percentages—of the order of 1% or 2%—of water initially. This water content may be an intentional ingredient, or an accidental one resulting from water contained in commercial products such as emulsifiers. But all water-washable penetrants are so formulated to incorporate those small amounts of water without harm.

However, since penetrant stations are usually adjacent to the wash station (washing being the process immediately following penetration), greater or lesser amounts of water will get into the penetrant bath in the course of time. Precautions to avoid this occurrence are and should be taken, but nevertheless water often does get into the penetrant.

Penetrants will "tolerate" a certain amount of such water addition without seriously—or at all—affecting the ability of the penetrant to perform normally. But at some point, which varies widely with different penetrants, the increase in water content changes the character of water-wash type penetrants completely. The penetrant thickens and actual

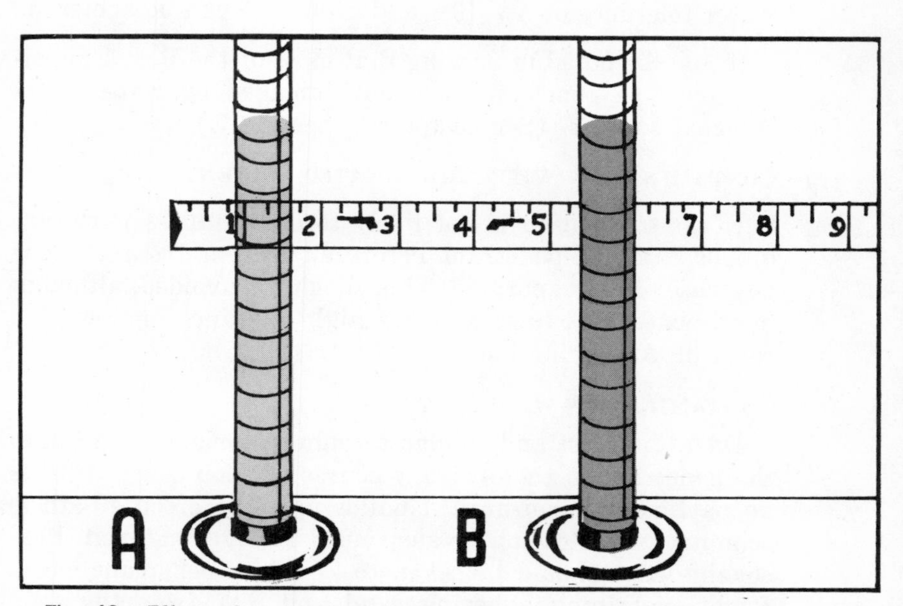

Fig. 40—Effect of contamination with water on a) Penetrant having 15% water tolerance, with 10% water added. Transparent. b) Penetrant having 5% water tolerance, with 10% water added. Thick and opaque.

the penetrant can no longer be used and must be discarded. Figure 40 shows the effect of adding 10% of water to two penetrants, one (a) having a high water-tolerance (15%) and one (b) having a low water-tolerance (5%). The penetrant in the cylinder on the left remains transparent, having assimilated the added 10% of water without apparent change. The penetrant on the right has separated and has become thick and opaque.

From a simple economic standpoint, therefore, it is evident that a desirable property of water-washable penetrants is an ability to "tolerate" — i.e., absorb without change of properties—large amounts of water, thus prolonging the useful life of a bath of penetrant.

Early water-wash penetrants were quite susceptible to damage by water from external sources—as little at 2% over the amount originally incorporated being enough to render the penetrant unusable. Improvements in formulaation have greatly increased the ability of modern water-washable penetrants to absorb or "tolerate" water, so that water tolerance of 5%, 10% and even 20% can be achieved.*

It may be noted in passing that most of the Post Emulsification type penetrants are not damaged by water from external sources. (See Chapter 8, Section 7.)

(c) CONTAMINATION WITH CHLORINATED SOLVENT.

Such contamination is not likely to occur unless parts are dipped into the penetrant before all solvent from a vapor degreaser has evaporated. This should be avoided, although most penetrants have a fairly high tolerance against this form of contamination.

(d) CONTAMINATION WITH DIRT.

Dust, dirt, lint and similar foreign material does get into the penetrant in the ordinary course of shop usage. It does no particular harm until it builds up to where the bath is scummy with floating or suspended foreign material. Reasonable care should be taken to keep the penetrant clean. Parts containing adhering sand and dirt from the shop floor should be cleaned before dipping in the penetrant.

*See here also Appendix I for further discussion of water tolerance of penetrants.

It seems incredible, but such things as cigar and cigarette butts and candy wrappers have been found in used penetrant baths.

(e) CONTAMINATION WITH OIL AND GREASE.

Contamination of this type is common and does no particular harm unless it becomes excessive. However, ordinary care should be taken to avoid any continuing source of oil or grease. Parts containing oily rust preventives or cutting oil residues should be cleaned before dipping. This is more important from the point of view of cleaning out cracks than from avoiding contamination.

Operators have been observed washing greasy hands in penetrant. This is harder on the operator than on the penetrant!

(f) OTHER CONTAMINANTS.

Various substances or liquids added to penetrants may render them useless. Such additions are not likely to occur except by accident, such as obtaining a drum of glycol from the stockroom instead of penetrant. Glycols cause most water-washable penetrants to separate and render them useless. A more likely accident is the mixing of penetrants of two different types. This, too, may cause separation. Almost any kind of acid will destroy fluorescent penetrant —both by changing its consistency and by damaging or destroying the fluorescent dye.

11. OPERATING TEMPERATURE RANGE. These penetrants should never reach temperatures over 120° F, and preferably not over 100° F, to avoid loss of volatile constituents. Some penetrants are formulated with higher boiling liquids which do not evaporate rapidly at 120° F, and these may be used at higher temperatures. A good rule of thumb is to keep the bath temperature at least 10° F below the flash point of the penetrant.

If hot parts are dipped, cooling coils may be required to avoid undue temperature rises, though this is not likely to be necessary unless the rate of inspection of parts is high.

At the other end of the scale, most penetrants will function at temperatures as low as 40° F. Operation at this temperature is, however, not recommended. The preferred operating temperature is around 70° F. Parts, whether they are hot or cold, should be allowed to reach ambient temperature before dipping. If parts are hot from the degreaser, and are intentionally dipped hot, means for cooling the bath may be needed, as stated above. Cold parts may "sweat", and this condensed moisture builds up the water content of the penetrant bath. An even worse effect of condensed moisture on parts is that it may block penetrant from entering defects. Parts should therefore be *dry* before dipping. (See Chapter 6, Section 2.)

12. CONSUMPTION OF PENETRANT. Economics demand that the amount of penetrant used to inspect a part be as little as possible. The greatest source of penetrant loss is the amount carried out of the bath by adherence to the surface of a part. If the part has a rough irregular surface, as for instance a sand casting, much more penetrant will be carried away than in the case of a machined part having smooth surfaces. The geometry of the part also may affect drag-out, and care should be taken when removing a part from the bath that all blind holes and recesses are emptied and that the part is so disposed on the drain rack that the penetrant can, to as great an extent as possible, drain away freely from all surfaces.

Drain time has an effect on penetrant consumption in that a very short drain time, though perhaps sufficient to achieve penetration of all defects, may not permit as much penetrant to drain away from the surfaces of the part, as a somewhat longer time would. This is an economic factor to consider, and longer drain times must be balanced against the necessary pace of production through the inspection process. Longer drain times can be secured without affecting production rates by simply providing more space for draining, so that parts will automatically have more time to drain.

Viscosity of the penetrant also affects drag-out. (See Chapter 4, Section 4.) Viscosity of a penetrant is determined by the manufacturing formula. It may be affected in use by various contaminants, especially oils and greases, and water. Viscosity increases somewhat at low temperatures—a reason for operating in the 70° to 80° F range. Loss of volatile constituents by evaporation also tends to increase viscosity somewhat.

The drag-out Table (Table II, Chapter 4) gives some clue to the consumption of penetrants due to this factor alone. A rough figure of 3000 square feet per gallon is indicated. However, this test was made on fairly smooth aluminum surfaces and consumption of penetrant might be much greater on rough-surfaced parts. It would vary also with different types of penetrants.

Contaminants play a part in penetrant consumption. When a bath becomes unusable due to build-up of contaminants, it must be dumped and the container refilled with new penetrant—an excellent reason for avoiding contamination. Since contamination with water is the most common form, penetrants which have a high water tolerance—i.e., can absorb large percentages of water before they become unusable—will have a longer life, if water contamination occurs, than penetrants having a low water-tolerance.

For example, if we consider a 30 gallon bath and assume a water pickup of four ounces per day, this would constitute an increase of approximately 0.1% in the water content of the penetrant. After 50 days of use, water content would have increased by 5% —and a penetrant having only a 5% water-tolerance would have to be discarded. With 10% tolerance a penetrant would have a life of 100 days; 15%, 150 days; and 20%, 200 days. Such rates of water pickup would be likely to occur only under conditions of constant use or considerable carelessness. The addition of new penetrant to the bath to make up for drag-out would lengthen the time before dumping is necessary. Smaller rates of water absorption would also lengthen the useful life of the tankful of penetrant, while larger rates would shorten it.

13. DEVELOPERS FOR WATER-WASH PENETRANTS. Standard developers as described in Chapter 5 are used in the water-wash penetrant process. Either wet or dry developers may be used.

If dry developers are used only the usual precautions must be taken (Chapter 5, Sections 7 to 10). The surface must be dry and the powder dusted on lightly and uniformly. A dust-collection system may be indicated for production operations. (Figure 28.)

If wet developers are used, they are applied by dipping, flowing or spraying, immediately after the water-wash and before drying.

14. CONCENTRATION OF WET DEVELOPERS. The concentration of wet developers is of great importance to the success of the inspection, especially when very fine cracks are sought. A sufficient film thickness of developer is essential, but an excessively heavy coating rapidly cuts down on sensitivity, since the minute amount of penetrant available at a fine crack cannot show through a very heavy coat.

The optimum suspension provides a coating of sufficient thickness to produce good indications. Lighter concentrations of developer powder to water are sometimes used, usually with the belief that a thinner film is more easily removed after inspection. This, however, does not follow and exceedingly light coatings are not recommended. Since the developer incorporates ingredients to facilitate the removal of the film by washing after inspection, very thin coatings may actually be *more* difficult to remove due to insufficient amounts of these ingredients. Also, very light suspensions may be too dilute in wetting and suspending components to give satisfactory coverage over the parts.

Details for mixing Zyglo developers and checking and maintaining bath concentrations will be found in Chapter 17, Section 47.

15. OPERATING TEMPERATURES. As is true for the entire penetrant process, optimum temperatures for wet developer are in the 70° to 80° F range. Since the suspending medium is water, temperatures must never fall below freezing. On the other hand, heating the developer bath to temperatures above ambient does not improve developer performance and increases the rate of evaporation of water from the bath.

16. DETERIORATION OF DEVELOPER BATH IN USE. The most serious cause of deterioration in use is the evaporation of water, which increases the concentration of the solid ingredients, both dissolved and suspended, in the bath. The remedy for this is proper checking of concentration by the methods recommended by the manufacturer (see Chapter 17), and adding back the proper amount of fresh water.

Miscellaneous dirt and dust tends to get into the bath while in use, and this can accumulate to such an extent that the bath may become unusable.

Another source of deterioration has been noted which is not so easily corrected. This is loss of the liquid portion of the bath, including the dissolved ingredients, through fine leaks, such as at the seal of the agitator pump. In such a case the concentration of *suspended* solids in the bath goes up, but addition of water to bring this down dilutes the dissolved ingredients and throws the bath out of balance. When such a condition exists, the leak must be found and corrected.

Chapter 7

WATER-WASHABLE FLUORESCENT PENETRANTS

Applying the Water-Wash Penetrant Process

17. Preparation of the Parts. Before applying penetrant, the surfaces of the part, including all openings and especially suspected defects, must be clean. One or more of the following methods of cleaning are commonly used.

(a) Mechanical Cleaning. Loose dirt, rust, scale, etc., can best be removed by wire brushing. If not removed such materials not only may mask a defect but may also absorb and hold penetrant to such an extent that washing after penetration cannot produce a surface free from background fluorescence.

Sand blasting or grit blasting can accomplish the same purpose as wire brushing, and may do a more thorough and quicker job of cleaning. Paint may also be removed by this means. However, the sand or grit used must be such that a cutting and not a peening action results. Peening may close defects so tightly at the surface that detection with penetrant becomes difficult or impossible. If paint has been removed by this process, a vapor-degreasing operation should follow.

(b) Solvent Cleaning. Oil and grease may be removed with solvents. These may be applied by hand but care must be taken to do a thorough job so that all openings, including suspected defects, are free of contamination. Liberal use of fresh solvent is necessary. Naphtha is frequently used, but if it is, the fire hazard involved must be constantly borne in mind.

Much the best method of removing oil and grease to give maximum assurance that cracks and other defects are clean, is use of the vapor-phase degreaser with chlorinated solvent. Parts come from the degreaser clean and hot, which also insures that they are free of water.

(c) Water Cleaning with Detergent. Washing machines using hot water and detergents sometimes provide a convenient and satisfactory means for cleaning parts, depending on the kind of surface contaminant to be removed. Oil and grease are satisfactorily removed from exterior surfaces, but may not be as well removed from cracks as with the vapor-degreaser. If the water cleaning method is used, drying with heat is mandatory, as a crack filled with water will not dry out readily without heat, and the water must be driven out before the penetrant can enter. Also, residual water on the surface of the part would contaminate the penetrant.

(d) OTHER CLEANING METHODS. Various special cleaning methods are sometimes applicable in special instances. Forgings are sometimes pickled in acid to free them from scale. Here care must be taken that all acid is washed off and that the forgings are subsequently thoroughly dried.

(Courtesy Pan American World Airways)

Fig. 41—Preparing to dip large part into degreaser for precleaning.

The aircraft and automotive overhaul industries use special industrial cleaners to remove grease and carbon from a variety of parts. These are usually water solutions, and their use should be followed by a thorough washing with water, and drying.

(e) ULTRASONIC CLEANING. The use of ultrasonic methods of cleaning is increasing, but it is doubtful whether their use in the preparation of parts for penetrant inspection is generally of any value over simpler methods. However, in the case of cracks filled with some hard contaminant such as oxide, carbon or engine varnish, ultrasonic vibrations have been reported to have some effect in breaking up, if not actually removing such crack-fillers. When so broken up, some penetrants may be able to enter.

(f) SURFACES CARRYING CHROMATES. Chromates and chromic acid tend to kill the fluorescence of penetrant dyes. When present they should be removed, preferably by an acid or alkaline dip followed by detergent washing and thorough drying.

18. IMPORTANCE OF THE CLEANING STEP. This has been emphasized before but can bear re-emphasizing here. Since detection of a defect with penetrants is absolutely dependent on the penetrant first entering the defect, everything possible must be done to free the surfaces and the defect itself from any form of cover or filling that would reduce the chances of the penetrant getting in. Precleaning, therefore, merits some thought and study on the part of the inspector before he accepts parts as ready for the application of penetrant.

19. PENETRATION TECHNIQUES. Application of water-wash penetrants to the clean parts may be accomplished by any method which insures complete coverage of every surface of the part, providing opportunity for penetrant to enter any existing opening or defect. In practice various methods are employed to this end, most of the variations being dictated by requirements of size, shape and location of the parts, and the economic and practical problems of handling them at the required production pace with as little labor cost as possible.

20. SMALL PARTS DIPPING. Small parts are most quickly and conveniently handled in wire baskets. Baskets may be dipped into a bath of penetrant (Figure 42), or penetrant may be flowed over the parts from a hose or spray nozzle. Parts not too large to manipulate by hand may also be dipped individually, or hosed or sprayed. Care must be taken in dipping that air pockets in recesses in the

Fig. 42—Dipping basket of small parts into penetrant.

parts do not prevent any portion of the surface being covered with penetrant. If the flow-on or spray method is used great care must be exercised that no uncovered portions of surfaces remain.

In general, dipping of the parts or of baskets of small parts into the penetrant is preferred for hand operation, while flowing or spraying is more practical in automatic equipment. In the latter case the stream or spray of penetrant must be so directed that all surfaces of the part are covered.

Operators at the penetrant station should wear oil-resisting gloves and aprons to avoid continual contact of the skin with penetrant and to keep penetrant from the clothing. If penetrant does frequently come in contact with the skin, frequent washing with soap and warm water and the application of protective skin creams is recommended.

Heating of parts before dipping is sometimes practiced though its advantages are doubtful. Often parts are dipped while still hot from the degreaser. In the latter case time should be allowed for all degreaser solvent to evaporate from surface openings (including cracks) before dipping. When heated parts are dipped they should remain in the bath till they cool, and temperature of the bath should be watched so that it does not rise beyond safe limits (120° F for many penetrants).

21. SMALL PARTS—DRAINING. When baskets of small parts or individual parts are handled by hand, they are simply set aside after dipping or flooding with penetrant, on racks provided for the purpose. Excess penetrant which runs off is drained back into the penetrant bath. Care must be taken that parts are so disposed that recesses and blind holes have an opportunity to drain.

The draining time is important to the process, since it is in this interval that penetration of defects takes place. Recovery of penetrant is economically important, but not important to the process itself. Sufficient space on the drain rack must be provided so that the parts remain there for the time required for the type of defects sought. In automatic equipment proper drain time is provided by the length and rate of movement of the conveyors.

Penetration time (drain time) varies for different materials and for different types of defects. The actual time required in any given case cannot be critically defined, but experience has developed some broad guides. Table X lists some conventional penetration time requirements for various materials. Beyond this, when in doubt, penetrate for longer rather than for shorter periods. When very fine cracks are being sought penetration times may run to several hours. Since a drain time of longer than thirty minutes to an hour may result in drying of the penetrant on the surface of parts (after which proper penetration can no longer occur) re-dipping of the parts is necessary—or preferably, the parts are left submerged in the penetrant for the length of time deemed necessary. See here also Appendix VI for discussion of electrostatic spraying techniques.

TABLE X

PENETRATION TIMES FOR WATER-W[illegible]
PENETRANT FOR VARIOUS MATE[illegible]

Material	Form	Type of Defects	Time
Aluminum	Castings	Shrinkage Cracks	[illegible]
		Porosity	[illegible]
		Cold Shuts	[illegible]
	Forgings	Cracks	[illegible]
		Laps	[illegible]
	Welds	Cracks	[illegible]
		Lack of Bond	[illegible]
		Porosity	[illegible]
	All Forms	Fatigue Cracks	[illegible]
Magnesium	Castings	Shrinkage Cracks	[illegible]
		Porosity	[illegible]
		Cold Shuts	[illegible]
	Forgings	Cracks	[illegible]
		Laps	[illegible]
	Welds	Cracks	[illegible]
		Lack of Bond	[illegible]
		Porosity	[illegible]
	All Forms	Fatigue Cracks	[illegible]
Stainless Steel	Castings	Shrinkage Cracks	3[illegible]
		Porosity	3[illegible]
		Cold Shuts	3[illegible]
	Forgings	Cracks	6[illegible]
		Laps	6[illegible]
	Welds	Cracks	6[illegible]
		Lack of Bond	60[illegible]
		Porosity	60[illegible]
	All Forms	Fatigue Cracks	30

TABLE X, continued

Material	Form	Type of Defects	Penetration Time (Minutes)
Brass & Bronze	Castings	Cracks	10
		Porosity	10
		Cold Shuts	10
	Forgings	Cracks	20
		Laps	30
	Brazed Parts	Cracks	10
		Lack of Bond	15
		Porosity	15
	All Forms	Fatigue Cracks	30
Plastics	All Forms	Cracks	5-30
Glass	All Forms	Cracks	5-30
Glass-to-Metal Seals	All Forms	Cracks	30-120 +
Carbide Tipped Tools		Lack of Bond	30
		Porosity	30
		Grinding Cracks	10
Tungsten Wire	All Sizes	Cracks	1 hr. to 24 hrs.
Titanium and High-Temperature Alloys	All Forms	All	Use only post-emulsification Penetrant

22. LARGE PARTS—APPLICATION OF PENETRANT. The method of applying penetrant to parts too large or heavy to manipulate by hand is in general a matter of convenience or practicability. When the entire surface of a large and heavy article must be coated with penetrant, dipping may be the quickest and most economical method. Mechanical handling equipment such as conveyors, hoists or other devices are employed. Care must be taken that air pockets do not prevent full coverage.

Sometimes large parts can be flooded or sprayed with penetrant while they are lying on suitable drain tables so that penetrant can be recovered.

(Courtesy Consolidated Edison Co., New York)

Fig. 43—Spraying penetrant on steam strainer on floor of power station—expendable technique.

In some instances no attempt is made to recover excess penetrant. Instead, penetrant is applied either locally in suspected areas, or even over large surfaces, by means of pressure sprays. Only enough penetrant is sprayed on to coat the surface, so that drainage is small and consumption of penetrant is minimized. Examples of this application are the inspection of large, assembled steam turbine spindles and blades, and of the stainless steel welded lining of industrial processing tanks or lead-lined vessels.

Use of this "expendable" technique is facilitated, when coating of only local areas of large parts is necessary, by the use of pressurized spray cans of penetrant—or penetrant can be applied locally with a paint brush.

23. LARGE PARTS—DRAIN TIME. Drain or penetration time for large parts is the same as for small, being determined by the material and character of the sought-for defect. If long times are indicated, re-spraying may be necessary to maintain a fluid film of penetrant on the surface. Where large parts have been dipped or flooded, care must be taken that all openings and pockets in the part drain properly. If pools of penetrant remain in such recesses, washing of the part is made difficult.

CHAPTER 7

WATER-WASHABLE FLUORESCENT PENETRANTS

24. WASHING TECHNIQUES. Proper removal of all excess penetrant from the surface of parts is essential to satisfactory inspection. While water-wash penetrants are designed to be cleanly removed with water, success in this operation involves the use of proper techniques and is not automatically achieved. There is a *right* way to wash in all instances—not only to produce clean surfaces, but to avoid over-washing—i.e., to avoid washing penetrant *out of defects.*

25. HAND WASHING. The most common method of washing parts is by means of a hand water spray. The character, pressure and volume of this spray are all of importance. In general, a plentiful volume of water at moderate pressures—30 to 40 p.s.i.—is desirable. The water should be broken up into a spray of coarse droplets, which impinge on the surface, penetrate the film of oil-emulsifier mixture, and immediately flush it completely away.

Higher pressures are undesirable because by mechanical force alone they tend to penetrate into defects and wash out some of the penetrant. Fine sprays do not carry sufficient volume of water for the flushing action needed. If the oil-emulsifier-water mixture is not washed away at once, some dye will separate out and stick to the surface and further washing will not remove it. On the other hand, use of a solid stream of water, which produces plenty of volume, is not satisfactory because the stream impinges on too small an area to achieve proper emulsification, and areas where dye has separated and remains on the surface are usually the result.

Water at the temperature at which it comes from the lines is usually quite satisfactory. Washing with hot water makes the washing easier but increases the hazard of removing penetrant from defects. Perhaps the optimum temperature for wash water is 110° F. However, heating the water is an added expense and is in general not considered necessary.

The washing operation should be conducted under a black light and should not be prolonged. As soon as the surface shows no areas of fluorescence under the black light (except at areas of serious porosity, etc.) washing should be stopped, to avoid over-washing.

In washing large parts, the wash should start at the *bottom and move up,* so that water running down from above does not separate oil from emulsifier on the lower areas before the spray reaches them. The emulsified water-penetrant mixture from the upper areas will run off cleanly over the already washed portions.

When washing small parts in baskets care must be taken that all surfaces of all parts are reached, and that no areas are missed where parts may lie in contact. If parts are so shaped that they cannot be disposed in the basket without serious contact areas, spacers should be provided in the baskets to keep parts separate and accessible to washing. Care should be taken also, that the baskets *themselves* are well washed. If baskets retain some penetrant, this can contaminate parts later in the process and create false and confusing fluorescent indications. If this becomes a problem, the parts after washing may have to be transferred to clean baskets before going on to the drier.

The wash tank and surrounding surfaces should be kept free from fluorescent scum to avoid contaminating clean baskets or parts with fluorescent spots which confuse the inspection.

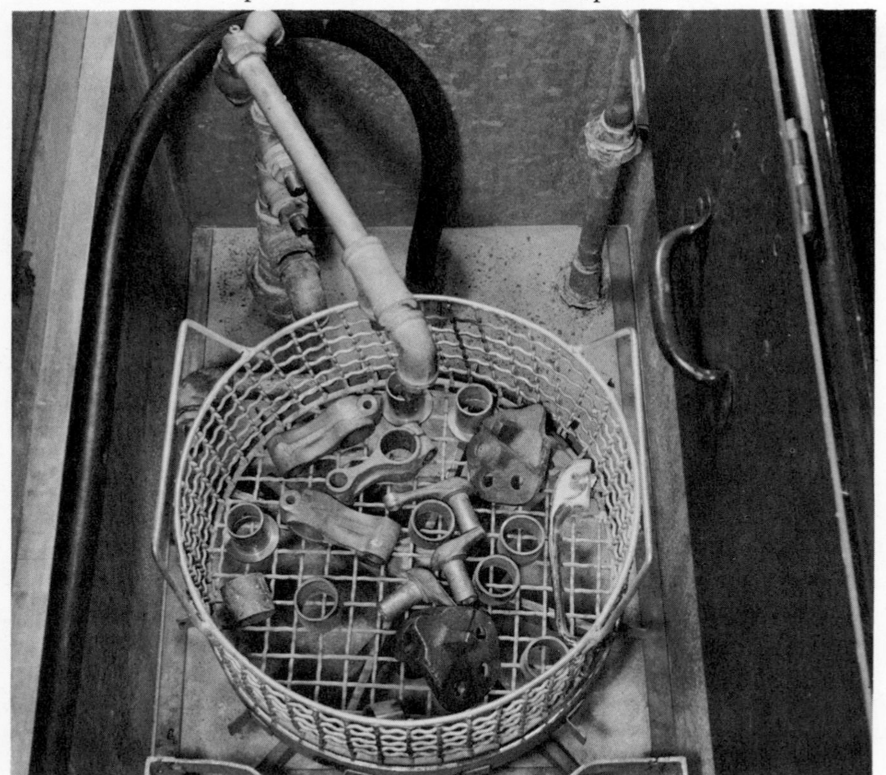

Fig. 44—Automatic wash for baskets of small parts.

WATER-WASHABLE FLUORESCENT PENETRANTS

26. AUTOMATIC WASHING. For small parts being processed in baskets, an automatic spray rinse has been devised which is far superior to hand washing. This involves use of a simple covered cabinet, similar to the usual hand wash station, equipped with spray nozzles directing a copious supply of water from all angles at the basket, which is being rotated. For most small parts, properly disposed in the basket to avoid undue contact between surfaces, this does a very satisfactory job.

On automatic units washing is accomplished with spray nozzles placed to suit the geometry of the parts being processed. Sometimes, an oscillating spray head is used instead of fixed nozzles. In one application in which the parts are long and of relatively uniform cross section, a travelling ring spray moves from one end of the piece to the other, thoroughly cleaning all surfaces in one pass.

27. DIP WASHING. Washing by simply immersing the penetrant-coated part in a bath of warm water and moving it about while submerged is a method that has been used with some success under certain conditions. Penetrant must be formulated so it will completely emulsify on contact with water and disperse readily into the water bath. The method has the advantage of simplicity, but has little value otherwise. It is not recommended for general use.

(Courtesy Consolidated Edison Co., New York)

Fig. 45—Washing steam strainer in power station.

28. WASHING LARGE PARTS. In the inspection of steam turbine rotors, washing is generally accomplished with a hose and spray nozzle. Other large parts which have been sprayed with penetrant may be similarly washed. Provision for draining off the wash water must be made. In such operations the washing should start at the bottom and work up all sides of the part. Figure 45 illustrates this procedure as applied to a steam strainer.

29. WASHING WITH WET CLOTHS. When spray washing is for any reason impracticable or not permissible, a good job can be done on limited areas using a wet cloth. The cloth should be thoroughly wet with water and the wiping over the surface should be rapid. The first swabbing should be followed at once with fresh water and a clean cloth. The method is obviously not suitable for use on large numbers of small parts or on large or irregularly shaped ones. For local checking in limited areas, however, it is a good cleaning method.

30. WASHING WITH DETERGENTS. Adding detergents to wash water is definitely bad practice, though it has been tried by some users. The proper amount of the best emulsifier for the purpose has already been incorporated in the penetrant itself. Adding detergent to the wash water may result in a nice clean surface, but penetrant will almost certainly be washed out of some defects.

31. DISPOSAL OF WASH WATER. For average size installations disposal presents no problem since the actual amount of penetrant carried into the drain in the course of an hour is small in relation to other wastes carried by the sewer. In some instances, especially for large operations, special precautions in disposing of wash water may be required. Usually this consists of collecting the rinse water in a tank, and adding an acid or suitable substance to break the emulsion. The oils containing the dyes will rise to the surface and may be skimmed off. The water thus freed of oily material and dye may then usually be safely run into the drain.

32. DRYING TECHNIQUES. Drying after water-washing is a necessary and important step in the processing of parts by the water-wash penetrant method. Results can be materially affected by the method of drying, particularly the intensity and definition of the indication. Therefore, the sensitivity of the test can be increased through proper understanding and application of suitable drying techniques. If dry developer is to be used, drying immediately follows the step of washing. If wet developer is to be applied, drying follows the application of the wet developer bath. Essentially, proper drying procedure is the same in both cases, though a few special considerations apply when wet developer is involved and these will be discussed in Section 52 of this Chapter.

33. WIPING WITH CLOTH OR PAPER TOWELS. This is a simple and quite satisfactory way to dry the surface of a part and is especially useful when a local area of a large part is being examined. After wiping dry, some minutes should be allowed before dusting on the dry developer powder, to permit the last film of dampness to evaporate off the surface. Use of towels is obviously slow and would be clumsy on parts of complicated shape and impractical for production inspection. Also, some of the definite advantages in sensitivity that result from the use of heat are lost when the wiping method of drying is used.

34. AIR-BLAST WATER BLOW-OFF. A strong blast of compressed air from the shop air system is a method of drying which is sometimes convenient and may be quite effective, but is not generally recommended. One objection is that too strong or concentrated a jet of air can mechanically blow some penetrant out of defects, and this must be guarded against. Shop air is not always free of entrained water and oil, and if either is present the air-blow-off will not be effective. Use of air, if properly applied and if dry, is sometimes useful in removing the major part of the water from the surfaces of large parts, thus reducing the time necessary to dry such surfaces completely. An air blast usually does not leave the surface absolutely dry however, and some further drying must be provided for.

35. DRYING AT ROOM TEMPERATURE. If the part or assembly is large, drying with heat may be impractical or impossible. If the washed part is allowed to stand long enough at room temperature it will, obviously, dry off. This is the slowest and possibly the poorest of drying techniques, though on occasion it may be the only possible one. One specific drawback to this method of drying is that, due to the time required, indications have time to bleed out excessively. This is no disadvantage if the defect is small and only a minimal amount of penetrant is in the defect in the first place. However, larger defects holding a larger reservoir of penetrant will have time to bleed excessively, and the indication will spread and lose definition. At room temperature the penetrant retains all its normal fluidity, since the volatile constituents do not evaporate as rapidly as the water dries, and this condition facilitates spreading.

36. WARM AIR DRYING. Blowing warm air over a part, as, for instance, by using a "hair dryer" type of blower, is only slightly better than open-air drying at room temperature. The air from such devices is seldom warmer than 130° F. when it reaches the surface of parts. Since the parts are cold, the increase in rate of evaporation of the water from the surface is not great. The quantity of heat supplied is not great enough to warm the part itself very quickly. Indications tend to spread excessively as in open-air drying. All in all, this method accomplishes little or nothing and is usually not worth the trouble and expense of setting it up.

37. OVEN DRYING. Placing parts in an oven maintained at, say, 225° F. is a somewhat better approach to the drying problem, though still not the optimum procedure. Here, if the power in-put of the oven is sufficiently large in relation to the mass of metal represented by the load of parts, the *part itself* becomes heated. If there is no provision for circulating the air in the oven (and this is the assumed condition for this discussion), absorption of heat and removal of the evaporated water vapor tends to be slower, and good control of both the time and temperature of the drying operation is difficult. Temperature inside the oven varies considerably, depending on disposition of the parts to be dried with respect to the heating element, resulting in uneven heating of the load, and leading to overheating of some parts.

Since the re-circulating hot air drier overcomes all these disadvantages, there is little to recommend the use of any other type of heated drier.

38. RE-CIRCULATING HOT AIR DRIERS. The re-circulating hot air drier is a device to dry parts properly and at the same time take advantage of all the favorable effects which heat can have on the brilliance and definition of indications, and, therefore, on the results of the inspection. The drier is an enclosed space consisting essentially of two sections. In one section is a bank of electric heaters of adequate power, with a fan to blow air over the heaters. A thermostat automatically maintains the temperature of the air leaving the heated space. From the heating section, the hot air is directed over and around the parts lying on a grill, and then back to the fan to be re-heated to the predetermined temperature. A

CHAPTER 7

WATER-WASHABLE FLUORESCENT PENETRANTS

Fig. 46—Recirculating hot air dryer for small parts.

certain amount of fresh air is constantly drawn into the system to reduce the water content of the air in the drying cabinet.

The temperature used for parts of normal size and thickness—say with sections 1/4″ thick or greater—is 175° F. to 225° F. Air at this temperature rapidly heats the surfaces of the parts and evaporates the surface water, carrying away the water vapor. Parts should be removed from the heat as soon as dry, when they will be quite warm but not yet at the full temperature of the air in the drier. Parts should not reach a temperature above 140° F.

39. ADVANTAGE OF RE-CIRCULATING HOT AIR DRIERS. With this technique several desirable effects are produced in addition simply to drying the parts. Water-wash penetrants are composed of liquids, some of which are fairly volatile and some non-volatile and more viscous. When a part is placed in the drier the penetrant begins to exude from the defect, and this process is aided by the heat absorbed by the surface of the part. In addition, as the penetrant reaches the surface the more volatile constituent tends to be carried away by the warm air. The more viscous non-volatile constituents tend to concentrate near the edges of the defect making for maximum brilliance and definition of the indication. Prolonged heating in the drier, or excessive temperatures, will increase the spreading of the more viscous liquids and thus reduce this concentration. For this reason both time and temperature of drying must be controlled.

40. PROPER DRYING TEMPERATURES. With normal penetrants the air thermostat should be set at 200° F, and temperature of the air in the drier should under no circumstances exceed 225° F. However, with very small parts, or parts having sections of 1/4″ or less, lower temperatures may be desirable. Depending on size and mass, drying temperatures may be as low as 150° to 175° F. Evaporation of the surface water may be somewhat slower, but the parts cannot reach temperatures high enough to produce spreading of indications as, because of quicker rise in temperature due to smaller mass, they would do with the higher drying temperatures.

41. AIR TEMPERATURE VS. PART TEMPERATURE. It should be understood that in this drying technique the part itself should not be heated above 140° F. Higher air temperatures will evaporate the water more rapidly and should accomplish this result while the surface layers of the part are being heated to, but not beyond, this point. It is evident that there must be a balance between the temperature of the air, the time the part is left in the drier, and the size and character of the part.

The material of which the part is made is also a factor in arriving at this balance. Aluminum and copper parts will transmit heat into the body of the part because of their high heat conductivity more rapidly than, say, a part made of stainless steel. *Surface* temperature of the latter may, however, rise more rapidly than in the case of aluminum or copper. An understanding of these factors and experience with the method are necessary to secure optimum results in any given set of circumstances.

42. OTHER DRYING TECHNIQUES. Various other methods and devices have been proposed and tried for drying parts; for the most part they are not satisfactory though they may sometimes have some value as a makeshift in the absence of suitable equipment. In judging such techniques it should be remembered that the time required and the temperature reached by the material are the critical factors.

Infra-red heat lamps might appear to be a simple and convenient source of heat for drying, whereas in fact they are quite unsatisfactory. Such lamps produce radiant heat, and tend to heat the part itself rather than the air around it. In the case of parts with shiny surfaces, the radiant heat is largely reflected, and *neither* the part nor the air will be heated. Rise of temperature in the part depends on the mass of metal involved. Thin sections will be heated faster than heavy sections and part temperature may get too high before the entire surface is dry. With heavy sections the reverse will be true. In addition the time required is usually longer than desired. This method is definitely inferior to the convection heating accomplished in the recirculating hot-air drier.

Heating parts by induction, utilizing the heating effect of eddy currents produced by placing the part in an alternating field, has also been proposed. Here again, the *part* is heated first and can reach undesirably high temperatures before the surface is properly dry.

High-powered unit heaters blowing hot air at parts may have some advantage in drying some very large part, but this is other wise an uncontrolled and wasteful procedure compared to an efficient, thermostatically controlled re-circulating hot-air drier.

43. DEVELOPING TECHNIQUES. A complete discussion of developers and their function in the process of inspection of parts with penetrants has been given in Chapter 5, and in Chapter 6, Sections 24-27. It has been emphasized that the application of developers is important as a step in securing maximum sensitivity and maximum definition and brilliance of indications; and, therefore, proper techniques in applying developers are of significance in the securing of good results, and may even in some instances be controlling. It is, of course, true that many indications appear after drying and before developers are applied, but a few trials on fine defects will quickly demonstrate the difference in the appearance of indications after the use of developers. See also Appendix II.

Wet and dry developers are both widely used in the water-wash process and the selection of the type to use is based on a variety of considerations, mostly not related to the question of sensitivity. (See Chapter 5 Section 28).

44. DRY DEVELOPERS. When dry developers are used, they should be applied as soon as possible after the surface is dry—the sooner the better. But the surface *must* be thoroughly dry, since damp areas will catch and hold excessive amounts of the powder. When parts come out of a hot-air drier, the developing step follows as soon as they can be handled, and there is no variable time factor involved. When parts are dried by less positive methods it may be less easy to tell exactly when all damp spots have disappeared. When developing is delayed, indications may bleed and spread excessively and definition is impaired, sometimes to such an extent that interpretation of the indication is made much more difficult or impossible.

45. APPLICATION OF DRY DEVELOPERS. The key to the use of developers to secure best results is to apply them in such a manner that all surfaces are covered, but with only a very light dusting of powder. Any method of application leading to this result is satis-

Fig. 47—Dipping basket of small parts into dry fluffy developer.

factory, and the selection of the method in any given case is largely a matter of availability and convenience. A bin containing the powder may be used with most dry developers. The parts are quickly dipped into the dust and the excess removed by tapping. Powder may be picked up by hand or in a scoop and thrown over the part, and the excess removed by knocking the part against the side of the bin. In this technique the character of the developer must be such that all but a very light film of dust will readily fall away.

In the absence of a bin of powder, spray bulbs containing developer have proved convenient and satisfactory. A dry paint brush has been used in some cases, but is not recommended since it tends to smear indications. A powder gun which blows the dust against the surface of the part is sometimes used. Care must here be taken, however, that the velocity of the powder is low when it reaches the surface, else it may all be blown off by the air stream. Powder carried to the parts by a low pressure, low velocity air stream through a soft rubber hose about 1 inch in diameter has been used very successfully. Another type of gun application is by means of a special design of electrostatic-charge spray gun, which applies an even coat of powder on the metal surface at low velocity.*

For production use a dust chamber has been used in some applications. The powder is kept floating in the air by means of air nozzles and the part simply passed through the cabinet. Here again the velocity of the powder at the surface of the part must be very low. If the cabinet is not well designed, the dust cabinet method may lead to poor results. (See Fig. 29, p. 94.)

46. DEVELOPING TIME. (See Chapter 6, Sec. 32.) Since the function of the developer is to hasten and facilitate the formation of readable indications, it is obvious that the time allowed for development is important. It must be long enough to insure that fine indications achieve maximum visibility, but not so long that larger indications have time to spread widely and thus lose definition. A good rule of thumb is to allow half the time for development as was allowed for penetration for the type of defect sought. This time is longer for very fine discontinuities and shorter for the more open, easily detected cracks.

47. CONTAMINATION OF DEVELOPER. It is important that developer bins and tanks be kept clean and free from all kinds of dirt or other foreign material. The most serious contamination in either dry or wet developer is droplets of penetrant. These, if present, will stick to the surface of parts and produce spurious spots of fluorescence which confuse the inspection. Drops of oil or moisture in the dry powder will cause balling up of the powder and adherence to surfaces in heavier amounts, or prevent free falling-away of excess.

*See Fig. 81, Chapter 11, Page 255.

Similarly, in wet developer, dirt and foreign materials tend to produce uneven coverage and uneven coatings.

48. USE OF WET DEVELOPERS. (See also Sections 13 to 16, this Chapter.) As has been stated, wet developers have a number of advantages, most of which are related to the expeditious processing of many small parts or parts of irregular shape. Time is also saved in that drying time and developing time proceed simultaneously, and by the time a part is dry, development is well underway although not complete in most cases.

49. PREPARATION OF THE DEVELOPER. The developer, furnished as a dry powder, is added to the water in the recommended proportion furnished by the manufacturer. This is usually of the order of from one third to one pound per gallon of water. However, some variation in developer concentration is sometimes indicated. Since the objective is to leave a sufficient but not too heavy coat of developer on the surface of a part after drying, it is self-evident that other factors than merely the *concentration* of developer in the bath must be taken into account. If the bath at one pound per gallon gives a suitable coating on surfaces which drain in a vertical or nearly vertical position, it may leave too heavy a coat on surfaces which drain less thoroughly, and especially if surfaces are horizontal and drain very little.

In the latter case as little as one third pound per gallon may give satisfactory results. *Too* low a concentration, however, reduces the wetting agent and other ingredients to a point where uniform coatings are not obtained. The proper concentration should be determined initially by experiment, to give optimum coatings for a given set of conditions and shape of parts. In some instances the shape may be such that no satisfactory compromise in concentration for all surfaces of the part can be reached. In such cases use of dry developer may be the best solution.

After thorough mixing, the bath should stand for an hour or more before use. Ingredients in the developer formula help to maintain the powder in suspension, but the operator should be sure that the bath is always well mixed so that the intended weight of coating be actually put onto the surface of the part. After standing overnight, a stirring of the bath with a wooden paddle is usually sufficient. The operator should make sure that there is no clear layer of liquid at the surface, but that the creamy consistency is uniform from top to bottom of the container. If the bath is in more or less constant use during the day the agitation provided by the dipping of parts will usually suffice to keep the bath stirred. In some installations, especially in automatic units, agitation is assured by a circulating pump, which then also may serve to apply the bath to the parts by flowing or spraying.

50. MAINTENANCE OF THE DEVELOPER BATH. (See Chapter 17 Sections 47-50.) It is obviously important that the prescribed concentration of the bath be maintained at all times. A specific gravity check for some types of wet developer, and a spot comparison test for others, enables the operator to be sure that the bath has not changed. The most usual maintenance problem is evaporation of water, which can easily be remedied by replacement of the lost water. Contamination with dirt, oil and grease or other foreign material should be carefully guarded against. Special care should be taken to avoid droplets of penetrant from getting into the developer bath.

(Courtesy Mallory Capacitor Co.)

Fig. 48—Dipping rack of capacitor cases into wet developer.

51. Application of Wet Developers. Dipping of the part into the developer bath is the simplest and most usual method of applying the developer to parts. Small parts are usually placed in baskets and the whole basket dipped. Parts should be stacked so that air pockets do not prevent developer from reaching all surfaces, and, conversely, so that no pools of developer remain in openings or recesses in the part. This may require some handling of the parts to drain out such recesses. In some special cases parts may be placed in jigs or racks (Fig. 48). Parts should be dipped briefly and not allowed to remain in the developer bath. *Prolonged* exposure to the wetting agent in the developer bath may tend to remove some penetrant from defects.

If parts are large enough to do by hand, either by dipping, or by flowing the developer over the surface with a hose, it is easy to be sure all surfaces are coated and no pools remain when the part goes to the drier. In automatic equipment, careful location and direction of streams of developer as well as carefully worked out placement of parts on fixtures are essential.

When using a circulating pump for agitation the system must be designed so that no air is sucked in by the pump, since such entrapped air may lead to excessive foaming of the developer bath. Foaming is caused by wetting agents in the developer formula, incorporated to ensure uniform spread of the developer suspension over the surface of parts. In some types of automatic equipment foaming may be a problem unless the system is arranged to minimize splashing or other conditions that cause foaming.

Anti-foam agents can be added to the bath, but these tend to reduce the wetting ability of the bath. Parts fresh from the wash station tend to have surfaces which, though not exactly oily, do not take the developer coating smoothly unless some wetting agent is present. In severe cases of foaming, special formulations may be necessary, or sometimes redesign of the developer station.

52. Drying the Wet Developer. Parts coated with wet developer should be placed in the drier after only a short interval for draining. Rapid drying is essential to secure a uniform developer coating, so that drying at room temperature is never satisfactory. The operator should position parts in the drier so that no pools or accumulations of developer liquid in fillets and recesses are likely to occur. It may even be necessary to turn parts in the drier after an interval to prevent such entrapment.

If for any reason it is not possible to use a suitable re-circulating hot-air drier, it may be preferable not to use wet developer at all, since other forms of drying are unsatisfactory. Obviously drying by wiping or compressed air blow-off would remove the developer suspension itself from the surface and defeat the result entirely.

53. DRYING TIME. Drying time should be no longer than necessary just to dry the surfaces of the part completely. In no case should parts be left in the drier for excessive periods—a limit of double the time required actually to dry the surfaces should be a maximum. Longer heating evaporates constituents of the penetrant present in defects and may prevent formation of indications of very fine cracks. Long drying periods also tend to cause excessive spreading of penetrant at large defects.

54. DEVELOPING TIME. With a proper coating of wet developer, development for most defects is practically complete as soon as parts from the drier are cool enough to handle. If, however, an uneven coat has resulted and there are areas where the developer is heavy, development times should be allowed as indicated in Table X, P. 146. Of course, if the amount of developer is excessive, no indication of a fine defect may appear at all, since the small amount of penetrant at such a defect may be insufficient to show through a heavy coat of developer.

55. THE INSPECTION. When development is complete, whether dry or wet developer has been used, the part should be inspected without excessive delay. Parts should not be handled more than is absolutely necessary before inspection since smearing of indications can easily occur. If left too long before being examined for indications, excessive bleeding and spreading of penetrant from larger defects reduces the sharpness of the indications and makes identification and evaluation of defects more difficult.

56. THE INSPECTION AREA. Since the fluorescent indication of a defect emits visible light, and thus glows, maximum visibility and contrast is achieved in complete darkness. As a practical matter, however, complete darkness is not necessary in most applications because of the brilliance of most fluorescent penetrants, although it should not be overlooked that absolute darkness is most desirable if exceedingly fine defects are sought. However, even if all outside light is excluded, as in a light-proof room, absolute darkness is not actually attainable since the black-light filters do not remove all light of visible wave length from that generated by the ultraviolet source. This is not a serious disadvantage, since the amount of visible light is small and does serve to furnish some illumination by which the operator can handle the parts better than he could in complete darkness.

57. CURTAINED INSPECTION BOOTHS. Nearly all fluorescent penetrant inspection is carried out in a curtained enclosure around a table, with suitable black lights conveniently mounted inside. The curtain black-out is complete above and at the sides and back of the table. The curtains which extend out in front of the table at the

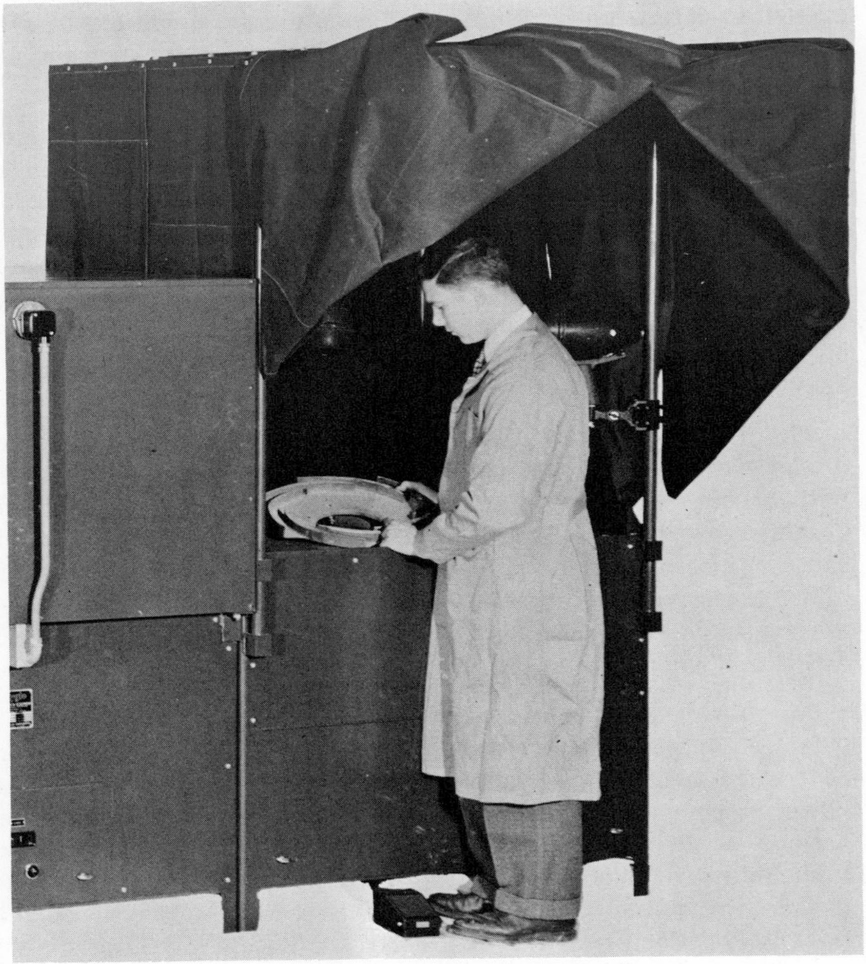

Fig. 49—Black light inspection booth.

ends and overhead across the front, to allow space for the inspector to stand in the darkened area before the table, usually need not be long enough to reach the floor, and often do not extend much below table height. Curtains which do not reach the floor admit some white light, but access to the booth is easier and the ventilation inside is improved. Usually this arrangement does not admit enough light to interfere seriously with good inspection under the black light on the work table. Painting the floor under the booth a dark color helps reduce the light admitted. Bright shop lights are undesirable in the inspection booth area.

Since the black lights generate considerable heat, small ventilating fans in the booth are often necessary. Usually a white light is provided in the booth to facilitate cleaning, etc., but this light should not be turned on during inspection of parts, since even very brief exposure to bright light quickly destroys the dark-adaption of the inspector's eyes.

The end-curtains of the booth are sometimes free so that parts can be pushed through from the drier onto the inspection table. The table may have a conveyor of some sort to facilitate the movement of large parts or baskets of small parts. Means for mechanical handling of parts becomes more important the greater the number, or the larger the size, of parts being inspected.

58. ENCLOSED ROOMS. Since a maximum exclusion of light is desirable from the point of view of best possible visibility of fluorescent indications, a completely enclosed dark room possesses many advantages. Such a room is provided with an inspection table or tables over which black lights of suitable size and number are suspended. Entrance to the room may be through a "light lock," and parts may similarly come in on a conveyor so that outside light does not get in. Ventilating fans and possibly air conditioning are needed for the comfort of the inspectors. White lights must be provided, of course, but should never be turned on while inspection is going on, unless time is subsequently allowed for the eyes of the inspectors to become dark-adapted again.

Such rooms are usually not justified unless the inspection rate is high and a number of inspectors are required, since the curtained enclosure is much less expensive as a first cost. Experience has also shown that some inspectors object to working inside a totally dark room. However, if properly designed, conditions are not materially different from a photographic dark room. Some illumination is provided by the black lights which, as has been said, do give off some visible light.

59. NEED FOR CLEANLINESS. Inspection tables under the black light should be kept clean. Dust and dirt on the table can smear indications. Care must be taken that spots of penetrant do not accumulate on the table for not only can parts pick up a false fluorescent "indication," but also stray fluorescent spots may give off enough fluorescent light to interfere seriously with the seeing of very fine indications of real defects.

60. SMALL DARK CABINETS. For occasional inspections of small parts, where complete facilities are perhaps not warranted, small table-top cabinets are often used. These consist of a box-like enclosure in which a black light is mounted. Parts may be held under the black light through an opening at the table top level and are then viewed by the inspector through a slot in the upper part of

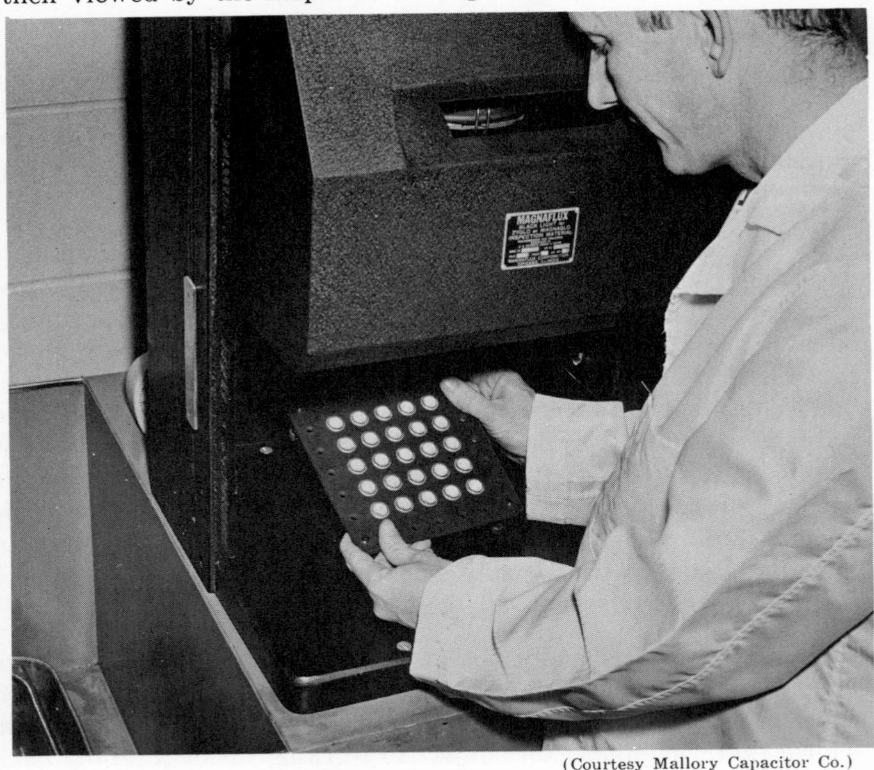

(Courtesy Mallory Capacitor Co.)

Fig. 50—Small black light viewing cabinet.

the cabinet. This device is not very satisfactory, since full dark-adaption of the inspector's eyes can not be attained, and very fine indications are difficult to see. However, parts can be held quite close to the black light bulb and a high black light intensity on the part can be secured. When used, the cabinet should be located in a dimly lit area, and the inspector should put his eyes to the viewing slot and wait a short time before attempting to decide that no indications are present. Of course, gross indications are easily seen without any dark-adaption.

61. INSPECTING IN THE OPEN. On the other end of the scale of favorable to unfavorable inspection areas, of which the dark room is perhaps ideal, is inspection with no exclusion of white light at all. This is quite often done, but never when extremely fine indications are sought for. Many types of defects, however, are known in advance to give strong indications if present. By using high-brilliance penetrants and high concentration of black light, good results for some types of inspection can be obtained without exclusion of white light. Even under these circumstances direct sunlight or bright lights should be avoided, and some sort of light barrier to throw the point of inspection on the part into shadow is usually possible and helpful.

Field kits are available for this type of inspection, in which penetrant, cleaner, developer and black lights are provided. By using the wiping technique for cleaning and drying, no equipment is needed beyond that included in the small portable kit. A 110 volt outlet is desirable for the black light, although low intensity battery operated black lights are available and are adequate in some instances. Penetrant as well as developer and cleaner are provided in pressurized spray cans, which make application easy and minimize "mess" and waste.

62. INSPECTING LARGE PARTS. Frequently inspection for cracks or other defects must be carried out on very large objects or structures. In such cases the inspection is usually made in place, since only portable testing means can be applied. Examples are very large forgings or castings; the blades of steam turbines assembled on the spindle; the welded linings of large processing tanks, etc. In such instances all the normal steps required to produce indications of defects must be gone through, although often ingenuity is necessary so that a wholly satisfactory inspection can result.

Portable black lights are employed for the actual location of indications on large parts, and since very fine cracks may be sought, light exclusion must be obtained by some sort of temporary enclosure or curtain—or sometimes the inspection can be made at night, in near-complete darkness. When the blades on a steam turbine spindle are examined, for instance, a frame with canvas curtains is often constructed to exclude light (Fig. 147, p. 343).

63. THE BLACK LIGHT. Black lights are a critical part of the equipment used in fluorescent penetrant inspection—both the water-wash and the post-emulsification type. A subsequent chapter (Chapter 9) will discuss their construction and operation in detail. From the inspector's standpoint, a few practical points should be mentioned here.

Fig. 51—Hand held black light in use.

The intensity of black light *at the point of inspection* is of utmost importance. The most common lights currently in use are 100 watt and 400 watt quartz tube mercury arc lights, covered with a special filter glass that transmits "black light" but excludes nearly all visible light and is opaque to short-wave ultraviolet rays. The 100 watt lights are furnished either as "spot" or 'flood", but only the "spot" type is recommended for inspection work. This light concentrates most of its output into a 3 inch circle, and insures a high level of light intensity at the point of inspection. The 100 watt flood light spreads its output so much that satisfactory intensity at any point is not obtainable. The 400 watt lamps give satisfactory light intensity over a 16 inch circle, and are used in inspection areas where large objects are being examined. The above areas of suitable black light illumination obtain when the lamp filter is 15″ from the work.

64. INTENSITY REQUIRED. The amount of light emitted by a fluorescent material is dependent upon the intensity of black light radiation used to energize it. Within limits, doubling the intensity of black light at an indication will double the brilliance of the indication. Therefore, black-light available *at the indication* must not fall below a safe minimum. Usually 90 to 100 foot candles is adequate, but for critical work it should sometimes be even greater than this.

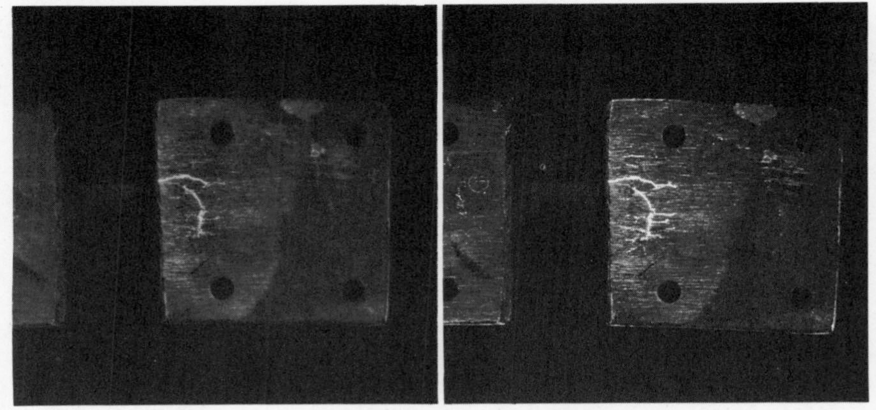

Fig. 52—Effect of intensity of black light on brilliance of indications. Same indication under weak (30) and intense black light (120 foot candles).

This intensity is obtained with the 100 watt spot light over a 3 inch circle when the light is 15 inches from the surface of the part. When a portable light is being used, much greater intensities are obtainable by holding the light closer to the work—or a small part may be held closer to a fixed lamp. The operator should remember that very little black light energy (20-30 ft. candles) is needed to light up a *gross* indication—but without sufficient intensity a fine indication may be missed entirely.

65. OPERATING CHARACTERISTICS OF BLACK LIGHT. Mercury arc black lights should be turned on 5 to 10 minutes before starting to use them for inspection. This is because the full output of ultraviolet light is not developed until the mercury arc gets hot, which requires at least 5 minutes. A certain minimum voltage is required to maintain the arc, so that a sudden line voltage drop may cause the light to go out. If this happens, the arc will re-establish itself, but not until the whole lamp has considerably cooled down, causing a delay of 5 or more minutes. Lights should therefore not be operated on shop lines subject to severe voltage variations.

The life of the mercury-arc capsule is shortened by frequent starting and stopping, so that it is usually more economical to start the light at the beginning of inspection and not turn it off again until its use is ended for the day, even though there may be considerable intervals during which it is not actually in use.

The output of black light falls off slowly over the life-period of the mercury arc lamp, which may be as much as 1000 hours. It is, therefore, desirable that the intensity of light be checked from time to time. (See Chapter 9, Section 17.)

66. BLACK LIGHT FILTERS. The black light filters should be kept clean in order that dust and dirt do not reduce the output of energy. Care should be taken against breakage. Since the lamp gives off much heat, the glass filter becomes hot—so much so that a drop of moisture or contact with any cold surface may crack it. A cracked filter should not be used. This is because even though the visible light that gets through the crack may not be enough to interfere seriously with the inspection, the unfiltered *ultraviolet* light can do harm to the eyes of the inspector.

67. THE INSPECTOR. One of the most important factors in securing good inspection is the inspector himself. Certain personality characteristics are necessary to do a dependable job of inspection. Perhaps the most important of these is interest in the job, coupled with awareness of its importance. Usually this insures alertness, so that the inspector does not become perfunctory in his scanning of surfaces. Also, the inspector must have great patience and not become bored with the job when indications of defects occur only occasionally. If rejections are as low as 1% or less, patience and alertness must make sure that the 100 parts are all scanned carefully even though only one is actually found with an indication. Of course, good, normal eyesight is important—and if glasses are worn, it is important that these be such that the eyes will focus properly on the surface of the part, otherwise a fine line of fluorescence might not be seen, due to its not being in focus. Inspectors wearing bi-focal glasses might do well, for very critical inspections, to have a special pair of single lens glasses which focus properly at a comfortable distance from the surface of the part being examined.

68. DARK-ADAPTION. (See detailed discussion, Chapter 4, Section 38.) The human eye changes its ability to perceive objects depending on the amount of light available. Everyone experiences this effect when the light in a room at night is turned off. At first everything is black, then as the eyes "get used to the dark," it becomes possible to see many objects in the dim light. The converse occurs when a bright light is suddenly turned on, and the eyes are blinded by the intense light until the reverse adjustment is made. This effect is called "dark-adaption" and is accomplished automatically by contraction or expansion of the pupils of the eyes, together with changes within the eye itself.

In fluorescent penetrant inspection, it is absolutely essential that the inspector's eyes become fully dark-adapted before he begins to examine parts for indications. Usually five minutes in the inspection area is sufficient to accomplish this, although complete dark-adaption may take as long as 20 minutes. If the inspector leaves the booth and encounters bright light outside, or if the white light in the booth is turned on, the dark-adaption is lost, and must again be regained by time spent in the darkened booth.

69. HEALTH HAZARDS OF BLACK LIGHT. Black light is in no way injurious to the operator. The wave length range, peaking at 3650 Angstrom units, is below the shortest visible violet light in the spectrum, but is well above the wave length of ultraviolet light which causes sunburn and other injurious effects—3000 Angstrom units or less. However, the mercury arc of the lamp produces large amounts of this short-wave ultraviolet, which is completely removed by the black-light filter. Some small amount of short-wave ultraviolet gets through the glass envelope of the spot lamp, however, and the lamp should therefore *never* be turned on without the filter in place, and cracked filters should be immediately replaced.

70. AVOIDANCE OF OPERATOR DISCOMFORT. When working with black light the operator will quickly notice that many objects and materials have the property of fluorescence. The teeth and fingernails fluoresce with a bluish-white light. Dyes in neckties or other clothing may become startlingly bright, not always with the same color which they appear in white light. Men's white shirts usually, due to finishing materials used in laundries, fluoresce quite brightly with a blue-white color.

The human eyeball also fluoresces, and when black light is allowed to reach the eyes directly an unpleasant effect is experienced when this fluorescence is seen, as it were, from the inside. This effect, though it *is* unpleasant, is entirely harmless. But black light should not be allowed to reach the inspector's eyes in sufficient amount to create this effect, since he cannot see normally while it is going on.

71. EYE-FATIGUE. Although working with black light creates no direct health hazard, it is desirable to relieve inspectors frequently, since any operation requiring close attention of the eyes creates fatigue and this interferes with effective inspection. Two hours of continuous inspection is a reasonable limit before a "break". Sometimes a team will alternate jobs—one processing parts while the other inspects.

If eye-fatigue is complained of chronically, yellow-green tinted glasses are excellent as a means of reducing this effect. These glasses must be of the right composition to pass all the yellow-green light from the fluorescent indications, and to cut out the black light and most of the visible violet which passes the black-light filter. (See Chapter 9, Section 21 for more complete discussion of these glasses.)

72. CONDUCTING THE INSPECTION. Inspection should in most cases follow promptly after the proper developing time has elapsed. If inspection is long delayed, indications lose their definition due to bleeding and spreading of penetrant from large cracks or porosity. Of course, if very fine cracks are sought or expected, prolonged development time may be desirable, to give every possible opportunity for the fine indication to come up; but for most parts prompt inspection is desirable.

73. SMALL PARTS. These are usually examined under fixed black lights in some sort of darkened inspection booth. Care should be taken to pick each part up with minimum contact of the fingers with the surface, so as not to smear indications. Parts should be turned so that all surfaces and recesses are exposed to the black light. The inspector's hands should be clean of any fluorescent material, especially penetrant, so no false indications can be produced from such a source.

Usually any part showing an indication is put into a separate group, after marking the indicated location with chalk or grease-pencil. Parts showing *no* indications are passed on to the next operation. Often, however, certain types of indication which may not be caused by significant defects may be familiar and be recognized as harmless by the inspector at this point, although such on-the-spot judgment requires some experience.

Hand-held, portable black lights are not particularly well suited for inspection of small parts because of the need to turn all faces of the part to the light.

74. LARGE PARTS. Large parts are usually examined with a hand-held portable black light lamp since it is easier to shift the lamp than to move a heavy mass of metal. The part *must* be shifted to some extent, however, so that all surfaces, including that on which it initially rests, may be accessible to the black light. Again, care must be taken to avoid smudging of indications or introduction of false fluorescent spots from hands carrying penetrant.

When parts are so large they cannot be brought inside a booth they are examined outside with portable black-lights, but some means for darkening the inspection area should be provided. A "portable" booth can often be constructed by covering a wooden framework with opaque canvas or paper, or black plastic sheets.

75. AUTOMATIC HANDLING OF PARTS. Automatic handling of parts for inspection is often possible and often speeds up the process considerably. With very small parts this may be difficult due to the need of turning the pieces to expose all surfaces. But for moderately small to moderately large parts, many automatic units have been designed and built. In these, the part is mounted on fixtures for automatic processing, and on some of these the fixture is made to rotate in front of the inspector so that he does not need to touch the part at all. In most cases, however, the inspector lifts the part from the conveyor to examine it, but does not otherwise have to handle it.

76. CONVEYORS FOR MISCELLANEOUS PARTS. Any means to help the inspector move parts to, through and from the inspection booth is an aid to the effectiveness of the inspection. Thus roller conveyors are used extensively to bring baskets of small parts, or individual large parts, to the inspection station. Turntables are sometimes provided to make it easier for the inspector to rotate large or heavy parts. In some installations medium to large parts are suspended from an overhead conveyor and carried past the inspector. The part is at a height such that the inspector, with a portable black light, can see top and bottom, and is so suspended that it can be rotated without removal from the conveyor.

77. SOME PRECAUTIONS TO REMEMBER. To secure good inspections with water-wash penetrants, there are some precautions to be kept in mind and conditions to be avoided, which might bear repetition at this point.

(a) INTERFERING CONDITIONS. Acids in general and oxidizing materials in particular, such as chromates, will in most cases destroy the fluorescence of the penetrant. Consequently, preparation of the parts must be such as to wash off or neutralize all acids including any in cracks. Anodized surfaces may be inspected if the anodizing can be removed, but such surfaces are better inspected using post-emulsification penetrants, which do not react with the chromates.

In addition, paint and porous coatings of any kind will prevent proper inspection and should be removed. Sand trapped on the surface of castings, or oil burned onto the surface of engine parts, will interfere by absorbing penetrant and preventing thorough washing.

(b) POOR WASHING. A poorly washed part is not suitable for inspection since fluorescent background due to residual surface penetrant makes it impossible to identify true indications of defects. A poorly washed part cannot be rewashed; it must be reprocessed from the start.

(c) FILLED CRACKS. If a crack is already filled with a foreign substance, penetrant cannot enter and no indication will be formed. Whether cracks which may be present might be filled with some foreign matter can usually be predicted by knowledge of the past history of the part. Some causes of filled cracks are the following:

(1) WATER from some source, such as washing to clean the part, condensate on a cold part, accidental wetting,

etc. Wet parts must be heated to drive water out of cracks.

(2) SAND BLASTING may peen the edges of the crack, causing metal to flow to close the crack so tightly that even penetrants cannot enter. Such cleaning methods must be avoided. A crack may also be closed by flow of metal during machining. Sometimes a very light etch is sufficient to open the crack without damaging the part.

(3) OXIDE may clog a crack if the part has been heated after the crack was formed.

(4) CARBON or baked oil residue ("engine varnish") may fill a crack in an engine part after long service.

(5) PROCESSING OIL or grease may fill a crack—e.g., heat-treating oil, rust preventive coatings, drawing compounds, cutting oils, etc. Vapor degreaser pre-cleaning is recommended for all oily or greasy parts.

Some of these filling materials are extremely difficult and sometimes impossible to remove. This is especially true of the oxide and engine-varnish fillers.

(d) PARTS WHICH HAVE BEEN RUN ONCE. Second runs with water-wash penetrants are not always satisfactory since the emulsifier compounded in the penetrant, once the latter has dried in a crack from a first run, is not dissolved by new penetrant and acts to block the opening. The difficulty is much more serious in the case of very fine cracks than with larger ones.

(e) FLUORESCENT PENETRANT FOLLOWING COLOR-CONTRAST PENETRANT. No attempts should be made to run a part through fluorescent penetrant after it has been processed with the color-contrast type, unless elaborate precautions are taken. (See Chapter 10, Section 39) Color-contrast dyes tend to mask fluorescent dyes so that no fluorescent indication is likely to be obtained at a crack.

78. CLEANING AFTER INSPECTION. After inspection subsequent processes may require that parts be clean, necessitating removal of all traces of developer and penetrant. Careful washing before developing should have removed all penetrant except that in defects.

Developer, however, requires a separate step for removal. The best way to insure complete removal is a detergent wash in an automatic washer. Dry developer can sometimes be sufficiently removed by an air blast. Wet developer carries in its formula material that facilitates its removal with water, so that sometimes a simple wash will be adequate. A hydro-wash gun is another effective cleaning device, especially if large quantities or very small parts are not involved.

If parts are to be cleaned after inspection, it should be done without long delay, since fresh penetrant and developer are easier to remove then than later, after parts have lain around the shop for some days.

79. IMPORTANCE OF THOROUGH CLEANING. Some alloys can be damaged by residues of penetrant or developer remaining on the surface. Wet developers and most emulsifiers are alkaline, and if left on surfaces (like aluminum) which are attacked by alkalies, the surfaces may become pitted. This is especially true in moist atmospheres.

Some nickel alloys are susceptible to damage by sulphur when they are subsequently heated in processing or in service. In most instances thorough and careful cleaning after inspection will sufficiently remove all materials, but in some critical applications so-called sulphur-free penetrants, emulsifiers and developers may be desirable. The same precautions, but to a lesser degree, apply to the element Chlorine.

Chapter 8

POST-EMULSIFIABLE FLUORESCENT PENETRANT MATERIALS AND TECHNIQUES

1. Historical. Fluorescent penetrants were first offered to industry in mid-1942. The penetrants that were then made available were the water-wash type using a "built-in" emulsifier. Both materials and techniques were developed under pressure of wartime urgency, but the results were at once remarkably successful. During the following 10 years there was much improvement in methods and materials, so that by 1950 sensitivity levels were higher and equipment and techniques had been adapted to many needs so as to give greater speed and dependability to the inspection process.

With the development of the turbo-jet engine, however, a need arose to find minute flaws in the heat-resistant alloy turbine blades (also called buckets), which standard water-wash procedures would not locate. These blade defects were of two types, and though both might be very minute, they were extremely objectionable as stress-raisers in these highly critical parts. The defects might be very fine and crack-like, or they might be quite shallow and open—like a slight depression at a forging lap which itself might be oxide-filled or partially welded shut.

To fill this need, the post-emulsification method and materials were developed. The new process was suggested to the Department of Defense and the leading manufacturers of gas turbines in the early 1950's, and was quickly accepted and adopted as the only available means for satisfactorily inspecting the turbine blades.

The new method opened up important new inspection possibilities for many special and critical penetrant applications. The new penetrant was given the trade name of Zyglo-Pentrex*, and the method became the subject of a patent which was issued in September of 1957.** A still more brilliant and sensitive penetrant for this process was subsequently developed. It is sometimes called "Super-Pentrex". The method is today widely used in many applications other than the inspection of gas-turbine blades.

---

*Zyglo-Pentrex. Trademark registered in U. S. Patent Office. Property of Magnaflux Corporation. Also registered in Canada and Great Britain.
**U. S. Patent #2,806,959.

2. How the Post-emulsification Method Works. There is no really fundamental difference between the Post-emulsification (P.E.) method and the water-wash method. In both, penetrant enters the defect, the excess penetrant is removed from the surface by washing with water, the part is dried, developer applied and inspection for defects carried out under black light.

The essential point of difference lies in separating the emulsifier from the penetrant (in the case of P.E.), and applying the emulsifier in a separate step. This separation permits formulating the penetrant without regard to the problems encountered when incorporating emulsifiers in it. Penetrating ability can thus be at a maximum and dye solubility is improved, since most emulsifiers tend to diminish both these desirable properties when made an integral component of the penetrant.

In applying the emulsifier as a separate step, the *degree of washability* of the penetrant can be controlled by the operator, simply by allowing the emulsifier to lie in contact with the penetrant-covered surface a longer or shorter time before washing with water. Since the penetrant alone is not washable with water, this gives control all the way from no washability to extreme washability.

Fig. 53—Automatic post emulsification unit provides adjustable emulsification time by shifting emulsification station. (top left).

Thus penetrant which lies in a relatively open and shallow defect will not be washed away unless or until emulsifier is given time to diffuse down to it before washing starts. In order, then, to secure indications of nicks, laps or other shallow and wide surface blemishes if they are significant, the step of emulsification is held to a minimum length of time and washing started before emulsifier diffuses to the bottom of such depressions.

Therefore, with a brilliant penetrant of practically zero water-washability and maximum penetrating ability, the P. E. method achieves a high degree of sensitivity for very fine and tight cracks as well as the ability to produce indications of open shallow surface blemishes.

After emulsification and washing, the process is completed exactly as in the water-wash process, through the steps of drying, developing and inspecting with black light.

3. STRONG AND WEAK POINTS. Every successful process has some outstanding advantages which are its reason for existence—but inevitably the process will have some less desirable features, necessary perhaps to achieve the purposes for which the process was devised. This is true of the post-emulsification penetrant process. An analysis of its strong and weak points is given below:

ADVANTAGES

(a) Ability to show shallow and open defects which the water-wash method cannot find. This is made possible by the separation of the step of emulsification, thereby permitting control of the *degree* of washability.

(b) Has high sensitivity for very fine defects. Formulation without emulsifier usually favors maximum penetrability of the penetrant.

(c) Has high brilliance, since formulation permits use of high concentrations of fluorescent dyes.

(d) Penetration time is shortened. The emulsifier-free penetrant enters defects more rapidly.

(e) Acids and Chromates do not interfere as much as they do in the water-wash process. This is because acids and oxidizing agents react with the fluorescent dyes only in the presence of water. Since the penetrants of the P. E. process do not contain or tolerate water, there is no opportunity for the acids and chromates that may be present to react with the dyes.

(f) Parts can be re-run a number of times with good results. When water-washable penetrants enter a crack the contained emulsifier of course also enters. When attempting to clean out such a crack, as with a vapor degreaser, so that the part can be reprocessed, the *emulsifier* tends to separate from the penetrant and some of it *is not removed,* since it is not soluble in the degreaser solvent. This, then, leaves a residue in the crack which interferes with the entrance of fresh penetrant on a re-run.

Since there is no emulsifier in P. E. penetrant, vapor degreasing does a good job of cleaning out cracks, thus permitting successful inspection re-runs. Even if some penetrant remains in the crack, it is miscible with fresh penetrant and does not oppose the entrance of the newly applied penetrant.

(g) The penetrant does not absorb or tolerate water so that contamination with water is not a problem with respect to penetrant life.

DISADVANTAGES

(a) The principal disadvantage is that the P. E. method is a two-step process preceding washing. Obviously, to secure the advantage of being able to locate broad, open defects, separation of the steps of penetrating and emulsifying is necessary. This means, however, that somewhat more time, labor and equipment is needed to accomplish and control the separate steps.

(b) Controlling the sensitivity through careful timing of the emulsification step requires *close attention* to this step if successful and consistent results are to be obtained.

(c) Design grooves, such as threads, fillets, key ways, etc., may be difficult to wash clean since the emulsifier may not be permitted time to diffuse through all the penetrant at such locations. Special care must be taken at such locations to insure good drainage before emulsification.

(d) Cost. The overall cost of the two-step process in time, labor and materials, is usually somewhat greater than that of the water-wash method. The wide commercial use of P. E. penetrants today would seem to prove that the gain in results more than justifies the additional time and care, and therefore the additional cost of the process.

4. PENETRANTS FOR THIS PROCESS. Elimination of emulsifier from the penetrants gives considerably more latitude in the choice of penetrant liquids. There is no longer the restriction imposed by the need to make a homogeneous mixture of two frequently incompatible materials—penetrant liquid and emulsifier. Therefore, the penetrant liquid can be built up to combine desirable properties not only as to penetrability alone, but also as to such characteristics as viscosity, dye solubility, volatility range, etc. This permits more freedom in achieving optimum—or more nearly optimum—retention in discontinuities after cleaning, concentration at the defect and control of spreading during development of the indication.

5. TYPES OF PENETRANTS FOR THIS PROCESS. Two principal penetrants have been developed and are in wide use in the P. E. process. These are given the trade names of Pentrex and Super-Pentrex. They differ from each other in a number of details of

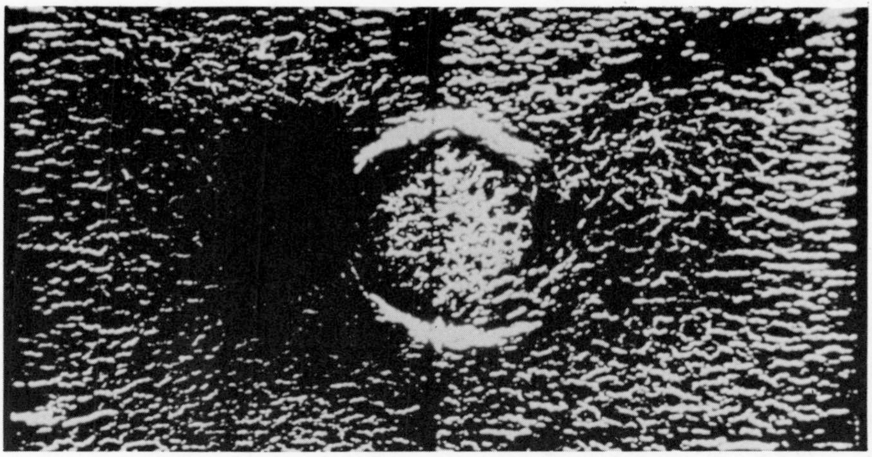

Fig. 54—Aluminum block comparison of Pentrex (left) and Super Pentrex (right).

formulation, but the important and effective difference between them is that Super-Pentrex is much more brilliantly fluorescent than Pentrex.

The normal Pentrex (Type ZL-2) is somewhat more brilliant than most of the water-wash penetrants currently available commercially, and is also somewhat more expensive. Super-Pentrex (Type ZL-22) was developed in response to the demand for a vastly more brilliant penetrant, and therefore one with greater sensitivity (due in large part to this increased brilliance) for very fine tight cracks. Since this increase in brilliance is achieved mainly through an increase in the content of fluorescent dye (the most costly ingredient) the cost of this penetrant is considerably greater than that of normal Pentrex. That the increase in sensitivity obtained justifies the increased material cost seems to be borne out by the wide and growing commercial use of this type over the normal Pentrex.

6. CHARACTERISTICS OF THESE PENETRANTS. Both of these penetrants are essentially high-flash, and non-irritating, and non-toxic to the degree that industrial chemicals of this general type are. Both contain a combination of low volatile and moderately volatile fractions to control spreading and increase concentration at the defect. Since they are composed of mutually soluble liquids which are good dye solvents, they are more stable than water-wash penetrants under large temperature variations during shipment and storage.

7. WATER TOLERANCE OF P. E. PENETRANTS. With these penetrants also, contamination with water is not the serious problem that it is with the water-wash type. These penetrants have no affinity for water, so that any water which gets into them does not alter their physical properties nor their crack-finding performance. If water finds its way into the penetrant tank it simply drops out and settles at the bottom—it does not combine with any of the ingredients of the penetrant.

Build-up of water in the tank can, of course, in time become so great that normal use of the penetrant bath would tend to stir the water up so that it appears as droplets in the penetrant on the surface of parts. This is undesirable perhaps, but not necessarily harmful. Water contamination is more of a problem where pump circulation is used to flow penetrant over the parts, especially in automatic machines using spray or flow-on application of penetrant, since in this case any water is constantly agitated and circulated with the penetrant. Even here the problem is not serious in the ordinary range of water build-up normally likely to occur.

8. DETERIORATION WITH USE. In general the P. E. penetrants deteriorate less in use than the water-wash type. They are less volatile so that evaporation losses tend to be lower. Water contamination as stated above, is not a serious problem. Care should be taken that ordinary dirt does not get into the penetrant, and that oil and grease carried into the penetrant bath are kept to a minimum. Normally, parts well cleaned in preparation for inspection will be satisfactorily free of oil and grease.

There is one type of contaminant that is more harmful to P. E. penetrants than to water-wash types. Cutting oils or compounds and fatty oils or fatty acids may harm the operation of the P. E. penetrant. Any appreciable build-up of such materials in the tank allows the penetrants to take up water to an extent which may be very undesirable, in contrast to their normal tendency to allow water to drop out without absorption.

9. OPERATING TEMPERATURE RANGE. Recommended operating temperature for this process is 70° F, although somewhat higher or lower temperatures are permissible. Being less volatile and having higher flash points, the upper limit of penetrant bath temperature may be somewhat higher than was given for water-wash penetrants. Still, unnecessarily high temperatures should be avoided, principally because drying of penetrant on the surface during drain time becomes more rapid at elevated temperatures. The upper limit of 120° F given for water-wash types is a good practical one to follow in the P. E. process also.

10. CONSUMPTION OF PENETRANT. Actual coverage obtained with the P. E. penetrants is not much different from that experienced with the water-wash type. Although the viscosity of P. E. penetrants is somewhat higher than that of the water-wash type, the drag-out loss is of the same order in both types (Chapter 4, Table II, P. 39).

Consumption of penetrant is affected by many factors, including degree of roughness of surface, blind holes, threads, etc., which tend to retain penetrant; and drain time. (Chapter 7, Section 12.)

11. FLASH POINT. P. E. penetrants now in use in general have higher flash points than the water-wash type. The two Pentrex penetrants have minimum flash points of 175° F and 185° F respectively, compared to 130° F and lower for water-wash. (Chapter 4, Table V, P. 45.) High flash points are desirable from the standpoint of fire hazard and operator safety, and to the extent that high-flash points reflect low volatility, evaporation losses are lower.

12. TOXICITY. The Pentrex and Super Pentrex penetrants contain no specifically toxic materials of the type which, in the public mind, sometimes are associated (most often erroneously) with fluorescent substances. More recently, however, some penetrants of the P. E. type have been offered containing crystalline fluorescent substances derived from coal tar, concerning which some question might be raised as to their complete harmlessness.

Since P. E. penetrants contain no emulsifiers in their formulation they have much less tendency to cause skin irritation than the water-wash type. They do, of course, consist of solvents which extract the natural oils from the skin, and can, therefore, cause drying and cracking of the skin if frequent or constant contact occurs. Operators are therefore advised to wear oil-resistant gloves and aprons as a protection. Frequent washing of the hands and application of oil-restoring skin lotions or creams are also recommended as preventive measures.

13. THE EMULSIFIERS. Although much of the advantage of the P. E. method lies in the excellence and brilliance of the penetrants, the secret of successful inspections by this method lies with the emulsifiers. These must be effective and give a clean surface after water-washing, free as possible of background, so that indications of defects can be readily picked up by the inspector; but their action must be controllable through their time of contact with the penetrant-coated surface before washing commences.

Some of the most important properties required of a suitable emulsifier are the following:

(a) It must be able to blend on contact with surface penetrant to make the penetrant water-washable.

(b) Blending must be slow enough to permit significant time-of-contact control by the operator.

(c) Blending must be fast enough not to delay the inspection process unduly.

(d) The emulsifier must be suitable for use in open tanks. This requires that it have

(1) A high flash point

(2) A low evaporation rate.

(e) It must have good tolerance for contaminating water.

(f) It must have good tolerance for contaminating penetrant.

(g) It should have no offensive odor.

(h) It should be non-toxic.

14. IMPORTANCE OF VISCOSITY. Assuming that the material has satisfactory emulsifying ability and meets the requirements of d, e, f, g and h, above, the next most important property of the emulsifier is viscosity. The viscosity of the emulsifier at the point of use determines the time required for emulsification to proceed to the desired point.

Viscous emulsifiers diffuse or blend more slowly. Thinner emulsifiers blend into the penetrant more rapidly. A viscosity must be chosen, therefore, that assures slow enough diffusion to give the necessary margin of control of emulsification time without unnecessarily prolonging this step of the process.

Another practical consideration affected by viscosity is the loss by drag-out. If too viscous, more emulsifier may be taken out of the bath with each part immersed than is necessary. Unnecessary consumption of emulsifier is obviously undesirable since it increases the material cost of the inspection.

15. AVAILABLE EMULSIFIERS. Currently three main types of emulsifiers are available and in general use. Two of these are essentially similar in composition and differ principally in viscosity. In many applications the broad-open type of discontinuity is not significant and is not sought. For fine to very fine defects, the P.E. method is used because of its greater sensitivity (brilliance and penetrating ability of the penetrant). Rapid emulsification and minimum dragout are thus desirable, since time of contact is not critical if the shallow open defect is not considered important. Therefore, a less viscous emulsifier is available for this specific use. A much more viscous product is provided for these applications where shallow-open defects *are* sought. The third emulsifier is used for special applications where the presence of sulphur in significant amount is considered undesirable.

In addition to these three main types, at least two others are available commercially. One of these is intended for use with penetrants being used in testing liquid oxygen containers or systems. The other is a cleaner-emulsifier in which a relatively small amount of emulsifier is combined with a solvent. This material may be used as a solvent cleaner, usually with a rag wipe-off technique, but may also be used as an emulsifier followed by a water-wash. Where used in this latter way it does not give as clean a background as is obtained with the first two emulsifier types. However, the solvent-emulsifier type is usually low in sulphur and chlorine, so may be used in applications where these elements are objectionable.

16. TYPES OF EMULSIFIERS. Following is a general description of the three main emulsifier types:

TYPE 2—This is a fairly fluid liquid which blends rapidly and gives an easily washable surface. Since contact time is brief, the possibility of emulsifier diffusing into the penetrant in relatively tight defects is slight. The material works well on rough surfaces because it *does* diffuse quickly and gets to the bottom of surface roughness, threads, fillets, etc., better and more rapidly than a more viscous emulsifier.

A red dye is incorporated in the emulsifier, fluorescing pink under black light, so that when washing a part under black light it is easy to follow the progress of removal of both emulsifier and penetrant.

TYPE 3—This is a much more viscous emulsifier and gives a much slower rate of blending with surface penetrant. The operator thus has time in which to control the depth of emulsification through shortening or lengthening the duration of surface contact before washing. The material may be difficult to use on rough surfaces if shallow discontinuities are being sought.

The red dye of Type 2 is also included in Type 3 emulsifier and is even more useful in following the progress of washing in this case.

TYPE 4—This emulsifier is intended for use in applications in which the presence of sulfur is objectionable. Certain nickel alloys when heated will absorb sulphur if present and become brittle—an effect which cannot be tolerated. *Complete* removal of sulfur-containing materials from the surface of parts after inspection would eliminate the danger, but complete removal cannot always be guaranteed, especially where design grooves and crevices exist.

The Type 4 emulsifier is of low viscosity and in general similar to Type 2, except for sulfur content. Sulfur is substantially absent from the product so that it has been found satisfactory for use on the critical nickel alloys mentioned.

A modification of Type 4 having high viscosity is also available for special applications.

TABLE XI

PHYSICAL PROPERTIES OF EMULSIFIERS

Type	Viscosity at 100° F Centistokes	Density	Flash Point Closed Cup	Water Tolerance % Added Water
2*	51.5	.947	300°F.	18%
3	118.0	.959	305°F.	20%
4	37.0	.946	375°F.	15%

17. WATER TOLERANCE OF EMULSIFIERS. If emulsifiers pick up appreciable amounts of water from outside sources their physical properties will become altered. Excessive amounts of added water will make them unfit for normal use. Since the wash station is usually immediately adjoining the emulsfication station, the possibility of water contamination exists. Some emulsifiers tend to thicken with the addition of small amounts of water, then thin out as more water is added. This initial thickening should not be great enough seriously to alter the viscosity of the emulsifier and thus affect its behavior. Table XI shows the amount of added water commercially used emulsifiers can pick up without seriously affecting their operating characteristics.

18. PENETRANT TOLERANCE OF EMULSIFIERS. Since parts, coated with penetrant, go at once to the emulsifier station after draining, there is also opportunity for contamination of emulsifier with penetrant, and this inevitably occurs. Emulsifiers must be able to absorb considerable amounts of penetrant before their performance is impaired. The principal effect of this penetrant pick-up is to reduce the ability to emulsify surface penetrant due to such penetrant already absorbed by the emulsifier liquid. Poor washing and unsatisfactory inspection results.

Type 2 and Type 3 emulsifiers have a high tolerance for penetrant contamination before their emulsifying action becomes so

*An earlier emulsifier designated Type 1 is now obsolete.

impaired that they must be discarded. Their tolerance for Pentrex penetrant is of the order of 20% by volume, although some users consider that the safe limit is much lower than this—in some cases as low as 10%. Actually this is to some degree a matter of opinion since the emulsifying action is bound to be affected to some degree by a dilution with penetrant of such large amount and the seriousness of the effect will vary with different applications. The maximum tolerance is the point where the emulsifying action obviously breaks down, and the emulsifier should be discarded before this point is reached.

Type 4 emulsifier has a much lower penetrant tolerance, of the order of 10% to 15%.

To prevent excessive penetrant carry-over into the emulsifier tank, drain time should be as long as feasible, but not less than 15 minutes. Of course, over-long drain time results in drying of the penetrant on the surface of the part, and this must be avoided.

19. OTHER PROPERTIES The emulsifiers in commercial use have other physical properties which are desirable for general applications. The flash points are high (Table XI), their evaporation rate in open tanks is not excessive, and they are practically odorless. Like all materials of this type, they are skin irritants and the customary precautions should be taken to avoid continual contact with the skin. Operators should wear gloves and aprons as protection.

20. DEVELOPERS FOR THE P. E. PROCESS. Developers for this process are the same as for the water-wash, and are applied in the same way. (See Chapter 5, Sec. 28 and Chapter 7, Sections 13-16 and 43-54). It is the opinion of many users that the fluffy-dry developer applied by dipping the part in a bin of developer is most sensitive in nearly all cases when very fine defects are being sought. Spray-can volatile-solvent-suspended developers can also be very sensitive for fine cracks, where their use is practical.

21. APPLYING THE PROCESS. The first step in applying the P. E. process is the same as for any penetrant inspection. The surface of the part must be cleaned of all dirt, foreign material, oil, grease, water, paint, etc. The defect must be clean and open to the surface, in order to be penetrated. This step has been fully discussed in previous chapters. (See Chapter 7, Sections 17, 18).

22. PENETRATION TECHNIQUES. Penetration techniques for P. E. penetrants are no different from those that apply for water-wash types. These are fully discussed in Chapter 7, Sections 19 thru 23. Whether dipped, hosed or sprayed, the main consideration is that *all* surfaces to be inspected are covered with penetrant. In the event that only part of the surface is to be inspected, pressurized spray cans are available and very convenient.

23. PENETRATION OR DRAIN TIME. One of the advantages of the post-emulsification method lies in the shorter penetration or drain time that these penetrants require. Table XII gives drain time for some typical materials and parts. In general, these drain times are about half (or less) those recommended for the same type of parts when water-wash penetrants are used. This is an important saving and in some cases may offset part of the increased cost of penetrant.

On the other hand, there is some advantage in prolonging the drain time to at least 15 minutes when the production rate or other requirements permit. Longer draining allows more penetrant to run off of the surfaces of parts, and although the penetrant thus recovered is a plus factor, the more important advantage is that the better-drained surfaces mean less or slower contamination of the emulsifier bath with penetrant.

It is highly desirable that, for a given inspection, the most advantageous drain time be established and then adhered to fairly rigidly. This is for the reason that emulsification time, which is critical, can also be established and can be expected to give consistent results if the film of penetrant to be removed is always the same.

If penetrant dries on the surface of parts, re-dipping may be necessary. As a practical matter with the short drain times and the lower volatility of the P. E. penetrants, re-dipping is seldom required.

24. PRECAUTIONS. There are no special precautions to be observed in applying the P. E. penetrants. Care to obtain full coverage, allowance of sufficient drain time, insuring that all blind holes, depressions, etc., are so disposed that full drainage can occur—these and other requirements are achieved with normal care when the process is fully understood.

TABLE XII

PENETRATION TIMES FOR POST-EMULSIFICATION PENETRANTS FOR VARIOUS MATERIALS

Material	Form	Types of Defects	Penetration Time (Minutes)
Aluminum	Castings	Shrinkage cracks	10
		Porosity	5
		Cold shuts	5
	Forgings	Cracks	10
		Laps	5-15
	Welds	Cracks	10
		Lack of bond	5
		Porosity	5
	All forms	Fatigue cracks	10
Magnesium	Castings	Shrinkage cracks	10
		Porosity	5
		Cold shuts	5
	Forgings	Cracks	10
		Laps	5-15
	Welds	Cracks	10
		Lack of bond	10
		Porosity	10
	All forms	Fatigue cracks	10
Stainless Steel	Castings	Shrinkage cracks	20
		Porosity	10
		Cold shuts	10
	Forgings	Cracks	20
		Laps	10-30
	Welds	Cracks	20
		Lack of bond	20
		Porosity	20
	All forms	Fatigue cracks	20

TABLE XII Cont.

Material	Form	Types of Defects	Penetration Time (Minutes)
Brass and Bronze	Castings	Cracks	10
		Porosity	5
		Cold Shuts	5
	Forgings	Cracks	10
		Laps	5-15
	Brazed Parts	Cracks	10
		Lack of bond	10
		Porosity	10
Plastics	All forms	Cracks	2
Glass	All forms	Cracks	5
Glass-to-Metal Seals	All forms	Cracks	5-60
Carbide Tipped Tools	Brazed joints	Porosity	5
		Lack of bond	5
	Tips	Cracks	10
Titanium and High-Temperature Alloys	All forms	All	15

It is well to remember that certain of the liquid components in P. E. penetrants are solvents, and these may attack some resins or plastics to an extent sufficient to prohibit their use. This is also true of water-wash penetrants, but the action may differ with respect to a given plastic. In the event of a reaction between penetrant and plastic, special penetrants can be made available for such an inspection.

25. EMULSIFICATION TECHNIQUES. The type of defect sought and the kind of material or part being inspected usually determines the choice of emulsifier to use. If only fine defects are being looked for, and shallow, open marks are not significant, the low viscosity emulsifier is indicated, since it acts more rapidly than the thicker type.

If wide, shallow surface discontinuities are to be detected, such as filled forging laps or even nicks or scratches, then the more viscous emulsifier should be selected. For very rough surfaces the choice may be restricted, since viscous emulsifiers may not diffuse rapidly enough into non-relevant surface depressions to permit satisfactory washing. Viscous emulsifiers work best on smooth surfaces, and it is, of course, on smooth surface that nicks, scratches, and the like are usually most objectionable.

If the parts being inspected are of a type likely to be affected by sulphur, then the sulphur-free emulsifier should be used.

26. APPLICATION OF THE EMULSIFIER. Emulsifier is perhaps best applied by dipping the part into a tank of the emulsifier liquid. The advantage of this technique lies in that the entire surface of the part becomes coated at practically the same time, thus giving more accurate control of emulsification time over the whole part.

Fig. 55—Automatic unit for tube inspection, applying penetrant and emulsifier by the flowing-on method.

Flowing or spraying is also a satisfactory method of application provided no appreciable time is required to coat the entire surface. In automatic equipment multiple spray or flow nozzles accomplish this result very well, and are often simpler mechanically than lowering and raising the part for dipping. Brushing-on of emulsifier is not recommended, since the action of the brush mixes the emulsifier with the penetrant prematurely and irregularly, and makes control of emulsification time impossible.

It is possible to use the "expendable" technique in applying emulsifier. In this case the station is combined with the washing station. Emulsifier is sprayed on the part, and after the proper lapse of time, the part is washed. Excess emulsifier is washed down the drain and not re-used. This method is rarely used and is apt to be wasteful of emulsifier, due to the need for speed in application to all surfaces, so that emulsification time can be properly controlled.

27. EMULSIFICATION OF VERY LARGE PARTS. When extremely large parts are dipped or sprayed, the actual handling time may be too long to permit washing as soon after coating with emulsifier as is desired, even if viscous emulsifiers are used. Emulsifiers with special properties have been devised to meet this situation, but since they are not generally applicable except in special instances, they are available commercially only upon request.

28. EMULSIFICATION TIME. This is the most critical factor in securing dependable results with the P. E. process. The finer or tighter (and deeper) the crack or discontinuity, the less critical is the time allowed for emulsification. Even the most active emulsifying agents cannot diffuse very rapidly into the penetrant held in a very small surface opening. But many defects are not so tight and the inspection must be so set up that *all* significant defects are located.

For this reason the importance of suitable emulsification times cannot be overlooked. Optimum times should be established by trial on typical parts. Normally the actual time required is from a few seconds up to about 3 minutes. In establishing the optimum for a given application, it is suggested that a series of tests be run, say at 3, 2, 1, and ½ minutes emulsification time, and results compared on the basis of ease of washing, amount of fluorescent background and excellence of indications at defects of the sought-for type.

It is not practical to prepare tables of emulsification times for different parts and types of defects, since any general or predetermined time may be wrong in any specific instance. Over-emulsification must be avoided, and a rule of thumb is to keep emulsification to the very minimum time necessary to produce a clean-washed surface. But this alone is not a sufficient standard, since the time necessary to accomplish this result may already be too long, and some significant indications on some types of surface may have been destroyed.

From the above discussion it may appear that this step in the process is so critical that the process itself is not reliable. This is, of course, not the case and as a practical matter suitable emulsification times are not difficult to establish provided the operator is aware of the various factors which have just been described.

29. DETERIORATION OF EMULSIFIER DURING USE. It has been stated (Sections 17, 18 above) that emulsifiers tend to become contaminated with penetrant and with water. If care is taken to keep ordinary dirt and foreign material out of the bath, the most serious source of deterioration is the inevitable accumulation of penetrant in the emulsifier bath. Types 2 and 3 emulsifier will in many applications still perform their function reasonably well with penetrant accumulations of the order of 20% by volume, though established emulsification *times* will no longer be valid when this much penetrant has diluted the bath.

When the *expendable* method of applying emulsifier is used, no deterioration occurs because there is no contamination. However, because of the difficulty in applying uniform and minimum coatings of emulsifier with a spray, and because there is appreciable unavoidable waste, this technique is not often used.

Emulsifier baths must also be protected from water splashing back over from the wash station, which is usually adjacent. If available emulsifiers have reasonably good water tolerances, this is not ordinarily a serious problem.

30. WASHING TECHNIQUES. Once the necessary time has elapsed for proper emulsification of the surface penetrant, washing techniques differ very little from the spray-washing used with water-wash type penetrants. (Chapter 7, Sections 24-31.) Wiping with wet cloths is not suitable nor, obviously, is washing with solvents. Hand or automatic spray-washing is commonly used, with water as it comes from the tap. Temperatures of 70° F to 100° F are preferable, but *hot* water is not recommended.

31. DIP-WASHING. Washing by merely dipping the part in a water bath is generally not a sufficient, and therefore not a satisfactory, washing method for this process. However, when large parts have been dipped in the emulsifier, it is sometimes impossible to get the water spray over all surfaces before the maximum emulsification time has elapsed. Use of a water dip as a "stop" for emulsification has been resorted to, but it has not proved altogether satisfactory.

In this technique the part is submerged in a water bath when the pre-determined emulsification time has passed, so that all surfaces are immediately wet with water. This is intended to stop the penetration of emulsifier into the penetrant. The dip must be followed at once with a vigorous spray wash, if a satisfactorily clean surface is to be obtained. Water of the dip bath must be frequently renewed to remove penetrant which has separated out.

32. OVER-WASHING. With water-wash type penetrants prolonged washing may result in removing the penetrant-emulsifier mixture from some defects. There is little danger of this effect in the P. E. process. Prolonged washing does not remove P. E. penetrants from defects in any normal washing technique, since the penetrant itself (un-emulsified) is not miscible with water.

One precaution should be borne in mind, however. Some users have employed water sprays or streams at excessively high pressure. When this is done, clean background surfaces are more easily produced, but this is accomplished because the high pressure blast of water removes some penetrant mechanically, by main force. Obviously this is undesirable, because the heavy impact of water can then also remove some penetrant from defects—especially open defects.

33. POOR WASHING. If a part washes poorly, leaving spots of fluorescence over the surface, it is an indication that insufficient time has been allowed for emulsification. In such a case, do not *re-emulsify* the part—instead re-process it with penetrant, after cleaning and drying. Allow a longer drain time (unless this was already a maximum) to reduce the amount of surface penetrant to be removed. Then allow a longer emulsification time before washing, and repeat these steps, increasing the emulsification time in each case, until a satisfactory washed surface is obtained.

A point to remember here, however, is that on *very rough* surfaces the emulsification time to produce a clean surface may be too long to secure reliable indications of open defects. In such a case emulsification time cannot be lengthened to the point of optimum surface cleaning, but must be shortened and residual background fluorescence versus actual open defect indications carefully evaluated.

34. OTHER CLEANING METHODS. Emulsification and water washing is not the only way in which Pentrex penetrants can be used, although in most cases it is the most effective. If shallow or open defects are not being sought, the penetrants can be removed from the surface with a solvent, somewhat similarly to the cleaning of color-contrast penetrants. (Chapter 10)

Wiping with cloths wet with a solvent is a quite satisfactory method, if carefully done using a minimum of solvent. Kerosene, a less active solvent than naphtha, will remove surface penetrant without dissolviing penetrant from fine cracks to any serious extent. It will, however, also remove penetrant from open defects.

Usually the surface should be gone over twice in removal by wiping—the second time with a clean cloth and fresh solvent. Solvent can be sprayed over the surface and immediately wiped off with a clean cloth. The solvent should be allowed to dry off of the surface before developer is applied.

A quick dip in kerosene followed at once by a dip into emulsifier, and then washing with water, has been reported as an effective step in the cleaning process. Its use would reduce the rate of contamination of the emulsifier bath, because considerable of the penetrant would be carried away by the kerosene dip.

Cleaning by very brief exposure of the surfaces in a vapor-phase degreaser has been used. Such an extreme technique cannot be recommended, as the hot solvent and vapor actively dissolve the penetrant and will quickly remove penetrant from defects. Some users have reported satisfactory results from this cleaning method, but only in the hands of an experienced operator on particular types of parts. Certainly the danger of missing defects when this technique is used is considerable and if used, this hazard must be fully appreciated.*

35. DRYING TECHNIQUES. (See Chapter 7, Sections 32-42). All the considerations previously detailed under water-wash penetrants are equally applicable to the drying of parts after washing in the P. E. process. The use of re-circulating hot air at controlled temperature is by far the most effective method of drying. The aim is to dry the surface without allowing the temperature of the body of the part to go above 150°-175° F, and to accomplish this in the shortest time possible to minimize spreading of penetrant at indica-

*See here Appendix V for a discussion of removers.

tions. Oven air temperature should normally be 200° F, and never above 225° F.

Alternative methods of drying are blowing the water from the surface of the part with a strong blast of dry air, or simply wiping with a dry cloth until dry. Neither of these hand methods is at all equal to the controlled hot air method, since warming of the part has the added advantage of helping to bring penetrant back out of defects. This makes for stronger and sharper indications.

Use of high velocity warm air blowers or of infra-red lamps is not recommended. (See Chapter 7, Section 42).

36. DEVELOPMENT TECHNIQUES. The same developers and the same methods of applying them are used in the P. E. process as are used in the water-wash method. (See Chapter 7, Sections 43-54). Either dry or wet developers may be used. However, there is considerable evidence that in most applications the dry, fluffy developer is more sensitive than the wet for use with P. E. penetrants. To achieve maximum sensitivity with the dry fluffy developer, parts should be dipped into a bin of the developer, thus insuring full and complete contact of developer particles at the edges of defects. Dusting or blowing on this developer is not nearly so effective. Solvent spray-can developers are very effective in achieving maximum sensitivity in special cases.

If wet developer is used, special care must be taken that the developer bath is kept at optimum strength, and also that no heavy deposits of dried developer material can result at any point on the surface. On very smooth surfaces, the wet developer may sometimes have advantage, since very little—sometimes *too* little of the dry fluffy developer powder will cling to such smooth surfaces.

37. CONTAMINATION OF DEVELOPER. Care should be taken that drops of penetrant from any source are kept out of the developer bin or tank. Such contamination will lead to spots of fluoresence not related to defects, which make inspection very difficult.

38. IMPORTANCE OF DEVELOPER. A few operators have expressed the opinion that developing is a superfluous step in penetrant inspection. It is true that many indications appear on the surfaces of processed parts even before developer is applied. However, it is readily demonstrable that fine or border-line indications appear more readily and more clearly when developer is used, and some may not appear at all without developer.

To satisfy himself that this is so, it is suggested that the operator make a comparative test on a good aluminum test block, (See Chapter 17, Section 15) applying developer on one half and not on the other, and evaluate the speed of appearance and the intensity of some of the fine indications.*

39. DEVELOPMENT TIME. As in the case of water-wash penetrant inspection, the time allowed for full development of an indication is not especially critical but is usually about half the time for penetration, or longer. This may mean several hours for very fine defects, for which maximum penetration times have been allowed.

40. INSPECTION. (See Chapter 7, Sections 55-77). After development, inspection under black light is conducted just as in the case of water-wash penetrants. When very fine defects are sought, black light intensity must be high, and maximum possible exclusion of white light should be provided.

Intensity and appearance of indications at a given size and shape of defect will be somewhat different with Pentrex penetrants than with the water-wash type. If the part has been properly processed, Pentrex indications are likely to be sharper and more brilliant than comparable indications produced with water-wash penetrants. Operators who are experienced in interpreting only one type of penetrant indications should be aware of this fact if they shift to the use of the other type.

41. PRECAUTIONS TO REMEMBER. In Chapter 7, Section 77, a number of precautions to be observed for good inspection results are discussed. In general these apply equally when P. E. methods are used, with the exception that P. E. type penetrants give much better results than water-wash on parts which have been anodized or treated with acids. On such parts the P. E. method is much to be preferred. Development times should be kept as brief as possible to shorten contact of the fluorescent dyes with the anodized or acid treated surfaces. Black light intensities should also be high, to offset any possible deterioration of the dye by the acids.

The remaining precautions or conditions to guard against

*Appendix II gives a full discussion of the mechanism by which the developer amplifies the brightness and apparent size of fine indications.

discussed in the previous chapter are listed again for ease of reference:

(a) Interfering conditions—paint, porous coatings, etc.

(b) Poor washing.

(c) Filled cracks. Contaminants may be:

  (1) Water.

  (2) Peened edges of cracks.

  (3) Oxide or scale.

  (4) Carbon, baked oil (engine varnish).

  (5) Processing oil, grease, or rust-preventing coatings.

(d) Parts which have been run once. When P. E methods are used, re-runs are possible, but be sure parts and cracks are thoroughly dried before re-processing.

(e) Do not try to use fluorescent penetrants on parts which have already been processed with color-contrast penetrants.

42. CLEANING AFTER INSPECTION. Cleaning after P. E. penetrant inspection, when required, should be done as promptly as possible. Use of a hot detergent wash is probably the most effective method, preferably in an automatic washer if many parts are involved. A hydro-wash gun is sometimes useful when parts are relatively few or for large parts.

If the parts are likely to be affected by sulphur, especial care should be used to remove all penetrant and emulsifier that might have remained on surfaces after inspection. Of course, in such cases, the sulphur-free penetrants and emulsifiers should be used.

CHAPTER 9

BLACK LIGHT—ITS NATURE, SOURCES AND REQUIREMENTS

1. DEFINITION OF BLACK LIGHT. "Black light" is a term applied to near-ultraviolet radiation having a wave length shorter than the shortest in the visible spectrum. It has the property of causing many substances, such as certain minerals and dyes, to fluoresce. Though this radiation is not visible to the eye and is therefore characterized as being "black," it is produced by the mercury arc as a "by-product" of visible white light, along with other shorter wave-length radiation. The name "black light" is therefore a very appropriate name by which to call it.

Black light, to energize the dyes of fluorescent penetrants and make them glow, is an integral part of the application of such penetrants to the detection of flaws. The user of this process should therefore understand what it is and know how to make proper use of it and of the equipment which generates it. He should also be thoroughly familiar with what successful inspection requires of black light and its sources.

2. NATURE OF FLUORESCENCE. The terms *luminescence, phosphorescence* and *fluorescence* are used to refer to light produced at low temperatures, as opposed to *incandescence* which refers to light produced through heat.

Luminescence is defined in Webster's Dictionary as "any emission of light not ascribable directly to incandescence, and therefore occurring at low temperatures. It may be produced by physiological processes as in the fire fly, or by chemical or electrical action."

Phosphorescence is "luminescence caused by the absorption of radiation, such as X-rays or ultraviolet light, and continuing for a noticeable time *after* those radiations have stopped."

Fluorescence is the "property of emitting radiation as the result of, and *only during,* the absorption of radiation from some other source." The distinction here is that fluorescence disappears as soon as the energizing radiation is cut off.

Specifically, in our application, dyes are used which have the property of absorbing short wave, invisible "black light" and re-emitting this energy in longer wave-lengths in the visible range. The various fluorescent dyes, with the same energy source—i.e., black light—give off light in different parts of the visible spectrum from red to blue, depending on the individual dye selected.

Dyes commonly in use in fluorescent penetrants give off light in the yellow-green or green-blue portion of the visible spectrum. Special penetrants for special applications, however, are formulated with dyes that fluoresce in the red, yellow, orange or blue ranges.

3. ULTRAVIOLET LIGHT. Ultraviolet light is the term applied to radiation of wave length shorter than the shortest visible violet wave length—from around 4000 Angstrom units down to 2000Å. In general, the shorter the wave length the more penetrating and active is the radiation.

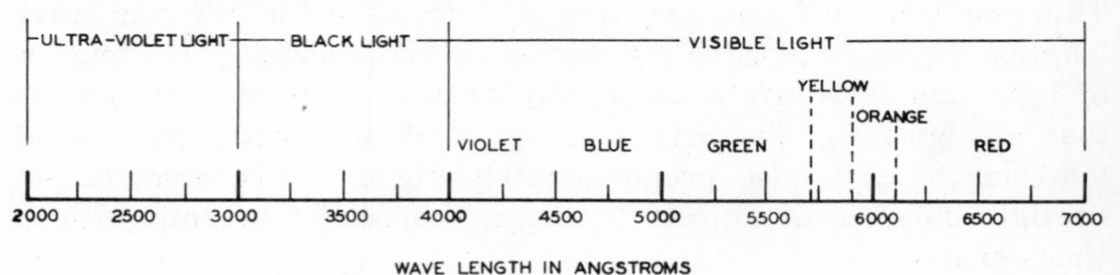

Fig. 56—Spectrum of light through the visible, "black light", and ultraviolet wave lengths.

However, the band between 4000Å and 3200Å is relatively inactive when compared to the band from 3200Å down to 2000Å. Ultraviolet of around 2500Å is very harmful to many forms of life—it will kill bacteria, cause sunburn, generate ozone and can be very injurious to the human eye. The electric arc, such as is used in welding, is rich in such short-wave ultraviolet, and welders (as well as watchers) must take special care to filter out these short waves before they reach the eye, or else not look directly at the arc.

4. BLACK LIGHT FOR PENETRANT INSPECTION. Welding helmets are fitted with very heavy dark blue or dark purple glass filters to safeguard the eyes. Filters are also used for fluorescent penetrant inspection, only in this case the filter is a special one devised to pass the maximum amount of the wave lengths which activate the fluorescent dyes, and to exclude all other wave lengths—i.e., both visible light and short wave ultraviolet—to as great a degree as possible.

The desired wave lengths are between 3500Å and 4000Å.

5. SUNLIGHT AS A SOURCE OF ULTRAVIOLET LIGHT. Radiation from the sun is composed of energy of a very wide range of wave lengths in addition to the visible light which the eye can see. In the range just below the visible light, there is strong invisible radiation in the ultraviolet. This energy will cause fluorescent dyes to glow, although the strong white light also present does not normally permit this to be apparent. However, the now familiar "daylight fluorescent" colors, paints and printing inks are energized in part by the natural ultraviolet in sunlight, to make them super-bright even in full daylight. Some of these colors react to short-wave ultraviolet as well as to "black light." At dusk and dawn there is a difference in light intensity and light distribution, due to the longer distance the sun's light must travel through the atmosphere. This results in different amounts of diffraction for different wave lengths. There is greater diffraction of the shorter wave lengths of light and these are consequently present in greater proportion than at high noon. The actinic energy striking daylight-fluorescent materials is thus also proportionately higher. This effect causes daylight fluorescent objects to appear especially bright at these times of day.

For the purposes of fluorescent penetrant inspection, however, it would not be very practicable to filter sunlight to secure the proper black light intensity. Therefore artificial sources must be utilized.

6. FLUORESCENT DYES. As has already been stated numerous fluorescent dyes are known and a considerable number have been used in fluorescent penetrants. (See Chapter 4, Section 44 and following sections.) The best dyes for this purpose react strongly when energized with black light of 3650Å wave length. The preferred dyes emit light in the green-yellow range—the most favorable range for easy "seeing" with the eye. Dyes especially adaptable for this purpose have been developed over the years so that the dyes now in use are far superior in fluorescent brilliance and color to those available twenty years ago. These dyes are also remarkably stable in their fluorescent light output during prolonged exposure to black light—a property of great importance for penetrant inspection, and one not possessed by many of the dyes which might otherwise be suitable.

For the purposes of fluorescent penetrant inspection, therefore, the need is for a reliable source of black light of 3650 Å which is of sufficient intensity and which can be produced conveniently at the point of inspection.

7. SOURCES OF BLACK LIGHT. Although sunlight and artificial light from incandescent sources include a greater or less amount of ultraviolet, most such sources are not adaptable for the production of black light of sufficient intensity. However, the electric arc drawn between two metal or carbon electrodes, is especially rich in energy in the ultraviolet range. The enclosed mercury-vapor arc lamp also offers a convenient source which is high in output of the desired black light wave length. With few exceptions, black light

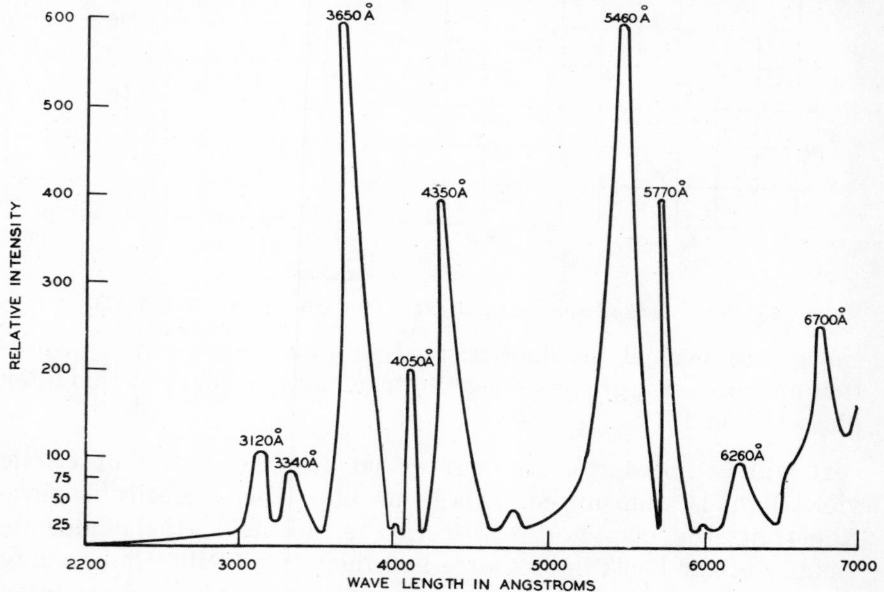

Fig. 57—Spectrum of output of high pressure mercury arc.

lamps used for fluorescent penetrant inspections employ the mercury arc in one form or another. Figure 57 gives the spectrum of light given off from a high intensity mercury arc lamp, and shows the energy distribution over the range of ultraviolet and visible wave lengths.

8. FILTERS FOR BLACK LIGHT. The glass filter almost universally used is a dense red-purple color. It effectively removes practically all visible light from the energy given off by the mercury arc. At the same time, it also removes all radiation of wave length below

3000Å—that is, it eliminates all the harmful short-wave ultraviolet. It passes ultraviolet radiation in the range from 4000Å (the lower edge of the visible violet range) down to 3200Å. The radiation passed by the filter peaks at 3650Å, the optimum for

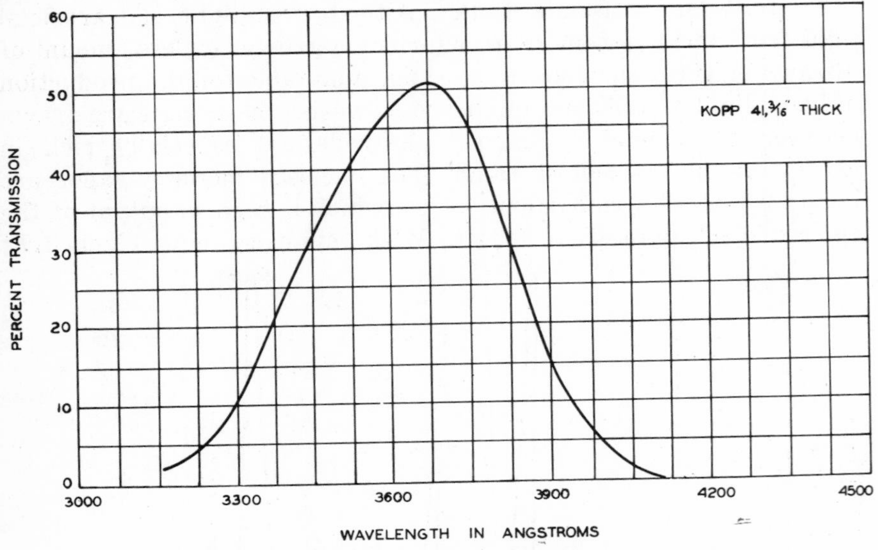

Fig. 58—Transmission curve of black light filter glass. (Kopp 41).

energizing most of the fluorescent dyes used for penetrant inspection purposes. Figure 58 shows the transmission curve of this filter glass (Kopp 41).

It will be noted from the curve that a small amount of visible violet light is transmitted. This is not altogether undesirable since it permits the inspector to discern the objects in the immediate vicinity of the black light source and therefore facilitates handling of parts during inspection. The filter also passes infra-red radiation of wave length longer than the visible red, but this is of no consequence whatever from the point of view of penetrant inspection.

9. FLUORESCENT EMISSION FROM DYES. It has been stated that fluorescent dyes may be selected to emit light in various parts of the whole spectrum from red to blue. Tests have determined that the eye finds a yellow-green light more "seeable" than reds or blues, so that the dyes most widely used for general purpose fluorescent penetrants are selected to give off light of this wave length range. Fig. 59 shows the emission curve of a typical dye of this type, when energized with black light of 3650Å.

BLACK LIGHT

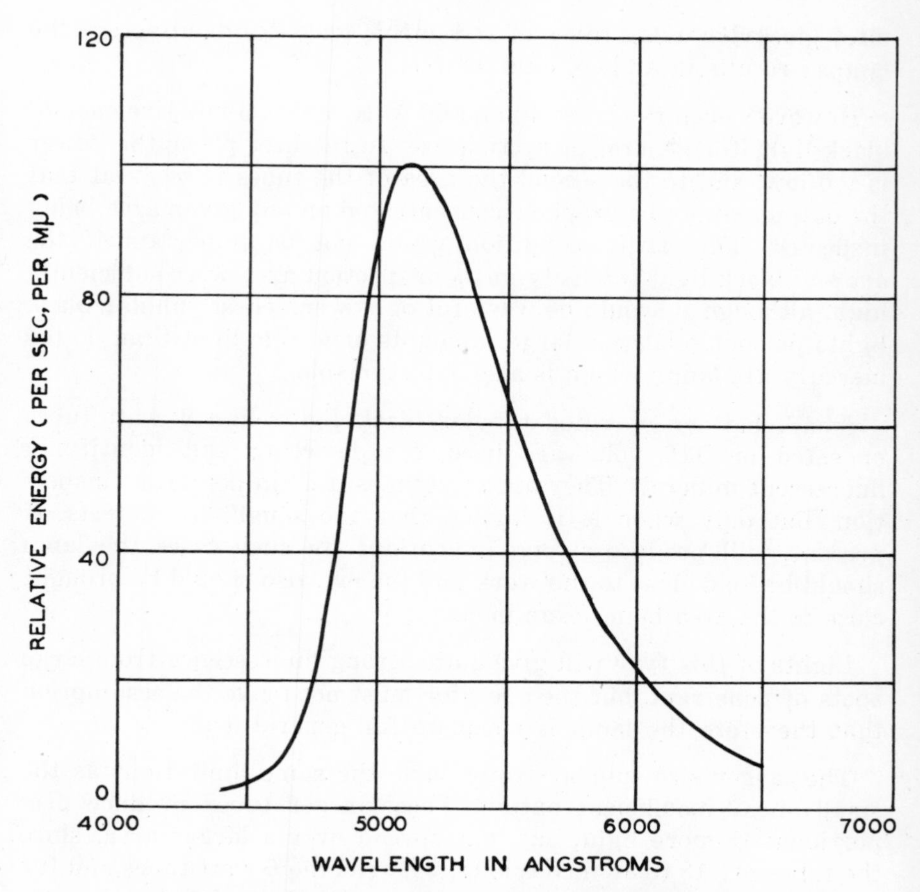

Fig. 59—Emission spectrum of yellow-green fluorescent dye.

10. BLACK LIGHT LAMPS. There are a number of types of black light lamps available commercially, though not all are satisfactory as sources of radiation for fluorescent inspection. Some of these lamps do not give sufficient energy in the 3650Å range to meet the *minimum* intensity requirements for inspection purposes, although all use filters of suitable glass to remove visible and short wave radiation.

11. TUBULAR BLACK LIGHTS. Tubular black lights are similar in construction and operation to the familiar fluorescent tubular lights used for general illumination. These employ a low pressure mercury vapor discharge, and the inside of the tube is coated with a phosphor which fluoresces under the energy of the mercury vapor discharge. Surrounding these tubes with larger tubes of red-purple filter glass (or using tubes of red-purple glass to manufacture the lamps) results in a black light source.

However, even the large 40 and 60 watt tubes do not give enough black light for general inspection use. In the first place, the power is too low, and in the second the area of the tubes is so great that the output cannot be properly concentrated on any given area being inspected. This latter condition would not be important if the *over-all* black light intensity in the inspection area were sufficiently high, although it would be wasteful of power. These tubular black lights put out relatively larger amounts of visible light than do the mercury arc lamp, which is also objectionable.

Small, battery operated tubular black lights and 6 watt tubes operated on 110 volts are used for detecting and identifying fluorescent minerals. They are sometimes used in penetrant inspection, but only when it is known that the sought-for defects, if present, will produce strong indications. In such cases the lamp should be held close to the work and the eye also should be brought close to the area being examined.

Lights of this type will give quite strong fluorescence from large spots of penetrant, but the operator must not make the assumption that therefore the lamp is adequate for general use.

The larger size tubular lamps have the same limitations as the small ones—insufficient output. These larger tubes produce proportionately more light, but it is spread over a larger area, since the tubes are 18 to 36 inches long, whereas the 6 watt tubes and the battery lamps are only 5 to 6 inches long. Since the larger tubes are not portable, however, as the 6 watt units are, they have even less general utility. If mounted in banks of 4 or 6 they may give fair results if close enough to the inspection table (15 to 18 inches) but only if gross defects alone are being sought. The black light intensity level in even a bank of tubular lights is too low to insure the location of very fine cracks.

12. Incandescent Black Lights. A black light lamp has been on the market which is similar to an ordinary photo-flood incandescent bulb except that the bulb is blown out of the red purple filter glass. This is another low-output black light source of little or no value for penetrant inspection work. The incandescent filament does not put out a great deal of ultraviolet light, so that the amount of black light passing through the filter is not adequate.

Lamp life is short and heat output great. Like the 6 watt tubular lamp, its only utility is in the intermittent energizing of gross fluorescent areas. It must not be depended upon for any important flaw-detection work.

13. MERCURY VAPOR LAMPS. The enclosed mercury vapor arc lamp is by far the most important black light source for inspection work and is almost universally used. The construction of this lamp is shown in the drawing (Fig. 60). The mercury arc is drawn between electrodes enclosed in a small quartz tube, Q. E_1 and E_2 are the current-carrying electrodes, and E_S is an auxiliary starting electrode or heater. The resistor R limits the current in the starting electrode. This arc-cartridge is mounted and inclosed in an outer glass bulb B, which serves to protect the quartz cartridge, and also to focus the light emitted. The lamp is supplied current from a special current-regulating ballast transformer, which limits the current which the arc can draw.

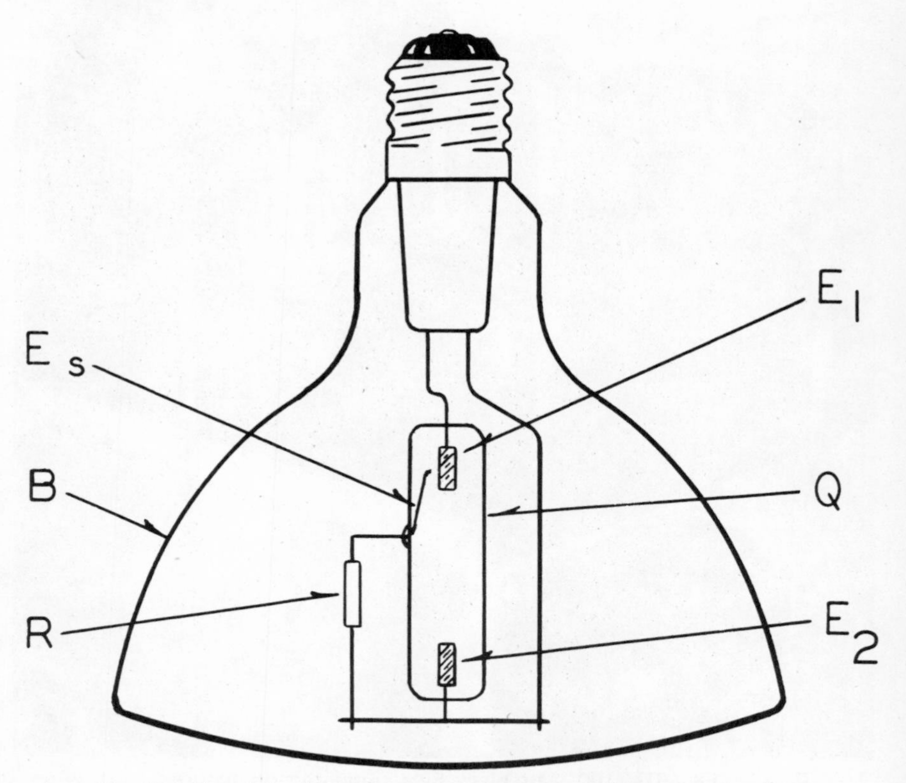

Fig. 60—Drawing of high pressure mercury arc lamp construction.

When current is first turned on, the mercury arc is not set up at once. A small, low current arc through the gas in the cartridge is first set up, bringing about sufficient vaporization of the mercury in the tube to start the arc between the main electrodes. This process takes about 5 minutes.

14. LAMP OUTPUT. The quartz inner capsule and the outer glass bulb pass energy of the higher ultra-violet wave lengths, as well as visible light (Fig. 57). The character of this spectrum is controlled by the design and manufacture of the lamp, principally by selecting the vapor pressure inside the quartz capsule. At high pressures (100 atmospheres) the spectrum is practically continuous over a wide range, but at lower pressures (10 atmospheres)

Fig. 61—100 watt black light, mounted on fixture.

the output is largely in the visible and ultra-violet range, and about equally distributed over that range, including the desirable black light wave-lengths. Lamps of this type yield the maximum energy in the form of black light after filtering, and it is this type that is used for inspection purposes.

15. COMMERCIALLY AVAILABLE BLACK LIGHTS. The self-contained mercury arc lamps illustrated and described in Sections 13 and 14 are available in several forms. A 100 watt reflectorized lamp is most commonly used in ordinary work. The 100 watt bulbs are made either as "spot" or "flood" lights. The latter gives a

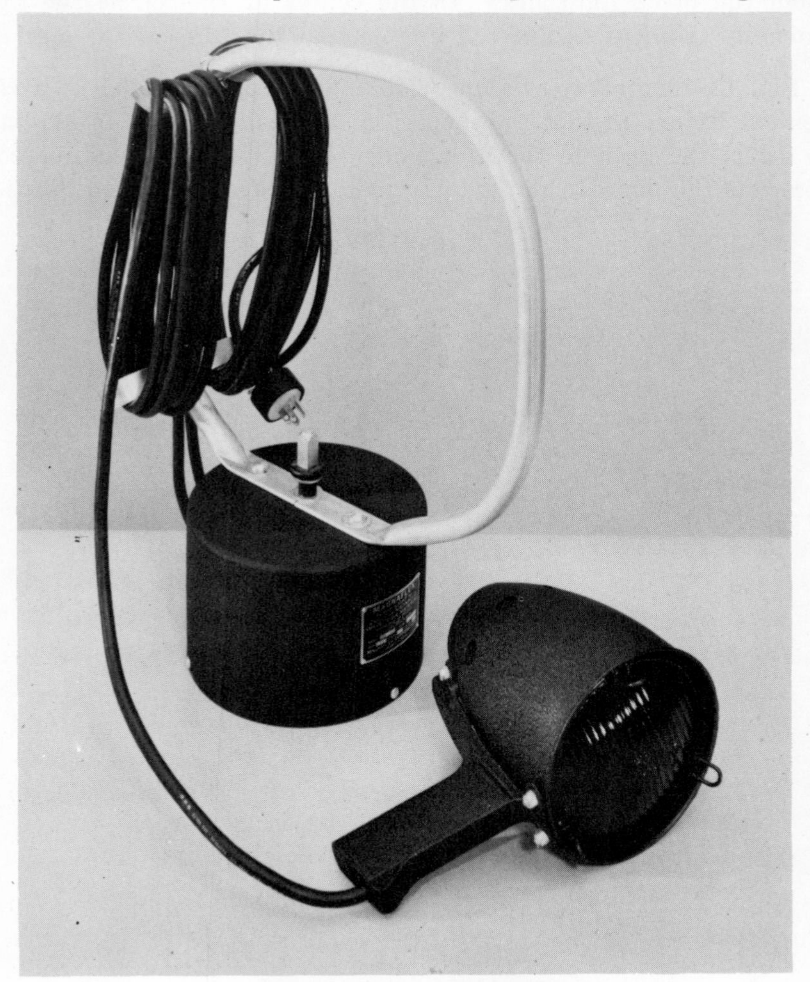

Fig. 62—100 watt portable black light.

more even illumination over a larger area than the "spot", but is not nearly as desirable for inspection use, since the illumination level is nowhere near adequate unless the lamp is held extremely close to the work. The "spot" lamp, on the other hand, concentrates much of its energy in a relatively small area, thus giving maximum illumination at the locations on which the eye of the inspector is focusing in looking for indications. More specifically, this type of lamp gives adequate intensity of black light for nearly all inspection purposes over a 6 inch diameter circle in a plane 15 inches from the black light filter. In the center of this circle the light intensity is about double the intensity at the edge of the circle.

Fig. 61 illustrates a lamp of the spot type, mounted in a convenient fixture so that the inspector can easily hold it in his hand to direct the light to the area under examination. A flexible cord connects the lamp to the transformer mounted in a fixed location.

Fig. 63—400 watt black light.

Fig. 62 shows the same type lamp in a portable fixture which includes the transformer. This type may be used in the field wherever a 110 volt source of current is available. The black light itself can be lifted from the fixture for hand use.

Fig. 63 illustrates the 400 watt mercury arc black light, similar in all respects to the 100 watt, except, of course, that its size is unsuitable for portable mountings. This light at 15 inches gives a much larger circle of maximum intensity than the 100 watt. It may be mounted much further from the work and still give adequate illumination over an area ten times as large as that covered by the 100 watt lamp. Batteries of the 400 watt lamps are used in large installations in which large areas must be adequately covered with black light, and in which added space for handling parts is needed.

16. INTENSITY REQUIREMENTS FOR BLACK LIGHT. Since the amount of visible light emitted from a fluorescent dye is directly

Fig. 64—Battery of 400 watt black lights mounted in an inspection unit.

dependent on the amount of black light energy supplied to it, the intensity of the black light at the point of inspection is of the highest importance.

Three factors determine how "seeable" an indication is: (a) the *amount* of dye at the indication; (b) the amount of *response* of the fluorescent dye, in the form of emitted visible light in relation to the energy supplied by the black light; and (c) the *amount of energy* supplied to the dye by the black light radiation. Given a penetrant formulated with a fixed amount of a given dye, the brilliance or seeability of a given indication varies with the intensity of the incident black light. This consideration is critical when seeking extremely fine indications.

Experience has shown that 90 foot candles *at the point of inspection* is the minimum black light intensity adequate for the location of fine cracks, such as grinding cracks. Larger or more open cracks may require only 70 foot candles, and 50 foot candles is sufficient for many gross defects. However, since one cannot be sure in advance how fine a crack it may be important to detect, no permanent installation should be set up to provide less than 90 foot candles at the working point. These levels assume substantial exclusion of white light from the inspection area.

As previously stated this intensity is provided over a 6 inch circle by the 100 watt spot lamps placed 15 inches from the work. At the *center of the spot* the intensity is at least double this amount. Fig. 65 shows the distribution of black light intensity, furnished

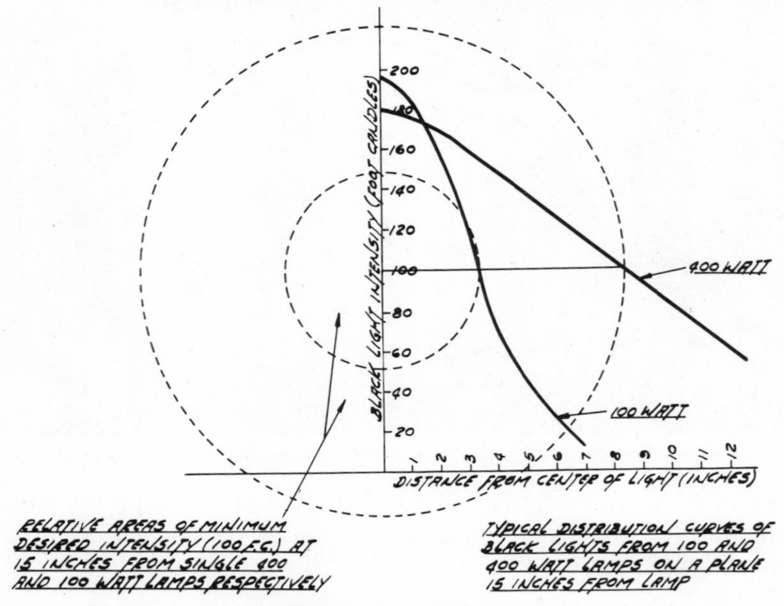

Fig. 65—Distribution of black light from 100 watt spot and from 400 watt black light lamp, at 15 inches from work table.

by the 100 watt spot lamp at 15 inches, from the center of the spot radially to the edges. Fig. 65 also gives similar data for the 400 watt lamp.

17. MEASUREMENT OF BLACK LIGHT INTENSITY. For the purposes of control of the inspection process, black light intensity should be checked at regular intervals for reasons discussed in the following section. Exact photometric measurements are not required, although reproducible determinations of intensity with reasonable accuracy are essential. Fortunately such a check can be easily and quickly made with very simple equipment.

Standard light meters, consisting of photo-voltaic cells and indicating micro-ammeters, give reasonably accurate reading of light intensity directly in foot-candles. Standard meters of this type are calibrated for white light intensity readings. However, the meters

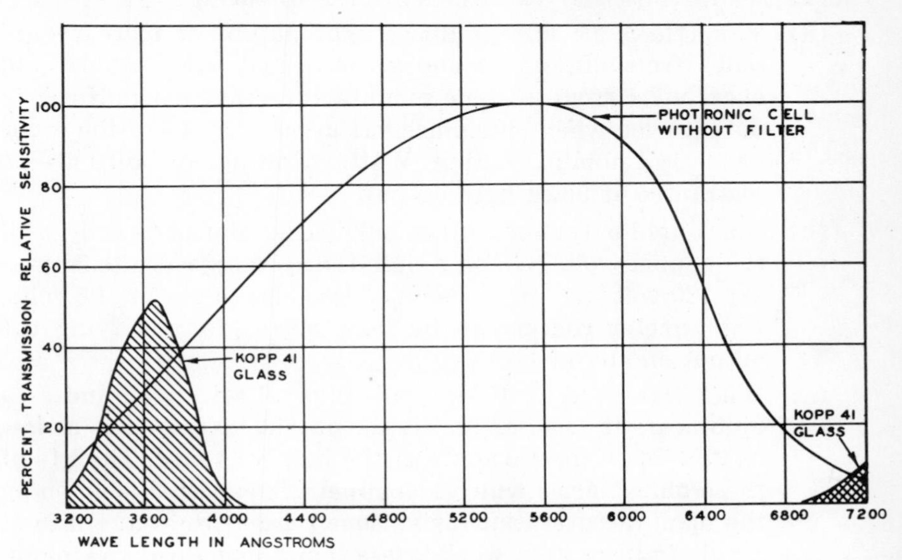

Fig. 66—Transmission curve for black light filter glass (Kopp 41) and response curve for photo-voltaic cell.

have a reasonable response in the black light wave length range as can be seen from the curves in Fig. 66 in which the response of the photo-voltaic cell is superimposed over the curves of light transmission by the black light filter glass. Readings taken under black light will not be numerically accurate but are reproducible, and therefore serve adequately as a measure of *relative* black light intensity.

The meters generally used are the Weston Model 703 Type 3 Sight Light Meter, and the General Electric Light Meter, Model No. 8DW40Y16. The meters are calibrated from 0 to 75 or 0 to

100 foot candles with multiplier masks to multiply readings by 10 for higher intensities. In use the meter is exposed to the black light, face up, at the point the measurement is to be made, and foot-candle readings taken directly from the meter scale, using the multiplier mask when needed. "Viscor" or other filters which pass only visible light and filter out black light should of course not be used in making such measurements.*

18. CAUSES FOR VARIATIONS IN BLACK LIGHT INTENSITY. It has been stated that the intensity of the black light at the point of inspection should be checked at intervals, because a lower-than-optimum intensity may seriously affect inspection results. Some of the causes for intensity variations are the following:

(a) VARIATIONS IN BULBS. Black light output of mercury arc bulbs from different manufacturers may vary widely, and even bulbs from a single manufacturer are not uniform in output even when new. Such variations may be of the order of 50% of nominal output. Wattage ratings of bulbs are no guarantee of black light output.

(b) Black light output of a given bulb varies almost directly with the applied voltage, and a bulb that gives good intensity at say 120 volts will produce much less black light at 105 volts. Light meter checks are the best means for verifying the output on any given line.

(c) Black light output of any bulb falls off with age, and as a bulb nears the end of its life the output may drop to as low as 25% of what it was when the bulb was new. The life of these bulbs varies widely. Nominal life expected is given by the manufacturer, but for various reasons the actual life of a bulb in inspection work is less than this figure. The manufacturer's life tests are based on continuous, steady operation in a fixed and well-ventilated position. Black lights used in inspection are subject to numerous starts and shut-offs and to rough handling. In addition, due to the needs of filtering and portable housing, such lights may operate at higher temperatures than are desirable. (See also Sec. 19 below).

(d) Accumulations of dust and dirt on the bulb and on the filter seriously reduce the black light output, sometimes by as

*Here see Appendix III for description of light meter for direct measurement of black light intensity in micro-watts per square inch.

much as 50%. This cause of variation can be avoided by keeping the filter clean, but an output check with the meter is the only safe way to make sure that the cleaning has been effective.

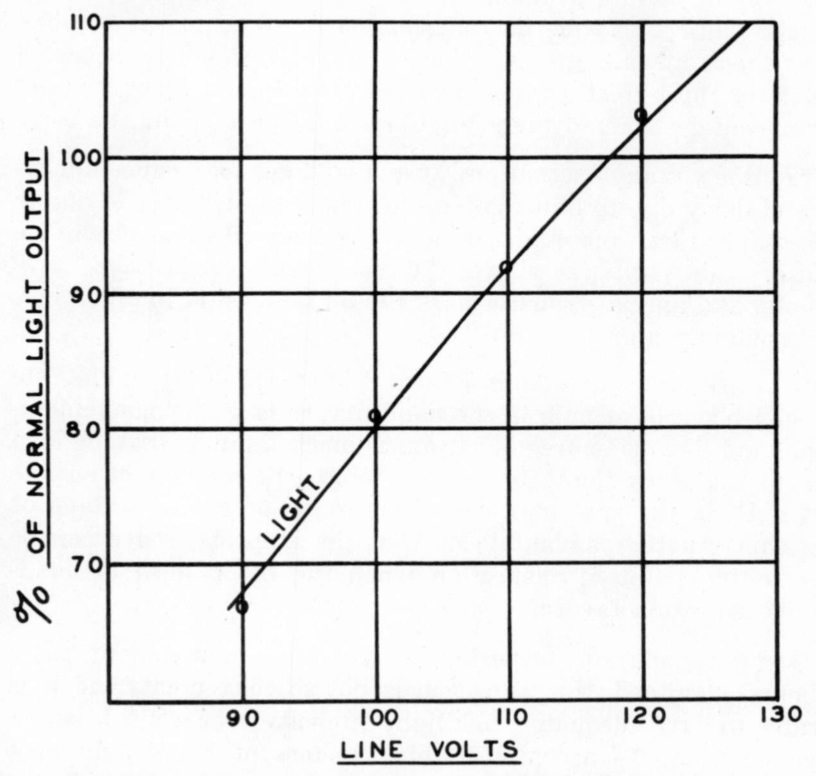

Fig. 67—Output variations with varying voltage. 100 watt "spot" black light.

19. BLACK LIGHT OPERATING CHARACTERISTICS. As has been stated, when the current to a black light bulb of the mercury arc type is first turned on, it takes about 5 minutes for the bulb to warm up to its full output, and no inspection should be started till this time has elapsed. If for any reason the arc is extinguished, as by interruption of the current, the bulbs will not immediately respond when the current is again turned on. Time must be allowed for the lamp to cool somewhat, and then for the arc to re-establish itself. This takes up to 10 minutes. Customarily, a black light, once in operation, is best left on even when not actually in use continually.

Another reason to leave the light turned on is that *each start* affects the life of the bulb, possibly reducing it by as much as 3 hours. It is therefore better, from the standpoint of bulb life, to leave the light on all day, even if it is only in actual use for a few hours.

Low voltage will extinguish the mercury arc and where line voltage is subject to wide fluctuations, with low points at 90 volts or less, the lamp may go out. Black lights should not be operated on such circuits if it can be avoided, but if it cannot, special constant-voltage transformers for the black lights should be used.

Large line voltage fluctuations at low voltages may cause annoyance and delay due to bulbs going out, and loss of bulb life due to unnecessary starts, but high voltage surges also decrease bulb life seriously. Line voltages above 120 volts may cause very early burnouts, and special transformers should be used if line voltages are consistently high.

20. ACHIEVING ADEQUATE BLACK LIGHT INTENSITY. The 100 watt spot black light bulb in the hand fixture is a very convenient, reliable and flexible source of adequate black light. It may be held closer to the work than 15 inches, though the amount of visible violet light in the spot may cancel out some of the advantage of doing this. Another advantage is that the inspector's eye can be closer to the point of inspection when the black light is hand-maneuvered into a favorable location.

In some installations, especially where large numbers of parts are being examined, this approach is not so convenient, and it is desirable to have adequate black light intensity over a much larger inspection area. To accomplish this, clusters of black light spot lamps can be directed on the inspection area. In a few cases banks of tubular black lights have been adequate. Where still larger areas are to be illuminated, a number of the larger 400 watt lamps are used. (See Chapter 11 on Equipment).

21. EYEBALL FLUORESCENCE. Reference has been made several times to the fact that the eyeball fluoresces when black light is directed at it. Although this effect is harmless, it is not only annoying but interferes with vision while it exists. In the location and manipulation of black light fixtures, this occurrence must be avoided. Black light is reflected from surfaces just as white light is, and if reflected into the eyes will cause such fluorescence to occur. Placement of black lights therefore must avoid reflections as well as direct radiation into the eyes.

Chapter 9
BLACK LIGHT

When the hand-held light is used, the surface of the part being examined should be at an angle so that reflection into the eyes does not occur. Although it is sometimes necessary to bring the eye close to the work when looking for fine indications, this must be done without getting into any direct or reflected black light.

Yellow glasses (such as "Wilsonite" sunglasses) may be worn by the inspector to cut out all black light from the eyes; in cases where the operator is bothered by the fluorescence of his eyes, this is an effective remedy. The lenses of these glasses pass all of the green-yellow fluorescent light from the penetrant but exclude black light. Yellow glasses also exclude most of the visible violet, and therefore many operators do not like to wear them since they give the effect of working in almost total darkness. Before adopting, the light transmission curve of the yellow glass should be checked. Of course such yellow glasses should be used only with penetrants that fluoresce in the green-yellow range.

22. Black Light Borescopes. Inspection of interior surfaces with black light is often quite difficult. Special viewing devices have been built and are available, employing light sources, mirrors and

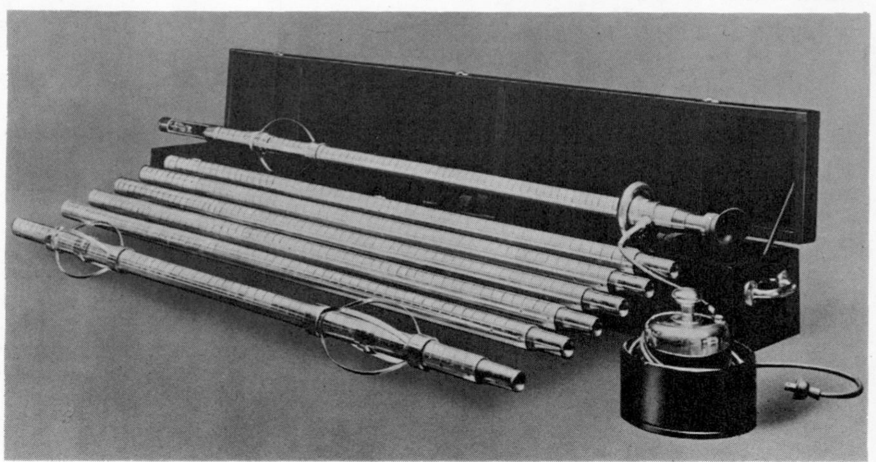

(Courtesy Lenox Instrument Co.)

Fig. 68—Black light Borescope.

lenses to permit the use of black light in the inspection with penetrants of the interior surface of tubes, gas cylinders and similarly inaccessible areas. Fig. 68 illustrates one of these devices. Specially constructed mercury arc black light bulbs are necessary to achieve both the size and shape needed to work with these devices.

23. BLACK LIGHT PHOTOGRAPHY. Recording of fluorescent penetrant indications is often desirable. There is no ready and easy method of making such a record. Sketching the location of the indication on an outline of the part does not really give a record of the indication itself, but only of the inspector's observation of it.

Photography is the best means of securing an actual record, but this again is not easy, is time consuming and requires considerable practice and skill. Still, with experience, good photographs of the fluorescent indication can be taken under black light. In addition to the technical skill required of the photographer, he is also under the obligation to see that the photograph neither exaggerates the size and brilliance of the indication, nor minimizes it. This requires good objective judgement, since photography in this instance can easily give a false value to the appearance of the indication as compared to what the eye actually sees.

In spite of all this, photographs are often highly desirable and the following outline, based on experience, will be of help to the photographer who has never attempted to take pictures under black light.

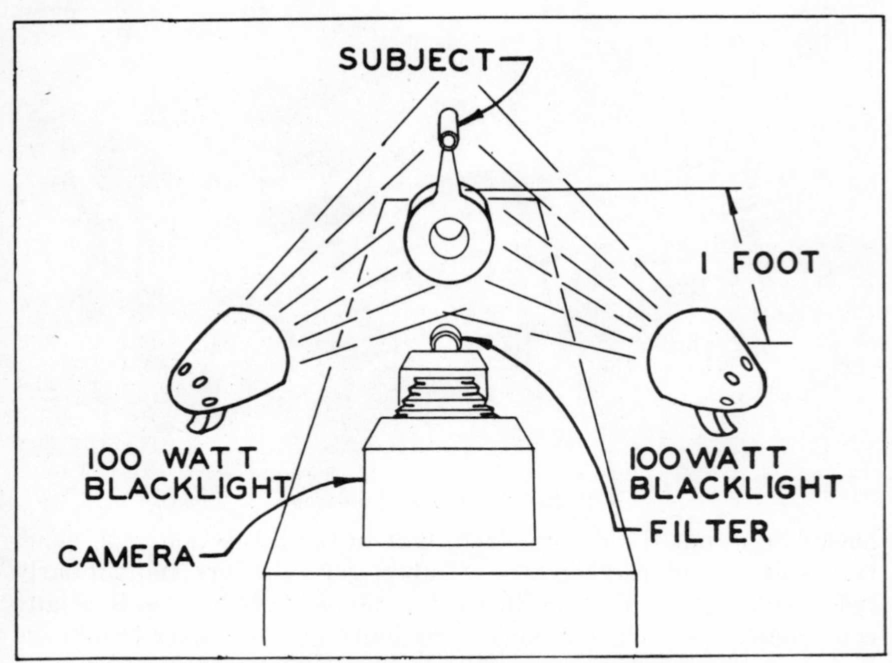

Fig. 69—Diagram of set-up for black light photography.

Fig. 69 shows diagramatically a suggested set-up for this purpose. A K2 or G filter over the lens of the camera is essential, to filter out the *black* light which would affect the film. A fast panchromatic film is preferred. The parts should be thoroughly cleaned of random fluorescent smears, and set up in a dark room with the two 100 watt black lights placed so as to bring out the brilliance of the fluorescent indications with as little reflective high-lighting of the part as possible. A light-colored non-fluorescent background is usually desirable so that the black outline of the part shows in silhouette against it.

The exposure time varies greatly with the brilliance of the indications. With a G filter, exposures vary from 20 minutes at f 32 for heavy bright indications to up to an hour at f 22 for fine indications of low intensity. If the thinner K2 filter is used, the exposure time is cut to about one-half and the definition of the part is improved, but undesirable highlights from reflected black light may come through stronger.

To increase the definition of the part as a whole and separate it from the background, white light may be used for a short time during the exposure, but the white light should be placed so that it does not illuminate the indication areas either directly or by highlight.

Since there is no practical means for pre-calculating exposures, one or more test negatives should be made for each set-up. The negative after normal development should show the indications solid black, but not spread wider than they appeared on the specimen. The rest of the negative should be thin, but with parts clearly defined. It should be checked especially for highlights interfering with or resembling the indications. Such highlights can often be moved, weakened or diffused, or eliminated by repositioning the lights.

Printing can be handled normally, usually on medium contrast paper. The object is to produce a quite dark impression of the part as it would appear under black light, with clear white indications in the picture where fluorescent indications appear on the part.

Photography with color film is sometimes useful, but exposure time and lighting are even more difficult than with black and white film. The photographer must first have mastered the technique of black and white photography, after which the challenge of fluorescent pictures in color may be attractive to him. It is not, however, recommended as a method of *recording* indications.

Use of the high-speed Polaroid camera may have advantages in some cases. Exposure times may be very short, and time needed for preliminary exposures greatly reduced. Details of this technique have not been generally explored, and must be worked out individually if its use seems desirable.

NOTE: See Appendix VI for suggestions in producing color photographs of fluorescent indications.

CHAPTER 10

COLOR-CONTRAST PENETRANTS—MATERIALS AND TECHNIQUES

1. HISTORICAL. The first "penetrant" method to be used industrially was the old "oil and whiting" method (Chapter 1, Sec. 6). This method employed essentially the same general technique as the color-contrast penetrant method today. It relied—as does the color-contrast method—on the stain produced on the white background of chalk or whiting by the penetrant (in that case dirty lubricating oil) re-emerging from the crack. The color-contrast method today uses better penetrants, achieves much better contrast by the use of red dyes, and employs better developers, thereby greatly improving the sensitivity and the dependability of the method.

At the time R. C. Switzer did his initial work which led to the patent covering the fluorescent penetrant method (U. S. Patent #2,259,400), he also made application for patent covering the color-contrast penetrant method using non-fluorescent dyes. His applications on color-contrast methods and materials were subject to many delays in the Patent Office, including the issuance of patents to others for similar developments and lengthy interference proceedings between these patents and the Switzer applications. Some of these complications were finally cleared up on June 24, 1958, by the issuance of Patent No. 2,839,918 to R. C. Switzer on the color-contrast method.

For some years after the introduction of the fluorescent penetrant method (in 1942), there was no apparent demand for any other type of penetrant because fluorescent penetrants seemed to offer the maximum in sensitivity and usefulness. At that time, however, fluorescent materials and techniques had not yet reached the high state of development that exists today, and problems arose in flaw detection which appeared beyond the ability of the water-wash type fluorescent penetrants then available.

Color-contrast penetrants were first commercially proposed in 1944 by Rebecca (Smith) Sparling and her co-workers, as a possible means of increasing sensitivity to fine defects over that of those water-wash fluorescent types then in use. The problem was to find shallow and open flaws as well as exceedingly fine cracks, in jet engine turbine blades then under development. In looking back, it seems clear that the success in this area achieved at that time by the color-contrast penetrants was due, not to the change from fluorescent to color-contrast dyes, but rather to the change from water-wash type penetrants to penetrants containing no emulsifier, and to different removal methods.

More recently, the development of the fluorescent post-emulsification process recognized the advantages of a penetrant containing no emulsifier, and resulted in a superior technique for finding the critical flaws in the turbine blades with all the large advantage in "seeability" added by the use of fluorescent dyes.

2. FIELD OF USEFULNESS OF COLOR-CONTRAST PENETRANTS. In the interim much work was done with color-contrast penetrants. Their commercial availability brought about their use for a large number of flaw-finding purposes. Their attractiveness lay in the extreme simplicity of the operation—they could be used anywhere, and no power or equipment was required. Enthusiasts at first tended to magnify this advantage and minimize the less desirable characteristics of the method.

Color-contrast penetrants do have a very definite field of usefulness in the family of penetrant methods, as will be discussed in later sections. However, the limitations of the method should be clearly understood. The method is *not* a broad substitute or equivalent for other flaw-finding nondestructive testing methods, penetrant or otherwise. As among penetrant methods, the choice as to which type is best suited to any given inspection problem should be made on the basis of the requirements of the problem and the abilities of the methods. Cost should not be ignored in this decision. (See Chapter 12, Sections 14-19).

3. ADVANTAGES AND DISADVANTAGES. If these two penetrant systems (color-contrast and fluorescent) are examined objectively it quickly becomes evident that the greatest advantage of the color-contrast system lies in its extreme simplicity and portability, and its small initial cost. No black light is needed, and removal of excess penetrant from surfaces can be accomplished simply by wiping with a cloth. A small kit can contain all that is needed to apply the test at any location.

It also quickly becomes clear that color-contrast penetrants have little else in the way of advantages, although in many characteristics they are equally as effective as fluorescent penetrants for some types of applications. In penetrability they can be and usually are fully as good as the fluorescent types, since the ability of a liquid as a penetrant is not affected by the type of dye dissolved in it. As to techniques, color-contrast penetrants lend themselves equally as well as fluorescent penetrants to the water-wash and the post-emulsification systems.

4. EFFECT OF DEVELOPER. Developers and developer techniques favor the fluorescent system, and tend to affect adversely the crack-finding ability of color-contrast penetrants. This is due to the requirement that a flat white background, produced by the developer, is needed for maximum color contrast. The relatively heavier powder film laid on for this purpose is a hindrance to the formation of a readable indication from a very fine crack, since the minute amount of red liquid may not be enough to show through the developer layer.

In the case of developers for fluorescent penetrants, the layer of powder is very much thinner. In addition, particles of developers for fluorescent systems have the ability to transmit black light, so that even penetrant on the under side of the developer particles becomes energized and fluoresces. No comparable effect is possible with white light and color-contrast penetrants.

The need for relatively heavy and opaque coatings of developer is an added, though possibly less important, drawback for the method in that in practically all cases the developer must be cleaned off the surface after inspection.*

5. SEEABILITY. The most important difference between the color-contrast and the fluorescent systems is the fundamental one of *visibility of the indication.* This is the *major* factor in determining the effective sensitivity of any penetrant method or material. Experience shows that an inspector is much less likely to miss the glow of fluorescence from an indication viewed in near-darkness, than he is the fine line of a small indication produced by color-contrast penetrants. (See discussion of sensitivity, Chapter 4, Section 25 and following sections.) The *maximum* possible contrast for color-contrast penetrants is of the order of 9 to 1, whereas for fluorescent indications the contrast ratio is many times greater—even thousands to one. (Chapter 4, Section 37.)

*See Appendix II for a further discussion of developer action.

This does *not* mean that fluorescent systems are a thousand times more sensitive than color-contrast types. For large indications there is little apparent difference in sensitivity between the two systems. It *does* mean, however, that with very fine cracks giving minute indications—in really *critical* cases—the fluorescent system is vastly more effective, and is able easily to show evidence of flaws which color-contrast methods are unable to show at all.

Fig. 70 shows two photographs of the same aluminum test block. (a) shows the indications produced with color-contrast penetrants photographed in white light. (b) shows the same indications produced with a fluorescent penetrant and photographed

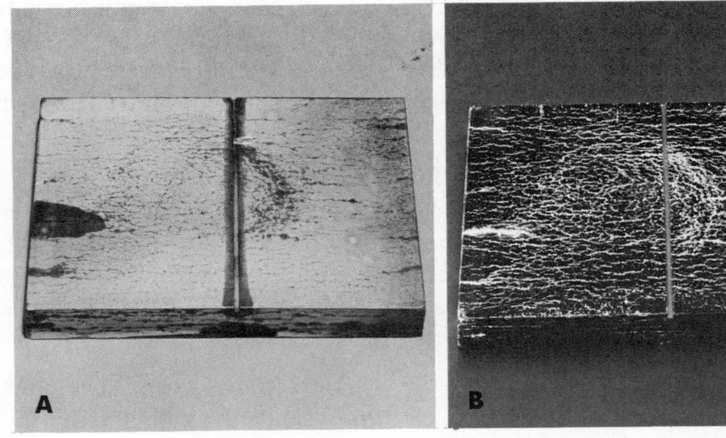

Fig. 70—Comparison of color-contrast and fluorescent indications. a) aluminum block color-contrast indications. b) Same block—fluorescent indications.

with black light. These are not shown to compare the two methods in any quantitative way, since photographs taken under such widely different conditions cannot be directly compared. They do, however, give an idea of the degree of contrast between indication and background which is broadly typical of the two systems.

6. COST. Many people have the impression that fluorescent materials are very expensive and that therefore non-fluorescent materials must be much *less* expensive. Actually this is not necessarily true, and the commercial price per gallon of color-contrast penetrants is consistently higher than that of most fluorescent types. Therefore, cost is not an advantage for the color contrast system, if the two systems are used on a comparable basis as to number and type of parts inspected. If used on a basis of local "spot" checking the difference in cost may be insignificant.

The reason for the higher cost of color-contrast penetrants lies mainly in the fact that much larger proportions of dye are needed than in their fluorescent counterparts. This fact more than offsets the difference in price per pound that may exist in the dyes themselves.

7. USE IN PRODUCTION INSPECTIONS. The fact that both water-wash and post-emulsification techniques can be applied to color-contrast penetrant systems does not in itself make this process an attractive one for production inspection of large numbers of parts. The reasons why color-contrast systems have had very little acceptance as production inspection tools may be summed up in the following comments:

(a) There is actually no demonstrable advantage of color-contrast over fluorescent systems for production inspection. Sensitivity for fine defects is actually lower because of the better seeability of fluorescent indications, although when low sensitivity is adequate or desired this is not a drawback. There is no manipulative advantage, since the steps are pretty much identical for both systems. Developer application tends to be more critical for color-contrast systems.

(b) Cost tends actually to be higher for color-contrast systems. Equipment required for production inspection is comparable in type and cost with that necessary for fluorescent systems, with the single exception of the darkened booth and the black light fixtures which color-contrast methods do not require. Offsetting the latter, good white light illumination must be provided for color-contrast inspection. But of great significance is the higher cost of color-contrast materials consumed, especially the penetrant, over those used in the usual water-wash or post-emulsification processes. These are a continuing charge against the over-all cost of the inspection, and there is no outstanding or even demonstrable advantage to justify a higher-cost method.

(c) The intense red dye of the color-contrast penetrant increases the problem of waste disposal and operator dissatisfaction. The strong red color of wash water entering public sewer systems from large-scale use of color-contrast penetrants is more likely to cause complaints due to color alone than is the waste from fluorescent systems. Both, however, may require special disposal facilities, but even here the red color is a complicating factor.

In addition, the red dye of color-contrast penetrants on skin and clothing of operators is vastly more objectionable than virtually invisible fluorescent "stains" which become conspicuous only under black light. Equipment and the immediate area around a color-contrast installation tend to become unsightly because of red-dye stains. Though perhaps minor, this is still undesirable from a "good housekeeping" point of view.

(d) If solvent-cleaning systems are used for production inspection, the low flash point of many color-contrast penetrants and cleaners is a definite drawback to open tank dipping or to spraying of parts. Not only is there a serious fire hazard but there tends also to be a substantial loss by evaporation. When the more highly volatile contituents evaporate, the penetrant loses some of its performance characteristics, in addition to shrinking in volume.

Non-flammable penetrants and cleaners are now available and their use would eliminate the fire hazard. There would still be a tendency to loss by evaporation in most of these if used for dipping or spraying large numbers of parts.

(e) The white developer coating remaining on the surface of parts after inspection almost invariably must be removed, requiring a separate step. Developers used with fluorescent penetrants may also require removal, but since the amount of coating is much less, this is easier and frequently not necessary.

None of the above considerations carry the same weight, as objections, when color-contrast penetrants are used in the applications for which they are especially well suited—namely, in smaller scale or local inspections, or on a spot-checking basis.

8. THE PENETRANTS. Color-contrast penetrants are available commercially in a number of variations depending on how they are to be used. These are:

(a) Normal solvent-clean type.

(b) Water-wash type.

(c) Post-emulsification type.*

*Please refer at this point to Appendix IV for additional color-contrast techniques.

Chapter 10
COLOR-CONTRAST PENETRANTS

9. Non-water-wash Penetrant. Since the factor in the sensitivity of a penetrant for the detection of fine defects which derives from the *seeability* of the indication is limited in all color-contrast types by the limited color-to-background contrast, these penetrants should be formulated to take the fullest possible advantage of every other factor of sensitivity. Thus, a good color-contrast penetrant of the non-water-wash type should first of all be an excellent penetrant so as to penetrate all defects as completely as possible.

The character of the liquids used varies widely. Most contain a proportion of relatively low boiling-point material along with a substantial amount of high boiling-point liquid. This is to reduce viscosity and through evaporation of the low-boiling point fraction, to reduce the tendency of the indication to spread. Liquids used may be petroleum distillates, or aromatic solvents or esters, or a combination of two or more of these along with other materials.

10. Dye Solubility. Whatever liquid is used, it must be a good solvent for the dye which is to be incorporated. The red dyes generally used have a reasonably high solubility in oils and other liquids commonly used as penetrants. This is essential because rather high concentrations of red dye are needed to give strong indications. The amounts used may be several times greater—of the order of 5 to 1—than those necessary for high brilliance fluorescent penetrants.

Solubility for dye must be good enough that, at the concentrations used, no re-crystallization or settling out of dye will occur on storage of the penetrant. Re-crystallization is especially likely to occur at low temperatures. Settling out of dye material not only removes it from useful solution in the penetrant, but causes much trouble by clogging valves when the penetrant is dispensed from aerosol cans. Fluorinated propellants often used in aerosol cans are themselves poor dye solvents and aggravate the tendency of dyes to settle out in the cans.

11. Flash Point. The flash point of any penetrant should be as high as possible to minimize the fire hazard. Danger of fire when volatile flammable liquids are used is especially great when open-tank dipping or spraying of parts is employed on a large scale basis. Even when used for only local checking the fire hazard is present though not so acute.

Many pentrants include a substantial proportion of low-boiling petroleum fractions, and these contribute to a low flash point for the penetrant. Flash points of 140° F (closed cup) or higher are considered reasonably safe, but some color-contrast penetrants will flash at very much lower temperatures. (See Chapter 4, Section 9 and Table V.) However, color-contrast penetrants are available which are formulated so as to have a safely high flash point or even to be completely non-flammable.

12. EASY REMOVABILITY. Since removal of excess color-contrast penetrants of the non-water-wash type is by dry wiping or by dry wiping with solvents, it is important that the dye-carrying penetrant liquid be easily and completely removable. At the end of the penetrating time, much of the volatile portion of the liquid has usually evaporated from the surface of the part. The residual material must then be readily soluble in the cleaning fluids provided for the purpose, so that no excessive use of solvents is required. Solvent for removing penetrant must not be used too freely, since it may remove penetrant from defects as well. Cleaner-emulsifier materials have this controlled removing action. (See Section 20 below. See also Appendix V on removers.)

13. ODOR. The odor of penetrants should not be objectionable. For maximum effectiveness of the inspection, the operator should not be annoyed by offensive odors or by breathing of vapors which may become disagreeable on long exposure. An ideal penetrant would be odorless, though this would be difficult to achieve.

14. TOXICITY. Obviously a penetrant should be as free of toxic properties as possible. No acutely toxic material should be employed. Many industrial materials in common use are mildly toxic, especially if they are not used with ordinary precautions. Penetrants should not be toxic in contact with the skin, although some may be skin irritants if contact is more than occasional. It is customary to wear protective gloves when working with color-contrast penetrants. Usually operators need no urging to do this (as they sometimes must be urged when using fluorescent pentrants), because contact with color-contrast penetrants means a deep red stain not easy to remove.

Use of chlorinated solvents in penetrant formulation should be limited to those types of solvent approved for general industrial use. Unnecessary breathing of such vapors should be avoided. Penetrant liquids should not be virulently poisonous, even though the likelihood of any penetrant being swallowed is remote. Most penetrants, if swallowed, would produce mild to violent gastric disturbances, and a physician should be called if this should occur.

15. DYES. Red dyes are universally used in color-contrast penetrants. This is because the red color gives a high degree of contrast against the white developer background and yet is a color easily distinguishable from other stains such as from oil, grease or dirt. Red dyes available commercially have excellent solubility in the liquids used for penetrant formulation—an important consideration.

16. SPECIAL FORMULA PENETRANTS. When color-contrast penetrants are used on certain nickel alloys, the presence of either sulphur or chlorine may be objectionable. Presence of even small residual amounts of these elements is highly objectionable on the surface of some alloys which are subsequently operated at high temperatures or are used in connection with certain nuclear energy applications.

For such use, special formulations are available which are sufficiently free of these elements to render them acceptable. Cleaners and developers are also available for this special purpose.

The flash point of these special penetrants may be low due to the use of petroleum fractions. Non-flammable chlorinated solvents, as well as certain other high-flash materials commonly incorporated in penetrants, are obviously not desirable in this application, although chlorinated solvents which leave no chlorine-containing fixed residue on evaporation are usually permissible.

17. WATER-WASH PENETRANTS. Water-wash color-contrast penetrants are commercially available but have a rather limited use. They incorporate an emulsifying agent as do their fluorescent counterparts. Properly formulated, they will yield a clean surface when rinsed off with a suitable water spray. In general, however, there is little incentive to use this type of color-contrast penetrant for production inspection, which is the chief application for water-wash techniques. Equipment and labor and time costs are the same as for the fluorescent version, but the generally lower sensitivity level of the color-contrast system is a strong deterrent. (See discussion above, Section 7.)

18. POST-EMULSIFICATION PENETRANTS. This process is now also readily applied to color-contrast penetrants and results in a rather more satisfactory inspection than does the straight water-wash technique. For P. E. use no special penetrant is required, the standard solvent-cleaning type being used. These, being non-water-washable, act in the same way as the special post-emulsifiable fluorescent penetrants, and give indications of both fine cracks and shallow open defects. Emulsification and washing are accomplished by use of a special emulsifier formulated for use with the usual color-contrast penetrants, followed by a suitable spray wash.

In this process also, for the same reasons applying to the water-wash version, there is little advantage over the fluorescent processes, other than the general advantage of portability and elimination of the need for a black light, possessed by all color-contrast penetrants.

19. OPERATING TEMPERATURES. Optimum operating temperatures are similar to those applicable to fluorescent penetrants. 70° F is a desirable temperature, and the surfaces being inspected should preferably not be below 50° F. Higher temperatures above 80° or 90° F ambient, increase the rate of evaporation of the volatile constituents of the penetrant, and are therefore undesirable. For this reason, as well as for the increased fire hazard, the penetrants should not be applied to very hot surfaces.

20. CLEANERS OR REMOVERS. These are the liquids used to remove the excess penetrant from surfaces after penetration, and consist of some type or mixture of solvents. They should readily remove both penetrant and dye, and leave a clean dry surface. They should be sufficiently volatile to dry from the surface in a short time without the use of heat.

Two types of cleaners are in general industrial and maintenance use—one a close-cut fairly volatile petroleum distillate, and the other one of the approved types of chlorinated solvents. The petroleum distillate types are usually rather flammable, and therefore in many applications the non-flammable "fire safe" solvents are preferable.

A third type of cleaner is used in many nuclear and aerospace applications. This is a high-boiling petroleum distillate of the kerosene range to which a small amount of detergent has been added. This may be used in a manner similar to the wipe-off removers; or the surfaces may be sprayed with cleaner and then flushed off with water. There is a tendency for a faint oily film to remain on the surface when this technique is used.

Cleaners (except Type 3) furnished for general use with color-contrast penetrants serve an additional purpose in that they are a readily available source of solvent for pre-cleaning surfaces before applying penetrant.

In addition to the solvent cleaners, the emulsifier for use in the P. E. process is available for use with water for this pre-cleaning operation. Cleaners are also sometimes used to remove developer from surfaces after inspection.

21. DEVELOPERS. As has been repeatedly stated, developers for the color-contrast process serve two purposes. One of these is the usual one of drawing penetrant out of surface openings. The second is to provide a white background to give contrast for viewing the colored stain produced by the penetrant re-emerging from the surface openings.

Developers commonly consist of a white powder suspended in a quick-drying liquid. The requirement for a dead-white opaque coating limits somewhat the choice of powder materials, and some of those suitable for fluorescent penetrant developers are not satisfactory. The solvent used was originally alcohol (a carry-over from the oil and whiting method), but now, in addition to alcohol, other solvents are used, including non-flammable solvents.

The white powder must, of course, be a good absorber and disperser of small amounts of penetrant liquid. The coating which it forms should be lightly adherent and readily removable subsequent to inspection.

22. FUNCTION OF DEVELOPER LIQUID. The primary function of the liquid in which the developer powder is suspended is to provide a carrier for applying the developer powder evenly and in the right thickness of coating over the surface being inspected. It should also dry rapidly so as not to delay inspection unduly.

The liquid also serves another purpose. Being a solvent, it tends to help bring penetrant in the defects out to the surface, and then leave it as a stain on the developer coating. Actually it is better if this solvent is not too active, else small amounts of penetrant would be diluted excessively and the color contrast of the indication reduced.

23. OTHER DEVELOPER CHARACTERISTICS. The developer powder-liquid combination should be a stable one so that no deterioration occurs on storage. Chemical reactions between solvent and powder can cause pressure build-up in containers; decomposition of solvent can result in corrosion of metal cans, etc.

Solvents, if quick drying, are often inflammable and present a certain amount of fire hazard, especially when applied from spray cans. The solvent must also be acceptable industrially from a toxicity standpoint. When stored, the powder will of course settle out of the solvent, but it must not cake hard on the bottom of the container and must be readily suspended again by agitation.

24. OTHER DEVELOPERS. Water-base developers are used in connection with the water-wash version of color-contrast penetrants. These, as in the case of fluorescent penetrant wet developers, are furnished as a dry powder, which is mixed with water by the operator. Water-washed parts are coated with developer and dried in recirculating hot air driers exactly as in the case of the fluorescent process.

Some users have been reported to employ a dry powder developer as with fluorescent penetrants. Such a developing material and technique may be expected to function mechanically as well with color-contrast penetrants as it does with fluorescent types. However, contrast ratios of indication to background are invariably poorer, since no white background is produced. On bright surfaces fair contrast would result, but on dark or rough surfaces indications, unless gross, would be extremely difficult to see. Such a procedure is certainly not to be recommended for general use.

25. APPLYING THE PROCESS. Basically the use of the color-contrast system for inspections is entirely similar to the fluorescent process. The steps are:

(a) Pre-cleaning.

(b) Application of penetrant.

(c) Removal of excess penetrant.

(d) Development.

(e) Inspection.

These steps necessarily differ in some details from those used with fluorescent penetrants, but fundamentally the purpose of each step and the results obtained are the same. (It is suggested that the reader review the chapters on general techniques, especially Chapters 2 and 6.)

Fig. 71 illustrates these five steps as applied to a gear, using spray-can application of cleaner, penetrant and developer.

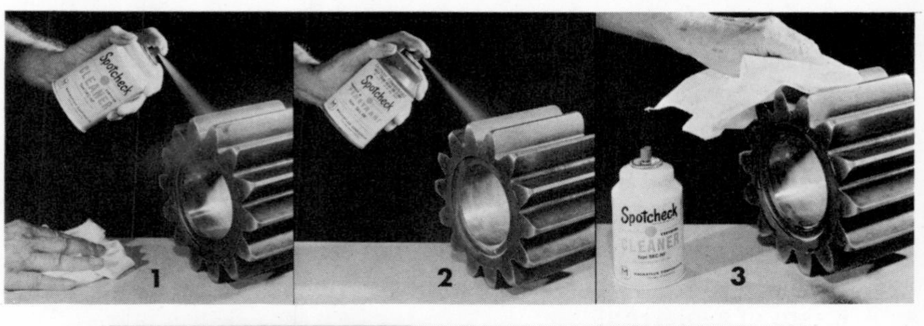

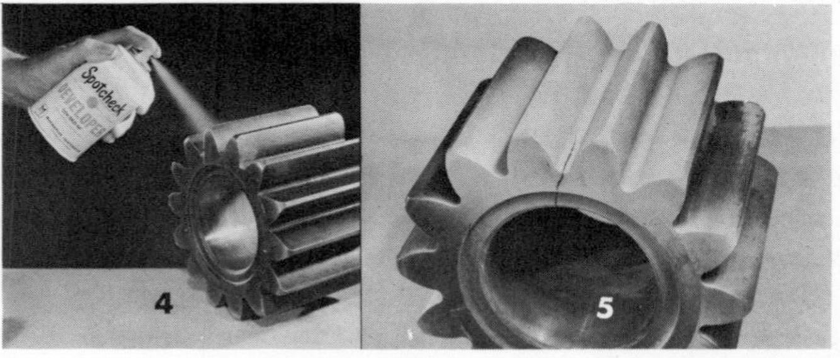

Fig. 71—The five steps in a simple color-contrast inspection of a gear. 1. Pre-clean. 2. Spray on penetrant. 3. Wipe clean. 4. Spray on developer. 5. Inspect.

26. PRE-CLEANING. For any penetrant method, success depends on the flaws being open to the surface. Pre-cleaning is therefore of the highest importance. All surface rust, scale and dirt should be removed by wire-brushing or other mild abrasive methods. Oil and grease may be removed locally with the cleaner furnished for use with the process. The cleaner should be used generously to insure best possible removal of oil and other contaminants from cracks. Cloths should be used to wipe the surface clean and dry.

When the process is used for the inspection of very local areas, pre-cleaning is readily and quickly accomplished by the use of spray-cans for applying the cleaner. These are now generally available.

If volatile solvents or kerosenes are used, ample time must elapse before penetrants are applied to make sure that such solvents have evaporated from cracks and flaws.

Vapor de-greasing is, of course, equally as desirable here as it is for fluorescent penetrant pre-cleaning, and should be used for small parts when it is available. It is, obviously, not practical for use when local areas of larger parts are being inspected.

Chemical, water-base cleaners are often used for very dirty, greasy parts. If used, the surface must be thoroughly rinsed free of any foreign residue, and heat must be used to insure removal of all water from surface openings.

27. TECHNIQUES OF PENETRANT APPLICATION. When used to inspect local areas of parts, penetrant may be applied with a brush. The application should cover the suspected areas generously but any spreading over areas not to be inspected should be avoided as a waste of penetrant.

A highly satisfactory method of applying penetrant is use of pressurized spray cans. With these it is easy to get coverage of the right amount and over the desired area, with a minimum of running which would result from excess applied penetrant. This technique is economical of penetrant, but of course penetrant in spray cans, pint for pint, is necessarily more costly than it is in bulk containers. The great convenience and speed of spray cans wipe out this disadvantage since, except for production applications, the amount of penetrant actually consumed is relatively small.

Parts can be coated all over by dipping into tanks but this is rarely done except in production inspection of small parts. (See Section 7). When this technique is used, baskets of parts may be dipped just as in fluorescent penetrant inspection. In such a case, the water-wash penetrant is to be preferred.

Since the red dye of the penetrant stains the skin and clothing, the operator should be prepared to avoid this by wearing gloves and aprons.

28. DRAINING. As in any penetrant method, time is allowed after penetrant is applied, to permit it to enter all surface cracks and other openings as completely as it will. When dipped, either individually or in baskets, the parts are disposed during the penetration time or drain time so that excess penetrant can drain back into the tank, as in the fluorescent process.

Times required for penetration are comparable to those applicable for the fluorescent version. The normal solvent-clean or non-water-wash type requires considerably less penetration time than water-wash varieties, the times being more nearly those used for the post-emulsification fluorescent penetrants.

Table XIII gives some typical penetration times suggested for materials that may be tested with color-contrast penetrants. (See also, Table X, Chapter 7, and Table XII, Chapter 8.)

TABLE XIII

SUGGESTED PENETRATION TIME FOR NON-WATER-WASH COLOR-CONTRAST PENETRANT FOR VARIOUS MATERIALS

Material and Condition	Types of Defects	Penetrating Time
On all materials	Heat treat cracks	2 minutes
	Grinding cracks	10 minutes
	Fatigue cracks	10 minutes
Plastics	Cracks	1-5 minutes
Ceramics	Cracks	1-5 minutes
	Porosity	1-5 minutes
Cutting tools:		
Carbide tipped or steel cutting tools	Poor braze	1-10 minutes
	Cracks in tip	1-10 minutes
	Cracks in steel	1-10 minutes
Metal—permanent mold castings	Shrinkage porosity	3-10 minutes
Die castings	Surface porosity	3-10 minutes
	Cold shuts	10-20 minutes
Forgings	Cracks	20 minutes
	Laps	20 minutes
Metal rollings	Seams	10-20 minutes
Welds	Cracks	10-20 minutes
	Pores	10-20 minutes

In most cases drain times are short enough that complete drying of penetrant on the surface of parts does not occur. Further, most penetrants have a sufficient content of low volatile liquids which do not dry rapidly. If drying does occur, re-spraying or re-dipping may be necessary, especially in water-wash types. When solvents are used for cleaning, these will usually remove partially dried penetrant without difficulty.

29. Removing Excess Penetrant. The non-water-wash penetrants are almost always used for local inspections, and these are best removed by wiping the area with cloths, either dry or wet with the cleaner-solvent. Dry-wiping with a clean cloth or paper towel is sometimes satisfactory, especially on smooth surfaces. The surface must be left entirely clean and free from any colored penetrant.

More often the cleaner-solvent is used. Cleaner is lightly applied from a spray can and immediately wiped off with a cloth. A second application, using a clean cloth, usually results in a good clean surface. Alternatively, a cloth may be moistened with cleaner and the surface wiped, removing most of the penetrant, after which a second wiping with a clean cloth moistened with cleaner will complete the job.

Cleaning should be done quickly and a minimum of cleaner fluid used. If the operation is prolonged or excessive amounts of cleaner used, some penetrant may be removed from defects. In all cases the surface should be wiped dry. For tests on nuclear or aerospace materials the cleaner-emulsifier is used for maximum sensitivity to fine defects.

This wiping technique is excellent for practically all crack-like defects and for porosity, but is not satisfactory if shallow *open* defects are sought. In this case the post-emulsification system and a water spray cleaning should be used instead, since wiping with a cloth will almost surely remove penetrant from such defects.

30. Dipped Parts. When parts are coated all over, hand washing with solvent is difficult and slow. If only a few are to be inspected this is no great drawback, but for large numbers of parts it is not very satisfactory.

Washing by dipping in a bath of solvent is rapid and gives a clean surface, but also dissolves penetrant from defects and is not in general satisfactory. In addition, dye quickly colors the solvent bath, and if this system is used two dips are needed, the second into clean solvent. The second dip increases the tendency to lose penetrant from defects. This technique is not recommended for general use.

Use of a vapor-degreaser is to be preferred over the solvent-dip technique, since it cleans quickly and thoroughly with only one exposure, and parts come out dry. If the exposure is brief, this method may be satisfactory for relatively large cracks and openings, as in castings. It cannot, however, be recommended for general use or in the hands of any but an operator who is experienced and understands the importance of keeping exposure to the hot solvent vapor at the very minimum.

31. WATER WASHING. Water-wash cleaning, when this type of penetrant is used, is identical with the same operation employing fluorescent penetrants. Water slightly above ambient temperatures works well (not over 100° F), but ordinary tap water is satisfactory. The spray should be strong with plenty of volume, and should consist of coarse droplets rather than a fine spray. (See Chapter 7, Sections 24-30.)

32. POST-EMULSIFICATION. The technique for post-emulsification cleaning differs very little from that used with fluorescent penetrants of this type, and the reader is referred to the detailed discussion in Chapter 8. Emulsification is accomplished by applying the emulsifier-cleaner after proper penetration time has elapsed. For local use or on small areas, by far the best method of getting emulsifier onto the surface is by use of spray cans. If parts have been dipped in penetrant, dipping in emulsifier is simple and satisfactory, although parts should not be left in the emulsifier more than a few seconds if the solvent-emulsifier is used. Drain time may be up to several minutes however, with solvent emulsifier, since the solvent evaporates rapidly, after which the surfaces wash better with water. Brushing-on of emulsifier is not a good procedure if shallow open defects are being sought, since it accelerates the mixing of emulsifier and penetrant.

Emulsification times should be established by trial, since broad rules cannot be laid down. Times usually are from one-half to three or four minutes. (See Chapter 8, Section 28.)

33. DRYING. Surfaces which are cleaned by the solvent-wiping method will self-dry very rapidly at ordinary temperatures, as the liquids used for cleaning evaporate rapidly. Heat is not needed as an aid to drying, although enough time must be allowed for all parts of the surface to dry.

Parts which have been washed with water should be dried in a re-circulating hot air drier, with all the precautions and procedures outlined for fluorescent penetrants. (Chapter 7, Section 38). If water-washing is used on local areas drying may be by wiping.

However, if the post-emulsification technique is being used in order to find shallow open flaws, drying by wiping may well wipe penetrant out of such flaws. In this case, when oven drying is not possible, a blast of warm air may be the only possible solution. (Chapter 7, Section 32 and following sections).

34. DEVELOPING. This is a critical step in the color-contrast inspection process. The objective is an even coat of developer thick enough but no more, to give a full white background over the entire area being examined. If bulk developer is used, a brush will give a satisfactory coating after some practice, although use of a spray gun gives best results. Application should be made as soon as possible after cleaning, before any appreciable amount of penetrant has come back out of any defect. If delayed, the brush will smear the indications and may actually so dilute the penetrant at a crack that no definite indication will be produced.

A convenient and safe way to apply developer is from a pressure spray can. The can must be vigorously agitated before use to be sure the developer powder is all in suspension. With a little practice, an even developer coating of the right weight can be sprayed on, with no possibility of smearing. A thin white coating is best.

The coating will dry quickly and should cover the surface so that it looks uniformly white. Thin spots can be re-touched.

35. OVER-ALL COATING. Parts which must be coated with developer on all surfaces are more difficult, and it is harder to achieve uniform coatings of proper thickness. Spraying (or brushing) is perhaps the best procedure here also, handling the part in such a way that no areas suspected of containing defects are touched. Parts may be dipped in a bath of solvent-base developer, but problems of agitation and drainage become more severe and this technique is apt to be rather unsatisfactory.

With water-base developers which are used after water washing, the developer powder is kept in better suspension and somewhat better results may be obtained from dipping. In this case, however, uneven draining is more serious, since the water-base developer dries more slowly than the solvent-base, even when hot-air drying is used.

36. DEVELOPING TIME. After the developer has dried, indications of many of the larger defects will appear at once. However, time should be allowed before inspection for all small indications to become as strong as they will. As with fluorescent penetrant inspection developing time, at least half the time for penetration should be allowed. When very fine defects are being sought, this time may well be prolonged considerably, even though excessive spreading of indications from larger defects will take place.

Where water-base developers are used, the same rules for developing time should be followed as were outlined in Chapter 7, Section 54.

37. INSPECTION. Inspection should be careful and thorough. The inspector should have good eyesight capable of focusing on very fine lines such as the indications at fine cracks. The inspection area should be clean with ample space for the handling of parts. White light illumination should be at a high level, though glare from the white background on parts, resulting from use of high-power spot lights, must be avoided. Eye fatigue from unnecessarily high levels of white light must be guarded against.

For local inspections in the field, a good shaded portable light must be provided, of high enough wattage that even small indications can be readily located. Ordinary incandescent lights of 100 watts or more in a hand-held shielded fixture give satisfactory illumination.

An inspector who has had experience with fluorescent penetrants must be especially careful when working with the color-contrast method, as indications do not stand out by their own light emission and must be carefully looked for. If developing time has been long, as when inspection is unduly delayed for any reason, the inspector must take this into account in estimating the severity of the defect from the size of the red stain, since spreading may have been excessive.

38. CLEANING AFTER INSPECTION. The opaque white coating covering the area or part after inspection is usually objectionable, and in most cases must be removed. A good developer will have been formulated with this requirement in mind, and usually the powder is only lightly adherent and will come off easily with a water spray. Another method of removing the developer is by wiping with cloths wet with cleaner or alcohol. Some developers can be removed in the vapor degreaser. A good detergent wash with water in an industrial automatic washer is probably the best procedure, if such equipment is available for this purpose.

39. RE-RUNNING PARTS. Parts may be re-run with color-contrast penetrants, but only after thorough cleaning with solvents. The vapor de-greaser is the only really dependable cleaning device before re-processing. Time must be allowed for all cleaning fluid to evaporate out of all cracks or other defects. The part may then be re-processed from the beginning, starting with penetrant.

Re-running parts that have been processed with water-wash types of penetrant is less satisfactory (Chapter 6, Section 34).

Re-running parts, using fluorescent penetrants for the second run after a first run with color-contrast penetrants is not satisfactory. This is for the reason that even very small amounts of the red dye from the color-contrast penetrant will mask the fluorescence of the fluorescent dyes. If it is absolutely necessary to make a re-run with fluorescent penetrant, very elaborate precautions *must* be taken to insure complete removal of color-contrast dye. The steps suggested are the following:

1. Vapor de-grease.
2. Scrub with detergent and water and rinse.
3. Dry at elevated temperatures.
4. Soak in a mixture of equal parts of trichlorethylene, toluene and acetone, at least over night.
5. Vapor de-grease again.
6. Allow to cool.

Fluorescent penetrant may then be applied with expectation of good success.

The same precautions are required, though to a somewhat lesser degree, when the color-contrast test follows the fluorescent. Fluorescent dyes have little color in white light and the fluorescent dye in the penetrant remaining in a crack dilute, and tend to dim color-contrast indications.

The reader is here again referred to Appendix IV for a further discussion of color-contrast techniques.

Chapter 11

EQUIPMENT FOR CONDUCTING PENETRANT INSPECTION

1. Need for Equipment. No special equipment is required for conducting penetrant inspection. In its simplest application color-contrast and fluorescent penetrants can be applied by hand, the excess can be removed by hand cleaning, and developer can be hand applied. With fluorescent penetrant the black light is the only piece of equipment that must be available.

Such hand application may be quite satisfactory when:

(a) Only a few parts are to be inspected.

(b) Maximum sensitivity is not required.

(c) It is the best that can be done because the part is too large or equipment to do a proper job is not available.

Color-contrast methods are ideal for such circumstances, since not even a power source for a black light is needed. Fluorescent penetrants will give greater sensitivity than color contrast types under such conditions if black light can be made available. Kits for employment of the methods under these minimum conditions are available and with care can give good results. (See Section 30)

However, equipment becomes essential for proper employment of the methods:

(a) When many parts are to be inspected in production. The by-hand technique here is impracticable, from the point of view of both speed and convenience. Equipment of suitable design makes handling of parts through the various steps possible at realistic speeds.

(b) When large parts are to be inspected regularly. In this case it is important that suitable means be used to insure proper application in each instance so that results will always be dependable and accurate.

(c) When a high level of sensitivity is required. Sensitivity cannot be constantly maintained at a maximum without proper facilities to insure optimum and uniform conditions at every step in the inspection.

(d) When consistent repetitive results are needed, as in production testing. Proper equipment makes it easy to employ the method in exactly the same way on all parts, so that variations in the appearance of indications are due to variations in the size and character of the defects and not to any variations in technique.

In addition to the above needs, there are other reasons for using equipment. Suitably designed units are economical, not only of time and effort, but of materials as well. The larger volumes of penetrant and developer which can be properly stored and which are instantly available for use with good equipment, permit better application of penetrant and developer (as by dipping) with minimum waste and loss by evaporation, and maximum recovery by draining excess liquids back into the storage containers.

In water-wash applications, the recirculating hot air drier is the only wholly satisfactory means for securing reliable inspection results from the points of view of speed and sensitivity.

2. ESSENTIAL EQUIPMENT COMPONENTS. The various components which usually are included in equipment for penetrant inspection correspond to the several steps in employing the different methods. These components, which may be combined to suit the requirements of the particular technique being used, are as follows:

(a) Pre-cleaning station. This is usually separated from the actual penetrant equipment line.

(b) Penetrating station, including the drain rack.

(c) Emulsifier station—used only for the post-emulsification method.

(d) Solvent-remover station—usually used only with color-contrast penetrants.

(e) Washing station—used in the water-wash and post-emulsification methods.

(f) Wet-developer station.

(g) Drier.

(h) Dry developer station, including the developing storage rack.

(i) Inspection station.

(j) Station for after-cleaning when required.

CHAPTER 11

EQUIPMENT FOR CONDUCTING PENETRANT INSPECTION

3. PRE-CLEANING EQUIPMENT. The processes and requirements for pre-cleaning parts vary widely with the character of the parts and the condition in which they come to the inspection station. During manufacture, the operation just preceding inspection may leave the part coated with oil or grease or other compounds or materials that must be removed. When a part is to be inspected on overhaul after service, grease, carbon, paint, gum or other interfering substances may have to be removed.

(Courtesy Phillips Mfg. Co.)

Fig. 72—Commercial vapor degreasing unit.

Suitable equipment must be selected to fit the individual case, and in nearly all cases such equipment is available commercially. Examples are vapor degreasers, sand or grit blasters, water-detergent washing machines, solvent or chemical tanks or sprays, Vapor Blast equipment, etc.

Pre-cleaning equipment is usually set up separate, or sometimes even remote, from the rest of the penetrant line of equipment. However, to minimize handling and transportation of parts, it is desira-

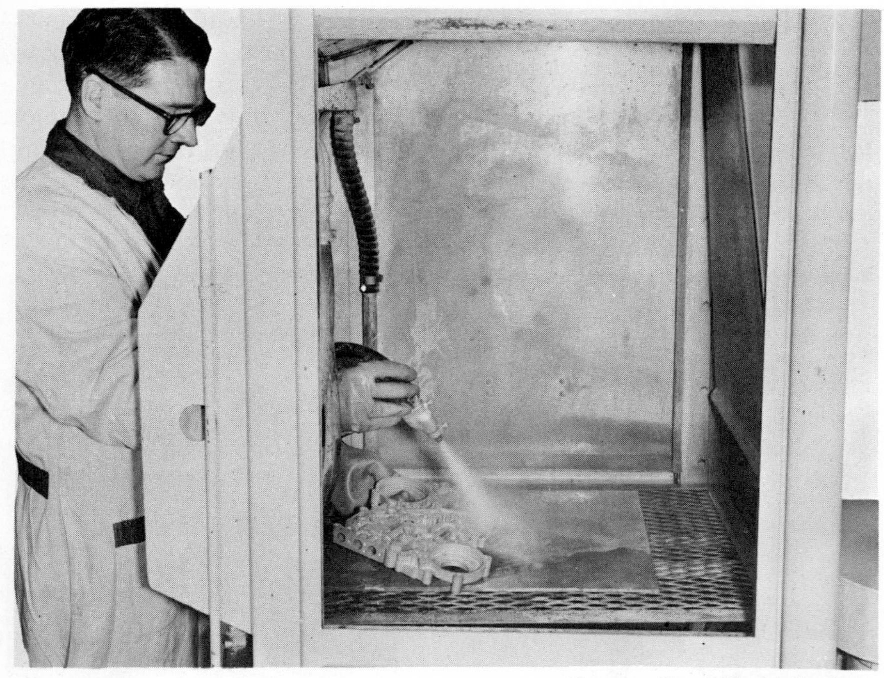

(Courtesy Vapor Blast Mfg. Co.)

Fig. 73—Vapor Blast cleaning station.

ble that pre-cleaning be carried out in the vicinity of the inspection station. The inspector will then be able to supervise the pre-cleaning operation and make sure that parts are in proper condition before applying penetrant.

The pre-cleaning station must deliver parts clean and dry. If solvents have been used, heat may be needed to make sure that all solvent has been removed from cracks or other surface openings. When water has been used, especially with detergent in solution, the need for heating is imperative. Water with detergent is itself a fairly good penetrant and may enter cracks and flaws during the washing process. To make sure that no water remains in flaws to prevent penetrant from entering, heat above the boiling point of water must be applied for a considerable time to ensure that all cracks are thoroughly dried out.

4. THE PENETRANT STATION. The principal requirement for a penetrant station is that it provide means for coating the parts with penetrant, either all over, as for small parts in production, or over limited areas of large parts when local inspection only is required. In addition, means should be provided for draining excess penetrant back into the penetrant reservoir, unless the "expendable" technique is being used. Draining racks usually serve the additional purpose of providing a storage place for parts during the time required for penetration.

5. PENETRANT STATION FOR SMALL PARTS. Small parts are most easily coated by dipping into a reservoir of penetrant, and then disposing on the drain rack. This may be done individually or in batches in a wire basket. Fig. 74 shows baskets of small parts on the drain rack after dipping in penetrant.

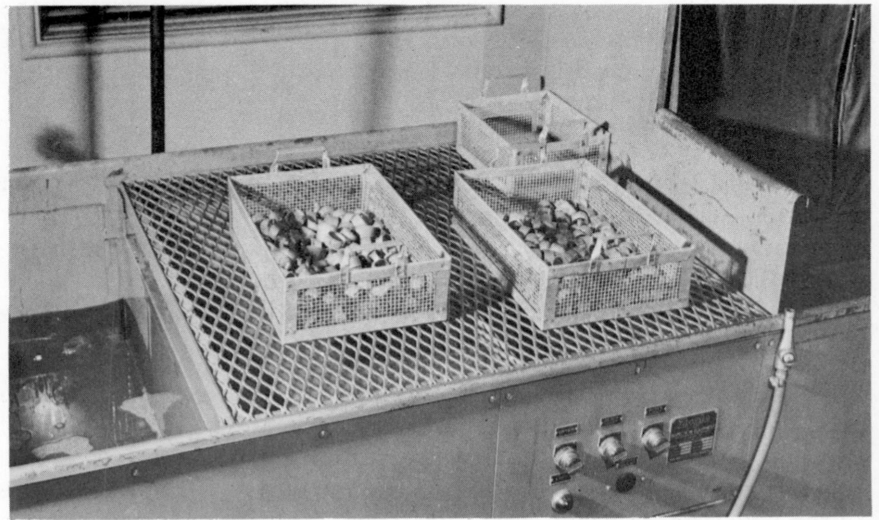

Fig. 74—Baskets of small parts draining after being dipped into penetrant.

Since good penetrants are homogeneous liquids, no facility for agitation is needed, and is not desirable. Some users have installed air agitation for their penetrant reservoir. This serves no useful purpose and has the undesirable effect of stirring up any sediment that may have accumulated on the bottom. Also, bubbling air through the penetrant increases losses by evaporation and seriously shortens the life of the penetrant. If the shop air line is not clean and dry, dirt, oil and water may be carried into the penetrant by the air stream.

The penetrant container should be equipped with an easily removable cover to reduce evaporation losses when not in use. A drain cock should also be provided to facilitate cleaning out the tank. Construction is usually of steel, but may be of other metal.

For water-base penetrants, stainless steel is the only satisfactory material.

Some penetrant stations are equipped with a hose and nozzle through which, by means of a small pump, penetrant can be flowed over parts which for any reason cannot be dipped into the bath.

6. PENETRANT STATION FOR LARGE PARTS. On large parts, penetrant is often applied by spraying or flowing. This is mainly a matter of convenience or practicability. It may also be a matter of economy, since the volume of penetrant needed to immerse a large object completely may be so great as to increase unnecessarily the original cost of the installation. A small reservoir of penetrant equipped with pump, hose, and a spray or flow nozzle is usually almost as fast a means for coating as is the dipping operation, on large parts.

The penetrant station in such a case consists of a booth, with a rotatable grill platform on which the part is set. A drain under the platform returns penetrant run-off to a sump from which the pump picks it up for re-delivery to the spray nozzle. The booth enclosure prevents splashing of penetrant on areas outside the penetrant station.

For heavy parts handling is facilitated by conveyors. These are commonly simple roller conveyors, but in some cases an overhead conveyor from which the parts are suspended is employed. If the inspection rate permits, the part may be allowed to drain in place in the penetrant station. If not, drain space on the conveyor outside the coating booth is required, with drip or drain pans to catch penetrant which runs off the part.

Fig. 75 is a general view of an automatic, conveyorized unit for the inspection of jet engine parts and assemblies. Fig. 76a is a close-up of the penetrant station of this unit. Parts are carried through on the conveyor and are sprayed with penetrant by means of the nozzles which can be seen in the picture. Fig. 76b is the automatic wash station on this unit.

7. PENETRANT STATIONS FOR EXPENDABLE TECHNIQUES. In some applications it has been found that the amount of penetrant which is recoverable and reuseable is not great, and this has led to the adoption of the expendable technique for some very large parts. In this case the penetrant is sprayed over the part in a booth similar to

CHAPTER 11

EQUIPMENT FOR CONDUCTING PENETRANT INSPECTION

Fig. 75—Automatic unit using overhead conveyor for large assemblies.

Fig. 76a—Automatic penetrant spray station showing spray nozzles.

Fig. 76b—Automatic wash station.

the one described in the previous section. Penetrant in this case may be stored in a separate pressure tank fitted with hose and spray nozzle. See Fig. 77.

The spray booth then is not equipped with sump to recover the excess penetrant. Instead it is fitted with water spray nozzles and drain, and serves the multiple purpose of penetrant, drain, and wash stations. Only the one station is then required and washed parts move directly to the drier.

If wet developer is to be used, this may be sprayed over the part after washing in the same station, the developer, of course, being also used on an expendable basis.

A decision to use this type of technique and equipment should be based on a careful analysis and consideration of all the factors of cost, time, rate of production and handling problems that are involved.

8. THE EMULSIFIER STATION. If post-emulsification penetrants are being used, the next step after penetrant application and drain is coating the part with emulsifier. It is important here that all parts of the surface be coated as nearly simultaneously as possible, since the time during which the emulsifier is allowed to act before wash-

Fig. 77—Unit for expendable technique on large parts. Combines penetrant, drain, wash, developer, and inspection stations (drier is separate).

ing is short—one half to three minutes or so. Dipping is by far the most satisfactory method for all parts.

For this purpose the emulsifier liquid is contained in a tank of sufficient size and depth to permit immersing the parts involved—either individually or in baskets. Covers are usually provided to reduce evaporation losses, and drain valves for clean-out when the bath has to be renewed. Suitable drain racks are also a part of this station to permit excess emulsifier to drain back into the tank.

If large parts must be coated with emulsifier, methods must be devised to achieve the fastest possible coverage. Multiple sprays or a copious flow of emulsifier from troughs or perforated pipes are used on some types of automatic equipment. For local coating of large parts, a spray is often quite satisfactory, using the expendable technique.

9. SOLVENT-REMOVER STATION. The solvent removal of excess penetrant is seldom made part of a fluorescent penetrant equipment line. In rare instances and under controlled conditions, a vapor degreaser has been used, parts being hung briefly in the vapor either individually or in baskets. When color-contrast penetrants are used on a production inspection basis rather than for local checking a dip-bath of solvent may be provided, or alternatively a suitable solvent spray gun with a spray booth and drain table. However, neither of these cleaning methods is dependable because such liberal use of solvents may remove penetrant from flaws that should be detected.

Color-contrast penetrants, if used in production, should be of the water-wash or post-emulsification type, in which cases the equipment is the same as for fluorescent penetrants, as described below.

10. WASH STATION FOR SMALL PARTS. Water washing of small parts is frequently done by hand, either individually or in wire baskets. Parts are held in the wash tank below table height, and cleaned with a hand-held spray using water at tap pressure and temperature. The wash trough or sink should be large enough and deep enough so that parts can be easily turned to clean all surfaces. Splash shields should separate the wash station from those on either side, which may be penetrant or emulsifier just preceding, and wet developer just following. Wash stations are always equipped with one or more black lights, so that the progress of removal of the penetrant can be easily followed. No light exclusion is necessary since un-removed penetrant areas fluoresce brilliantly.

11. AUTOMATIC WASHING. For production inspection, hand washing may prove to be too slow. Automatic cleaning of baskets of parts is quite satisfactorily accomplished by means of a rotating table on which the basket is set, and water spray heads properly located so as to rinse all surfaces of the parts thoroughly.

Specially-built automatic washers for parts which are large and of irregular contour have frequently been installed. Spray nozzles must be located to suit the individual part or parts for which the washer is designed, so as to clean all surfaces satisfactorily.

12. DIP-WASHING. Removal of excess penetrant by simply submerging the part in water is not generally recommended, although it has been used in certain applications. In nearly all cases, spray washing gives much superior results. When the dip method is used, the water bath must be large enough to receive and completely submerge the entire part in question in one dip. Penetrant emulsifies and is carried away with some agitation of the part. Some users of this washing technique find that air agitation of the water in the wash bath helps remove penetrant from openings and passages. The bath should be skimmed or frequently renewed to remove penetrant which has separated. All penetrants do not respond to this washing technique, so this type of wash equipment is seldom furnished.

A dip bath has sometimes been used in a post-emulsification line for large parts. In this case the bath of water must be large enough to submerge the part completely. This is not intended as a wash, but is for the purpose of stopping the emulsifying action at the proper time, and is then followed immediately by a spray wash. However, the dip is not very effective in arresting emulsification and the process is not generally recommended.

13. WASH-STATION CONSTRUCTION. Because of the nature of the process, the water-wash station is subject to corrosion. Steel construction should be protected by a rust-proofing treatment and paint. Most satisfactory, but more costly, is the use of stainless steel for this purpose.

14. DRYING STATION. The re-circulating hot air drier is one of the most important components of the penetrant equipment line. Successful inspection is to a considerable extent dependent on proper design and operation of the drier. This has been discussed at length in other chapters.

The drier must be of a size to handle easily the type and number of parts being inspected. Heat input, air-flow and rate of movement of parts through the drier, as well as temperature control, are all factors that must be balanced.

Entrance and exit of parts must be simple and easy but with minimum loss of heated air. Parts nearly always pass through the drier on a conveyor, either a hand-operated roller conveyor, or an automatic one the speed of which has been co-ordinated with the proper drying cycle.

Source of heat is frequently electric resistance elements, but may be gas, hot water or steam in special instances. The heat input is controlled by suitably located thermostats, and its amount is determined by the size, composition and rate of movement of the parts being processed.

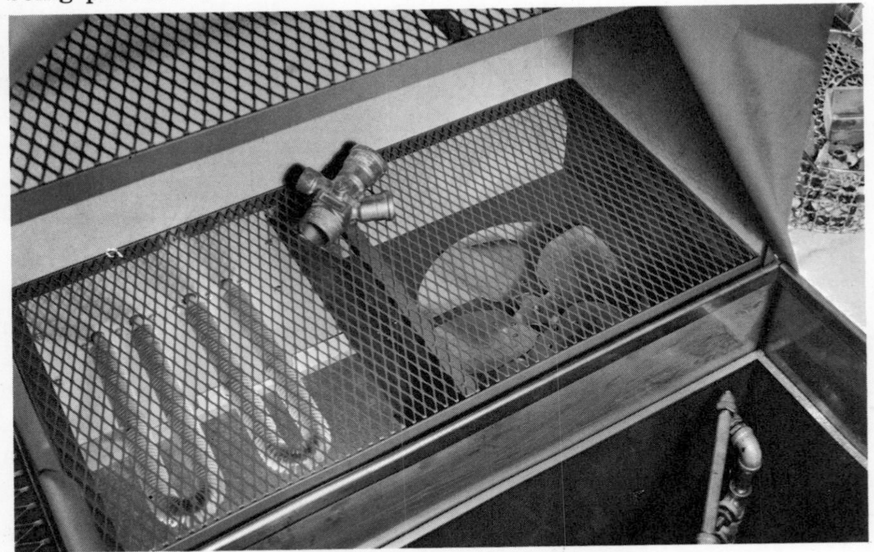

Fig. 78—Recirculating hot air drier.

15. Other Types of Driers. Integrated equipment invariably includes the recirculating hot air drier just described. Makeshift driers are sometimes used—in some cases because nothing better is available. Electric or gas hot-air blowers of commercial design have been used, but since no control of heat or temperature is possible, these are highly unsatisfactory and are ordinarily used only on an emergency basis. Infra-red lamps as a source of heat are also not suitable for drying washed parts, since the radiant heat which they deliver cannot readily be controlled so as to achieve desirable part temperature and at the same time dry all surfaces.

16. Special Purpose Driers. Equipment designed to handle parts of special size and shape requires a drier specially designed to suit the case. Many such have been built and are in use. Each one is a separate engineering problem involving the special combination of composition, mass, surface area, speed of movement and other considerations peculiar to the circumstances. Fig. 79 shows a special automatic drier used in the penetrant inspection of non-magnetic bars.

17. Developer Stations. The developer station incorporated into the equipment line, and its location in the line, depends on

Fig. 79—Special drier for bar stock.

whether dry or wet developer is to be used. If the former, the developer station follows the drier; if the latter, it immediately precedes the drier, following the wash station.

18. DRY DEVELOPER STATION. A rack, or space on the conveyor following the drier, is needed to permit time for parts to cool to handling temperature. Parts need not be completely cold and are usually given the developer coating as soon as they can be conveniently handled.

The dry developer station usually consists of a simple bin containing the powder. Dried parts are dipped into the powder and the excess shaken off. Larger parts may not be so easily immersed in the powder, so a scoop is usually provided for throwing powder over the surfaces, after which the excess is shaken off. The part is then moved on to another rack or continuation of the conveyor, which is of sufficient capacity to allow proper development time before the part reaches the inspection station.

The developer bin should be furnished with an easily removable cover to protect the developer from dust and dirt when not in use.

19. DRY-FLUFFY DEVELOPER STATION. The very light fluffy developer material behaves very much like a fluid, and submerging

Fig. 80—Dust-control installation on dry developer station.

of even quite large parts under the surface of the powder is quite easy. The powder is, however, very light and tends to float in the air. Dust control systems are sometimes needed when this developer is used in production. Control is accomplished by a suction opening across the back of the bin at the top, which draws off any developer dust that tends to rise out of the bin. The dust-laden air is passed through filter bags from which, if desired, it can be reclaimed for further use. (See also Fig. 28, P. 93.)

20. DEVELOPER GUNS. Developer powder can also be applied with air pressure. This system does away with the bin, but requires a booth or cabinet and makes dust collection almost a must. The system is seldom used in production work. (Chapter 7, Section 45.) An electrostatic gun for dry developer is shown in Fig. 81.

21. DEVELOPER DUST CABINETS. A system for automatic application of dry developer has been devised and has met with some success. This consists of a cabinet through which the dried parts are passed on a conveyor. The air in the cabinet is laden with dust kept agitated by means of a blower. As parts pass through, all

CHAPTER 11
EQUIPMENT FOR CONDUCTING PENETRANT INSPECTION

Fig. 81—Electrostatic gun for dry developer application.

surfaces are brought into contact with developer powder carried by the air.

Air must be exhausted from the cabinet and either recirculated or cleaned by passing through a dust-collecting filter.

22. WET DEVELOPER STATIONS. Wet developer, when used, is contained in a tank similar to that used for penetrant and emulsifier. It should be deep enough to permit parts to be submerged in the developer, and should have a rack or conveyor on which parts can rest after dipping to permit excess developer to run off, back into the bath. From this point parts pass directly into the drier, either by hand or on a continuation of the conveyor.

Developer baths tend to settle out when not in use. A paddle for stirring is usually provided. Pump agitation often leads to foaming and is not usually used for this purpose. Continuous agitation is not needed, since the settling rate is very slow. Pumps are sometimes used for flowing developer over the parts from a nozzle.

23. AUTOMATIC UNITS, WET DEVELOPER APPLICATION. Special means of applying developer are used in automatic units. Flow-on methods are frequently used, of such size and patterns that parts are quickly and thoroughly covered. Foaming of developer in sumps and reservoirs is sometimes a problem which must be guarded against.

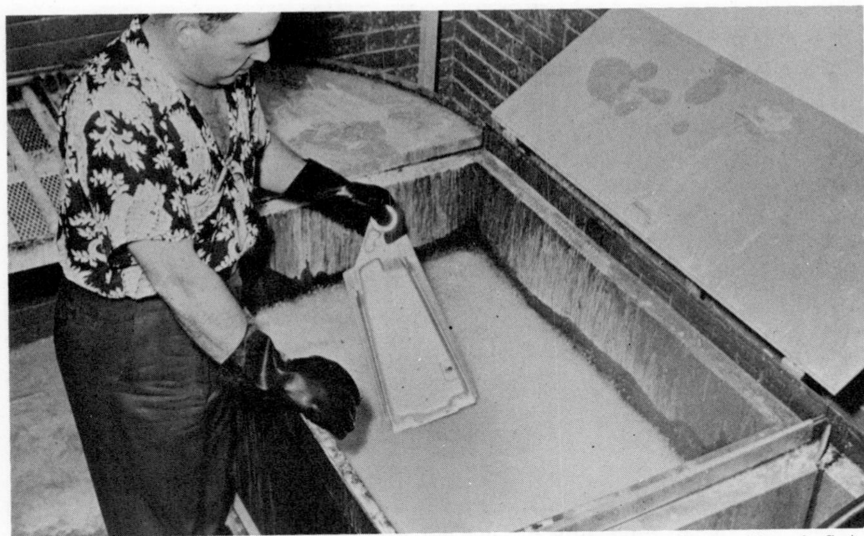

(Courtesy Cessna Aircraft Co.)

Fig. 82—Wet developer station.

24. APPLICATION OF EXPENDABLE TECHNIQUE. When the expendable technique is being used for penetrant application, wet developer is usually also applied by this means. Of course, solvent developer from spray cans (Fig. 83) is always applied on an expendable basis. Water suspended wet developer may be contained in a large paint spray pressure container which provides means

Fig. 83—Pressure spray can for wet developer application.

Fig. 84—Pressure tank and spray for dry developer application.

for agitation and for applying from a spray gun. Foaming is not so serious a problem here, since the developer is not re-circulated.

25. THE INSPECTION STATION. Essentially, the inspection station is simply a work table on which parts can be handled under proper lighting. For fluorescent methods the table is usually surrounded by a canvas curtain or hood to exclude most of the white light from the area. For color-contrast penetrants a hood is, of course, unnecessary.

Black lights may be batteries of 100 or 400 watt lamps for area lighting, or in small stations may be one or two 100 watt spot lamps mounted on brackets from which they can be lifted and moved about by hand. White lights are usually installed overhead, controlled by conveniently located switches. A ventilating fan is very necessary, since the temperature inside the hoods builds up rapidly from the heat thrown off by the black lights.

Parts are moved into the booth through a split curtain at one end, either by hand or on a conveyor. They are similarly passed out the other end after inspection, or are often simply dropped by hand into "accept" or "reject" containers standing inside the curtains.

26. INSPECTION ROOMS. In a few large installations, fully enclosed dark rooms hâve been built for black-light inspection.

(Courtesy General Metals Corp.)

Fig. 85—Typical inspection station.

Access is through a "light lock" of some sort. Inspection tables or conveyors, before which a number of inspectors can sit or stand, may run the length of the room, as in the curtained booths. White lights must be available, of course. Black lights may be of high power on an area-illumination basis, but are usually supplemented by a hand-held portable spot light for each inspector. Good ventilation is extremely important, and air conditioning is desirable.

It is important that inspection rooms be laid out so as to facilitate keeping rejected parts from inadvertently getting back into the production line. Unless the room is properly laid out and *correct procedures established,* janitors, new men or employees from other departments may unintentionally misplace rejects among the accepted parts.

27. AUTOMATIC UNITS, INSPECTION. Inspection on automatic units is accomplished at stations the design of which depends on

CHAPTER 11

EQUIPMENT FOR CONDUCTING PENETRANT INSPECTION

Fig. 86—Inspection station on automatic bearing race unit.

the size and nature of the part, the speed required and the number of inspectors needed to keep up with the output of the automatic processing unit.

Sometimes a single inspector with "accept" and "reject" gate controls is able to inspect rapidly enough, especially if he does not have to handle the parts. In other cases processed parts pass along the center of a table on a conveyor, from which several inspectors on both sides pick off parts, examine and dispose of them as accepted or rejected. Accepted parts may be put on a second conveyor for removal from the inspection station.

28. POST-CLEANING. Post-inspection cleaning is often necessary to remove all traces of penetrant and developer. As in the case of pre-cleaning, equipment for this purpose is available commercially and special designs are seldom required. Water-detergent washers are probably the most effective for this purpose, when parts are small enough and in enough quantity to make them feasible. If the cleaning is done by hand, as on a few parts or on large ones, a water spray with or without detergent is usually effective. This requires some sort of booth to keep the spray within bounds and to drain off the waste. Solvent sprays, using considerable force, are also sometimes used.

29. COMMERCIAL PENETRANT EQUIPMENT. Integrated equipment is available in many sizes and combinations. Module designs are widely used so that a line can be assembled from standard components to include the stations which a given situation requires. For many applications special units have been designed and built to inspect certain types of parts. In some cases units have been custom designed and built to inspect a specific part. The following sections will illustrate and describe a few of those which are typical.

30. MINIMUM FACILITIES. For occasional inspections in the field, or where extreme portability is a controlling consideration, minimal kits for carrying out either color-contrast or fluorescent penetrant inspections are available commercially.

Figure 87 illustrates such a kit for color-contrast work. Included are pre-cleaner, penetrant and developer, all in pressurized spray cans. Removal is by wiping with cloths or paper towels.

Figure 88 shows a similar kit for fluorescent work. Again, cleaner, penetrant and developer are supplied in pressurized cans. Here, too, cleaning is by the wipe-off technique, with or without solvent. A portable black light is included.

Other kits designed for use under special conditions or for special purposes are available.

(Courtesy Howell Tractor & Equip. Co.)

Fig. 87—Color-contrast kit in use.

Fig. 88—Fluorescent penetrant kit.

31. PORTABLE BLACK LIGHTS. These are available in several forms. The most widely used type is illustrated in Fig. 62 (p. 209). They are useful in many field inspections where penetrant is applied by improvised processes, as, for example, the inspection of non-magnetic blading of large steam turbines. A special, low output explosion proof black light is available for use where the mercury arc tubes are not permissible. These low-output lamps must be held very close to the work to secure sufficient black light intensity for proper inspection.

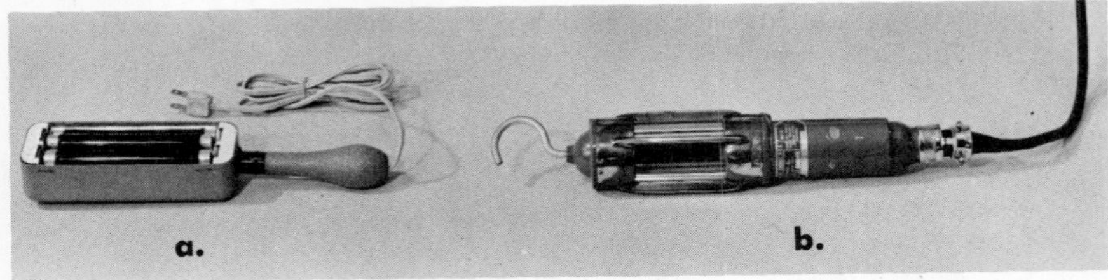

Fig. 89—Low output portable black lights. a) General purpose. b) Explosion proof.

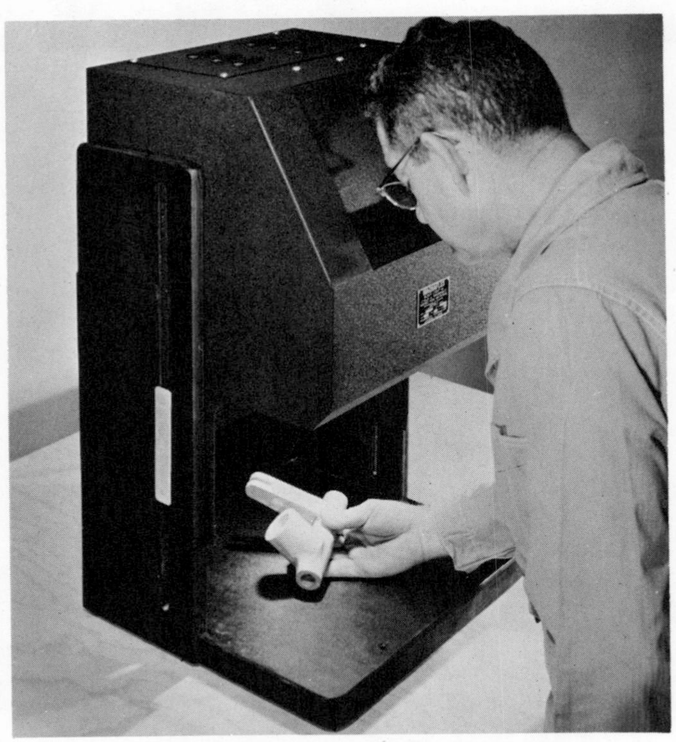

Fig. 90—Small black light viewing cabinet.

When 110 V circuits are not available in the field, the standard mercury arc spot black light bulbs may be energized by using small (400 watt) generators driven with chain-saw type gasoline motors.

A low output, low wattage light is available for maximum portability. This light may be operated with batteries by use of a converter such as is furnished in connection with electric razors when operated from 12 volt automobile systems. (Fig. 89a).

32. SMALL VIEWING CABINET. When a full scale inspection booth is not practicable, a small viewing cabinet is used to examine small parts.

This is shown in Fig. 90. A black light of the 100 watt spot variety is mounted in the top of the cabinet. The inspector looks through the slot at processed parts which he manipulates under the black light by hand. This is a reasonably effective inspection device, but has the drawback that, unless he holds his eyes to the "slot" for several minutes before looking for indications, the inspector's eyes are not dark-adapted and fine indications may

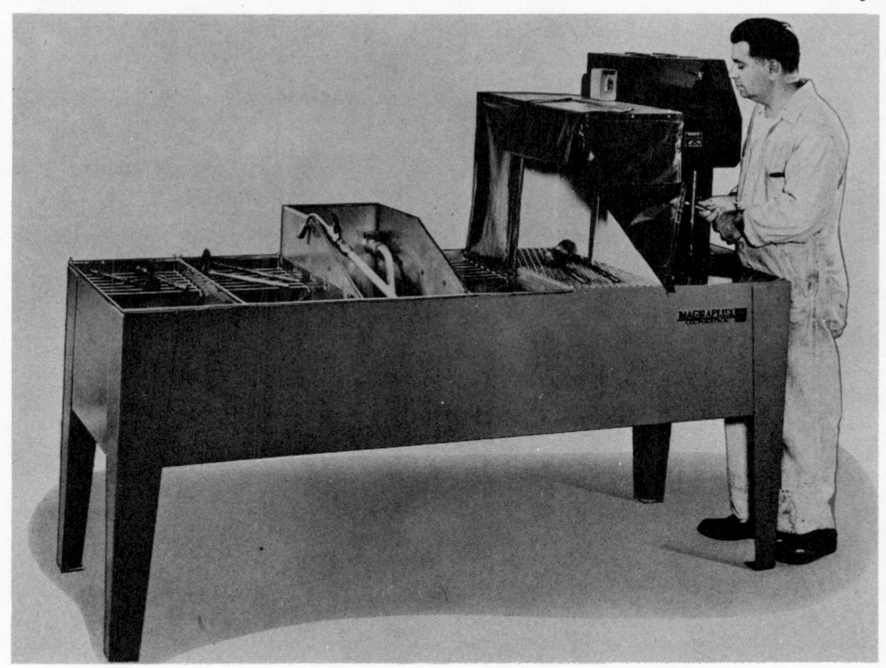

Fig. 91—Small integrated unit for fluorescent penetrant inspection of small parts.

easily be missed. To offset this to some extent, however, parts may be held very close to the spot light and thereby receive a very high level of black light illumination.

33. SMALL INTEGRATED UNIT. Fig. 91 illustrates a small integrated unit, widely used for the inspection of a large variety of small parts. The unit is complete in one frame and includes all the essential processing stations. It is, of course, hand operated throughout.

Somewhat larger units of this type are extensively used for the inspection of small parts in production but where the number of parts to be inspected is not great enough to warrant automatic equipment. Automatic washing of parts in baskets is often installed in the wash station of this type of unit, in addition to hand-washing. A typical unit of this type is shown in Fig. 92.

Fig. 92—Larger general purpose unit.

34. MODULAR UNITS. Fig. 93 illustrates one of the larger inspection lines built up of a combination of standard stations. The components and functions are as follows, starting in the foreground:

Penetrant.

Penetrant drain.

CHAPTER 11

EQUIPMENT FOR CONDUCTING PENETRANT INSPECTION

Courtesy United Air Lines

Fig. 93—Typical modular unit.

Emulsifier.

Wash.

Wet developer.

Drier.

"Rest" station.

Inspection.

Roller conveyors are used here wherever possible to make shifting of parts easier for the inspector.

Sometimes special variations of some of the stations are made, as shown in Fig. 94. This is an automatic wash station for the turbine wheel of a gas turbine engine. Water sprays above and below the wheel give a thorough wash while the wheel is rotated.

35. SPECIAL UNITS. Many units of special design have been built to do special jobs. These may be for hand operation, or may be semi-automatic, or fully automatic. Fig. 95 is an artist's sketch

Fig. 94—Special wash station for gas turbine wheels.

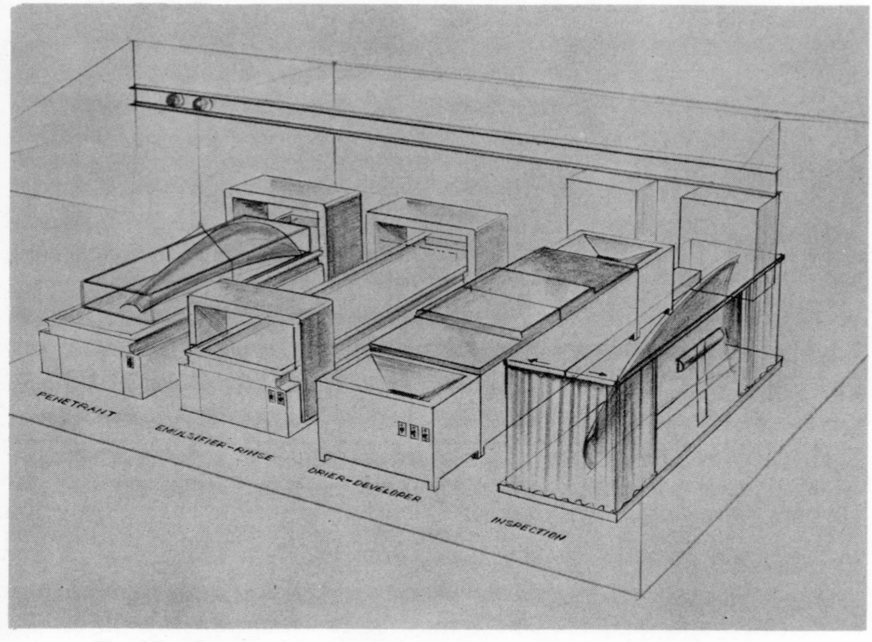

Fig. 95—Drawing of unit to inspect large rocket tank dome gores.

of a unit designed to inspect very large parts of rocket cases. Each station is automatic, but the parts are shifted from station to station by means of an overhead crane.

36. AUTOMATIC UNITS. Many special units are in use which are fully automatic, except for the viewing by the inspectors. Fig. 96 shows such a unit for the inspection of gas turbine blades. Blades are loaded at one end by an operator and are automatically

Fig. 96—Automatic unit for inspection of gas turbine blades.

processed through the various operations and finally are presented to the inspectors at the inspection station ready for examination. Other automatic or semi-automatic units will be described in Chapter 13.

Automation is currently moving ahead a further step. Units have been designed to program the variables of the penetrant process—penetration time, drain time, emulsification time, drying and developing time—by means of punched cards made up to suit the process specification for any given part. A pallet of parts, carrying process specifications with the suitable punched card is delivered to the inspector. He inserts the punched card into the control "slot", and the parts are automatically processed in accordance with the pre-determined program, varying the process for each part in sequence, as desired.

CHAPTER 12

DETECTABLE DEFECTS

1. GENERAL. In preceding chapters the Penetrant Method of defect detection has been discussed from many angles—what it is, how it operates, its advantages and limitations, and the materials, equipment and techniques required to apply it. Little has been said as to what the method will find or in what applications it has been found to be useful. In the next four chapters we will look at defects as such, and at specific inspection applications, as well as at the problem of interpreting what is shown by the indications produced.

2. DEFECTS DEFINED. There is an important distinction to be made in any discussion of defects as found by any nondestructive test. Nondestructive tests indicate the presence of some condition in the material or part—usually a condition which is a departure or variation from that desired or contemplated by the designer or manufacturer. This variation is indicated by a number of means in different types of tests. Any divergence from the norm may be shown by meter readings, tape or chart recordings, photographic film, cathode ray screens, or visual observation of some indicating medium directly on the surface of the part being inspected, as in the case of penetrants.

But it must always be remembered that the condition indicated may or may not be objectionable from the point of view of serviceability—it may be entirely harmless, or even an expected condition for which the designer *has allowed*. In such cases the condition is not a defect in the material for the particular use for which it is intended—though the same condition in material intended for some other service may be very objectionable.

It is therefore customary, in the language of nondestructive testing, to define a defect as a condition, fault or blemish which interferes with the intended service of the material or part and is therefore objectionable. Any condition indicated which is nonrelevant to the future use of the part is, in this sense, not a defect.

Penetrant inspection reveals discontinuities of whatever origin or significance, in the surfaces of the material being tested—but indications so produced may or may not be those of defects. Actually the word "defect" is often loosely used even by people who are fully aware of this distinction—it is a word more easily said than "discontinuity". But until a *discontinuity* has been properly determined to be a *defect,* the former term is the only correct one to use.

3. KINDS OF DEFECTS. When a part is to be stressed heavily in service, defects are those discontinuities which might lead to malfunctioning of the part or to actual rupture of the material, as in fatigue. The most damaging defects are therefore those which occur in high-stressed locations, and which are sharp-notched—as are most cracks—and are therefore stress-raisers likely to lead to fatigue or other early failure. The orientation and shape of such defects also affect their severity in any given occurrence.

On the other hand, a scratch on a mirror surface is a defect even though it may never cause breakage; or a crack in a porcelain enamel surface is a defect, which may lead—not to failure or breakage—but to corrosion or unsightly staining.

In the discussions which follow, the word "defect" will often be used in the loose sense to refer to discontinuities, partly because the word *is* easier to read or say, partly because in this discussion we are interested in and seeking discontinuities because they may be and usually are true defects. Nevertheless the distinction just made should always be remembered.

4. BROAD CLASSIFICATION OF DISCONTINUITIES. Discontinuities or defects may be classified in many ways from many different points of view, each useful for some purposes; and these will be discussed in the following sections. There is perhaps only one really broad classification which separates discontinuities into two groups, and for the purposes of penetrant inspection applications this is a truly basic separation. Discontinuities may be either *open to the surface* or they may be *wholly below the surface.*

Penetrant inspection will find *most* discontinuities which break the surface of a part, in *most* solid, non-porous materials, even though the surface opening is small and the greater part of the discontinuity does lie below the surface (as in some types of porosity). But Penetrant Inspection cannot locate discontinuities which lie *wholly* below the surface, since in this case there is no opening through which the penetrant can enter.

5. Important Characteristics of Defects. In considering defects (discontinuities) from the point of view of detectability by the use of penetrants, there are certain characteristics which determine whether they can be found or not, and whether they are significant, or how significant they may be, as defects.

It seems, therefore, of interest to list some of these characteristics so that they will be better understood in subsequent discussions. The following considerations are important:

(A) Defects open to the surface.

(1) Depth, D—measured in a direction normal to the surface.

(2) Width, W—at the surface, measured at 90° to length.

(3) Length, L—longest dimension measured at the surface.

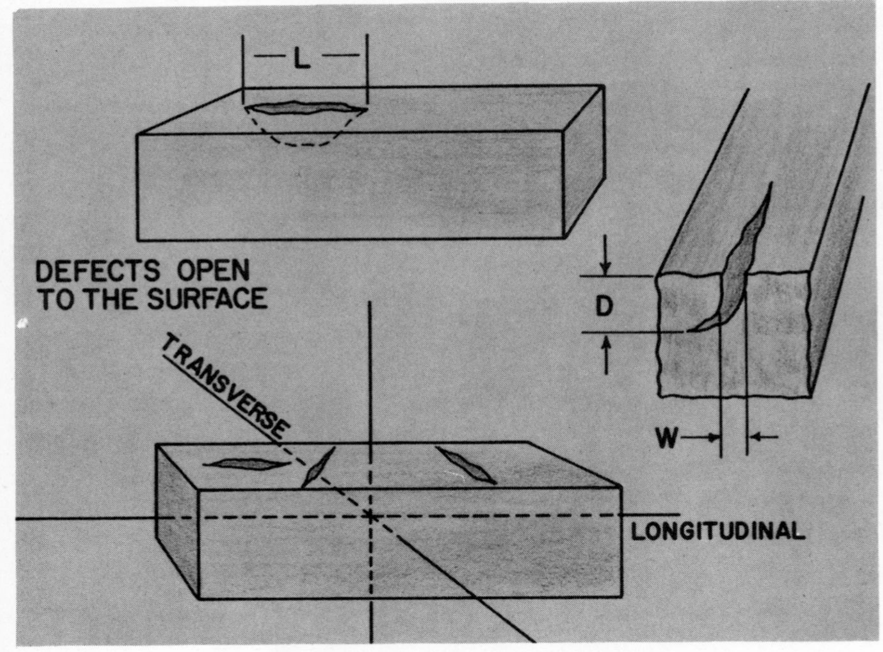

Fig. 97—Characteristics of surface defects.

(4) Shape—sharpness at bottom—V or U.

(5) Angle of penetration with respect to the surface.

(6) Orientation of principal dimension.

(a) With respect to longitudinal axis of part.
(b) With respect to transverse axis of part.

(7) Frequency—number per unit area.

(8) Interrelationship—grouping, alignment, etc.

(9) Relationship of all characteristics to stresses in the part and to critical stress locations.

(10) Stress-raising effect from all considerations.

(B) Defects lying wholly below the surface:

(1) Length, L—principal dimension parallel to the surface.

(2) Width, W—dimension parallel to the surface at 90° to length.

(3) Height, H—dimension normal to the surface.

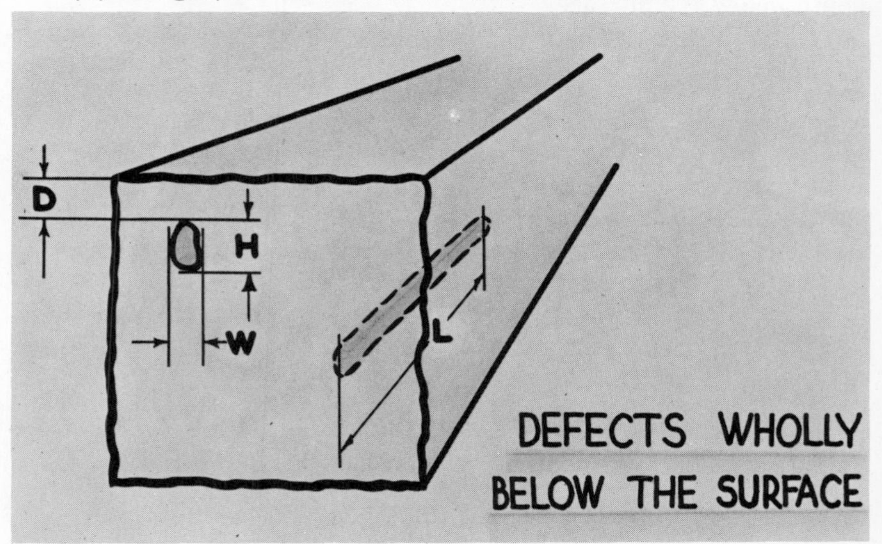

Fig. 98—Characteristics of subsurface defects.

(4) Depth, D—distance from the surface to nearest part of defect.

(5) Shape—globular, angular, flat, sharp-cornered, etc.

(6) Orientation of planes of principal dimensions:

(a) With respect to surface.
(b) With respect to longitudinal axis of part.
(c) With respect to transverse axis of part.

(7) Frequency—number per unit of cross section.

(8) Interrelationship—grouping.

(9) Relationship of all characteristics to stresses in the part and to critical stress locations.

(10) Stress-raising effect from all considerations.

There is at least one type of defect that has characteristics of both the above groups. This is the surface (or other) porosity commonly found in aluminum and magnesium sand castings. In these the bulk of the discontinuity lies below the surface, but there is, nevertheless, an opening to the surface by which penetrant can enter. In this case we may have a minimum of length and width at the surface, but appreciable length, width and height at a slight depth below the surface.

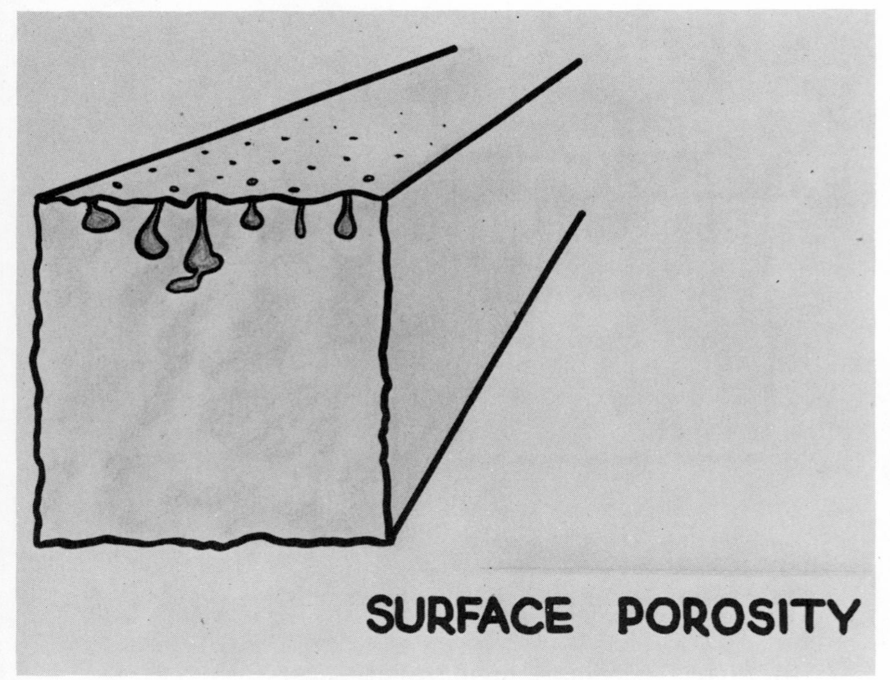

Fig. 99—Surface porosity.

6. POSSIBLE CLASSIFICATION OF SURFACE DEFECTS. Classification of defects for the purposes of magnetic particle inspection has long been based on their source or origin—inherent, processing and service. Magnetic particle inspection is, however, applicable to only one type of material—i. e., ferromagnetic metals, such as iron, steel and many alloys. These materials all have a common denominator in that they are produced and processed in essentially the same manner and are subject to the same types of defects from the same origins.

In trying to apply this system of classification to defects found by Penetrant Inspection, we at once run into difficulty because the latter method is applicable to a wide variety of materials made by vastly different processes. There is no common denominator as regards manufacture and processing among such diversified materials as ferrous and non-ferrous metals, plastics, ceramics, glass, etc., all of which lend themselves to inspection with penetrants. On the other hand, a crack is a crack and has certain characteristics regardless of origin or cause. And, of course, while cracks may occur in any of these materials it is also true that each material may have some defect peculiar to itself and not found in the group generally.

Thus we find we may usefully classify defects in a number of different ways depending on the purpose for which the classification is undertaken. Some possibly useful groupings are the following:

(a) by type.

(b) by dimension and shape.

(c) by source or origin.

(d) by materials in which they occur.

(e) by the form of the material in which they occur.

(f) by processes which produce them.

General classifications of defects should include both surface and subsurface varieties, although for the purposes of penetrant inspection only surface defects are of interest. Therefore, the classifications that follow, although not limited to surface defects, are nevertheless considered from the point of view of their usefulness in connection with the use of penetrants for their detection.

7. CLASSIFICATION OF DEFECTS BY TYPE. Considering defects as such, without reference to the material in which they occur we have the following groups:

a) Surface: fine, tight.

  (1) Shallow
  (2) Deep

b) Surface: broad, open.

  (1) Shallow
  (2) Deep

c) Porosity linked to surface

  (1) Shallow and fine
  (2) Gross

d) Entirely subsurface

e) Cracks or other openings extending entirely through the cross-section—i.e., leaks.

f) Non-relevant discontinuities or false indications.

Obviously such a classification could go into much greater detail and many sub-classes under each heading could be enumerated. For example, the entire group of sub-surface defects is here lumped under a single head, whereas these could be subdivided into many categories. But from the standpoint of penetrant inspection this would have little or no value, and sub-classification here is not warranted. And basically, the other groups cover all the essentially different types which penetrant inspection seeks to find, and the sub-types will be taken up later in considering specific applications.

8. Classification of Surface Defects by Dimension and Shape.

The above classification is strictly qualitative, and while it makes the distinction between "fine, tight" and "broad, open", and between "shallow" and "deep", it gives no clue as to actual sizes of openings which fit these definitions.

It would seem, therefore, that surface defects might be more accurately defined, especially for specification purposes, on the basis of dimensional characteristics—i.e., length, width and depth. Each dimension, for instance, could be divided into a series of numbered values in a significant range, and the defect described by three numbers. Such a designation might take the form L1 (Length) W3 (Width) D2 (Depth) or simply 1-3-2.

Following is such a possible classification.

TABLE XIV

LENGTH-WIDTH-DEPTH CLASSIFICATION CODE FOR DEFINING DEFECTS

Severity Number	Length L	Width W	Depth D
1	.001″ or less	.0001″ or less	.001″ or less
2	.001″ - .005″	.0001″ - .0005″	.001″ - .005″
3	.005″ - .010″	.0005″ - .0010″	.005″ - .010″
4	.010″ - .025″	.0010″ - .0025″	.010″ - .025″
5	.025″ - .050″	.0025″ - .0050″	.025″ - .050″
6	.050″ - .100″	.005″ - .010″	.050″ - .075″
7	.100″ - .25″	.010″ - .025″	.075″ - .100″
8	.25″ - .50″	.025″ - .050″	.100″ - .150″
9	.50″ - 1.00″	.050″ - .100″	.150″ - .250″
10	1.00″ or longer	.100″ or wider	.250″ or deeper

From this, a defect designated as L4-W5-D3 (or simply 453) would be a defect not over .025″ long, .005″ wide and .01″ deep.

Shape should have some place in such a system, since shape is important in judging the seriousness of a discontinuity in many instances. The most important shape factor is the bottom or end of the discontinuity—whether a sharp V notch or a rounded U. The designation W7-D2 is undoubtedly a wide shallow surface mark but does not tell whether the bottom is rounded or sharp. Perhaps the modifying letter V or U after the dimensional description would serve this purpose.

Such a system would make it easy to put numbers to the defects we now customarily speak of as fine and tight, or wide and shallow, and thereby answer the questions "how fine?" or "how wide?" or "how shallow?" However, the system would not pin down the shape factor very well, especially when considering subsurface discontinuities.

The important consideration of orientation of the defect with respect to the surface or the axes of the part, or with respect to stress direction, is also not designated by this system.

A globular opening, sub-surface, would not be too well defined by calling it L1-W3-D1 (i.e., .001″ x .001″ x .001″). For penetrant testing this disadvantage is not very pertinent, since a globular opening is necessarily sub-surface. However, porosity of various kinds does have shape characteristics not well defined by three dimensions. When connected to the surface—usually by very small openings—the size of the surface break is unimportant compared to the size of the sub-surface cavity.

By means of more modifying numbers or letters these situations might also be included in the classification, but the code designation would be so cumbersome as to be of doubtful value. An entirely separate system, applicable to sub-surface discontinuities only and ignoring the size of surface openings if they exist, would offer a solution, only an additional dimension should be added in this case—namely, the distance of the cavity below the surface of the material.

The system of classification as proposed in this section would probably be best applicable, and useful, only for *surface* discontinuities.

9. CLASSIFICATION BY SOURCE OR ORIGIN. This system of classification has for many years been used in discussing defects found in magnetic materials by the magnetic particle method and certainly has many advantages in identifying defects. But because of the much wider scope of the penetrant method, which is applicable to many non-metallic materials whose processing histories have little in common with those of metals, this system is not entirely applicable to all defects which can be located by penetrants. Still, penetrant inspection *is* applied to many metals, so that this system of classification does have some merit for this purpose, especially because, if stated slightly differently, it can be made to apply to materials other than metals.

Following in general the plan used for ferrous materials, the classes for penetrant inspection purposes might be:

(a) PRIMARY PROCESSING DEFECTS. These include all those produced in preparing the metal or other material into initial usable form, before any modifying operations of manufacture have been performed. This group would include the "inherent" defects in ingots, billets and castings, as well as those introduced in such processes as rolling, extruding and forging.

(b) FINISHING DEFECTS. These include all those introduced during the manufacture into finished form. Included are forming, bending, heat treating, grinding, welding and handling cracks, machining tears, drawing defects, cracks in fired ceramics, molded plastics, glass and glass-to-metal seals.

(c) SERVICE DEFECTS. This class includes all defects produced after the part or material has been placed in service. It includes fatigue cracks in metals, and defects from any other cause resulting from service.

Even with such modification this system does not appear to be too widely useful for penetrant inspection purposes, except in the application to metals.

10. CLASSIFICATION BY MATERIALS. Defects could be considered from the point of view of the materials in which they occur. Various materials are prone to particular types of defects characteristic of that material. Examples are fine porosity just under the surface in aluminum and magnesium, firing cracks in ceramics, shallow but serious seams in tungsten wire, etc. Thus defects peculiar to aluminum and its alloys could be listed, and, separately, those characteristic of magnesium, copper, brass, stainless steel and all other metals, as well as ceramics of various types, plastics, etc.

In actual fact, such classifications are used, whether consciously or not. When inspecting an aluminum article the informed inspector will be aware of the defects, characteristic of that metal in whatever form is involved, for which he must search. This is an *end use* of defect classification, but for purposes of compilation such a system would be very lengthy and would involve much duplication.

11. CLASSIFICATION BY FORM OF MATERIAL. Forgings, castings, extrusions, tubing, porcelain insulators—these various forms in which materials are produced often have defects characteristic of that particular form. Laps or bursts in forgings, thermal cracks in castings, tears in extrusions, all are characteristic defects sought when these forms are inspected. Thus we could list defects characteristic of:

(a) Castings—of whatever metal or other material.

(b) Forgings—of whatever metal.

(c) Rolled products and shapes.

(d) Bars.

(e) Tubing—seamless, welded.

(f) Extrusions.

(g) Sheets and strip.

(h) Drawn, spun, explosion formed products.

(i) Porcelain enameled products.

(j) Ceramics—green, fired.

and so on for a very long list. Again in actual inspection such a classification is known and used, even if not formalized. But as a *general* system of classifying defects it is not satisfactory, since it would be long and there would be many duplications. Furthermore, it would not lend itself to include various types of processing- and service-introduced defects.

12. CLASSIFICATION BY PROCESSES. An approach similar to the previous one, but more practical, would be to list defects by the processes or conditions which cause them. Such a listing would include:

(a) Solidification from fluid state (as in ingots)

(b) Rolling

(c) Forging

(d) Casting

(e) Extruding

(f) Piercing

(g) Drawing

(h) Welding

(i) Molding and firing (ceramics).

(j) Heat treating

(k) Grinding

(l) Machining

(m) Plating

(n) Glass-to-metal sealing

(o) Stress-variations (service and fatigue) and so on.

This is a useful manner of considering defects, since each process is known to produce types of defects which are characteristic of that process. We speak of forging laps, rolling seams, heat treating and grinding cracks; and when we inspect materials or parts known to have gone through one or more of these processes, we are on the lookout for these characteristic defects. If this system were to be attempted as a *general* classification of defects, however, the list must of necessity be very long or else some processes on some materials must be omitted.

13. DETECTABLE DEFECTS. For the purposes of this chapter the simplest and most useful method of classification is to consider defects on the basis of their own character rather than on the time or method of their production or the materials in which they occur. Detectability actually depends more on the defect characteristics themselves than on any other consideration. Chapters 13 and 14 will discuss specific techniques for the detection of defects of various characteristics and origins occuring in specific materials.

14. CHOOSING THE METHOD. The character of the defect itself is undoubtedly the paramount consideration in choosing which variant of the penetrant method to use for its detection. However, the level of sensitivity necessary to meet the requirements of the inspection is of almost equal importance.

It cannot be overemphasized that the prime objective of nondestructive testing is *not simply to find defects*. It is rather to assure that each manufactured article or each piece of material goes into service *free of all defects which would interfere with its satisfactory operation and life*. It is, therefore, of utmost importance that whatever nondestructive test be selected in any given instance, it be adequate in kind and in sensitivity to insure the *absence* of *significant* defects.

To make such a selection intelligently requires vastly greater knowledge and experience with regard to the abilities and the limitations of a test method than merely the easily demonstrated fact that it can and will find significant defects under certain circumstances. It also demands a knowledge of the particular part and its intended service, so that it may be known just which defects are significant and which are unimportant.

Failure to understand the importance of these two considerations leads all too frequently to errors in adopting a nondestructive test for a specific purpose. It is not enough to know that certain defects are present—assurance must also be given by the selected test that, if no defects are found, defects of that type actually are *not* present.

In applying this philosophy to the selection of a suitable penetrant method, one must realize that the available methods and techniques cover a wide range of sensitivities—from the color-contrast penetrants on the one hand to the super-bright post-emulsification fluorescent penetrants on the other.

15. Factors to be Considered in Choosing the Method. Following are some of the most important factors to consider in deciding which method, material and technique is best suited to a given inspection problem.

(a) What kind and size of defects are sought.

(b) What kind of parts are to be inspected—material, size, shape, surface condition, etc.

(c) What is the form and the stage of manufacture of the part—forging, casting, rough or machined surface, etc.

(d) What kind of defects are *likely* to be present. The kinds of defects that may be present are usually known from the material, and the processes the part has been through. In some materials the only significant defects that *can* be present are easy to find by low-sensitivity techniques.

(e) What kind of defects—size, character, etc.,—*can be tolerated.* It is not always necessary to find every defect of every kind.

(f) What is the service of the part—if it is critical even the most minute defects may be damaging. In this case the most sensitive method available probably should be used.

(g) Parts that have been in service and are suspected of being cracked may present peculiar conditions which may affect the choice.

(h) Size and number of parts to be inspected may impose operational limitations restricting the choice.

(i) Rate at which inspection must be made may be a factor.

(j) Availability of equipment or facilities may be a factor.

(k) Cost may be a factor.

16. AVAILABLE CHOICES. There are only two types of *penetrants* available today, namely

(a) Color-contrast types.

(b) Fluorescent types.

There are numerous special penetrants and tracer additives, but these too are either color-contrast or fluorescent. And basically there are only three fundamentally different *methods* of penetrant inspection in use commercially from which to choose. These are:

(a) Wipe (with or without solvent) and solvent developer.

(b) Water-wash.

(c) Post-emulsify and water-wash.

To these might be added special methods and techniques available for special materials and conditions.

There are, of course, numerous variations of materials and techniques within these basic methods. These are, however, more of the nature of operating variations than of fundamental method differences. The decision must be made as to exactly which of several penetrants of a given type to use—which developer—which emulsifier. Also one must determine what kind of equipment is desirable —drying means—inspection area—black light type—all these must be selected before actual inspection can begin. But the first choice has to be made among the above listed basic methods.

17. COMPARISON OF ADVANTAGES AND DISADVANTAGES OF PENETRANT METHODS. For purpose of comparing the basic penetrant methods, one with the other, a tabulation follows giving in summary their outstanding good points and weaknesses. In this tabulation penetrant methods as a group are not being compared with other types of nondestructive defect-detecting methods, but only among themselves.

FLUORESCENT WATER-WASH PENETRANTS.	
Advantages	*Disadvantages*
Brilliant, self illuminated indications. Fluorescence insures good visibility. Single step process. Fast—economical of time. Good on wide range of defects. Easily washes with water. Easily adaptable to many small parts. Good on rough surfaces. Good on key ways and threads. Relatively inexpensive.	Not reliable in finding scratches and shallow surface discontinuities. Affected by acids, chromates. Not reliable on anodized surfaces. Not reliable on second or third running of parts. Susceptible to over-washing. Water-contamination may destroy usefulness of the penetrant.
FLUORESCENT POST-EMULSIFICATION PENETRANTS.	
More brilliant than most water-wash formulas. Fluorescence insures high visibility. Highest sensitivity for very fine defects. Good on wide shallow defects. Washes well after emulsification. High production, especially on large parts. Short penetration time. Normally not affected by acids, chromates or anodizing. Parts can be re-run. Great brilliance permits use in field with minimum light exclusion for some applications. Not vulnerable to over-washing.	A two-step process. Emulsifier application requires additional equipment. Not as good as water-wash on threads, key ways and rough surfaces. Materials are more costly.

Color-Contrast Penetrants.	
Advantages	*Disadvantages*
No black light needed. No water required. Highly portable. Excellent for spot-checking. Parts can be re-run. Good on anodized parts.	Less sensitive for very fine defects. Visibility of indications limited. Must have white developer background against which to view indications. Red dye is "messy."

NOTE: The water-wash and post-emulsification versions of color-contrast penetrants have the advantages and disadvantages of their fluorescent counterparts except in the matter of visibility and sensitivity. The above listed *disadvantages* apply to all color-contrast versions.

Special Penetrants.	
Designed to meet special conditions not met by standard penetrants. May be only way to get a particular job done.	Not always readily available. Technique of use not the same as for standard penetrants. Sensitivity may be limited by special requirements.

Special Methods.	
May solve an inspection problem which normal methods are unable to do.	Equipment and materials not readily available. Evaluation of method necessary in every case.

18. General Discussion of Method Choice. From what has been said it must be clear that the decision as to how to proceed with a given inspection problem to obtain the best possible results with penetrants is not always an easy one. There are many factors that must be understood and balanced, and sometimes a compromise must be made because of some limitation imposed by circumstances or environment.

The level of sensitivity required for the type of defect expected, should first be established. This should be such as to give the assurance that, if no indications are produced, defects which cannot be tolerated are not present. The actual procedure selected should then be the one most easily applied under the conditions that exist. If highest possible sensitivity for fine and for open defects is demanded, then the post-emulsification method would probably be selected. If parts are small a standard inspection unit would be used, but if parts are very large, the expendable technique might be best and most economical.

In some cases there may be a lack of materials or facilities to perform the inspection in the most desirable or convenient, or most economical way, and a compromise may be necessary. If, for example, no power source is available from which to operate a black light, or if no black light is at hand, the fluorescent penetrants cannot be used even if it is most desirable to do so, and in such a circumstance the best possible job must be done with a color-contrast kit. Sometimes limitations imposed by the environment may be deciding. For example, flammable penetrants may not be permissible in certain areas, and water-base materials must be used; or a special formulation is demanded, as in the inspection of liquid oxygen systems where organic combustible substances must be scrupulously excluded. Some metals are liable to damage by the sulphur contained in many penetrants and emulsifiers, and in such instances the choice may be limited to available penetrants containing no sulphur, even though these may not be the most sensitive possible for the type of defects sought.

If the defects sought are of a type easily found, a less sensitive method may be employed. In such a case speed, convenience or cost may be the dominant factors in a choice. But it must be apparent from this discussion that, underlying every choice are the two basic considerations—namely, the type of defect sought and the level of sensitivity needed to assure that with no indications there are no defects of that type.

19. STEPS IN MAKING A CHOICE. From the point of view of what *can* be found given a free choice of methods and materials, the character of the defect is obviously controlling. However, the choice may then be modified by a consideration of what *needs* to be found as against what *can* be found. Here expediency as well as cost may further influence the choice.

Given, therefore, a type of defect to be detected, the first consideration is what is the best method most likely to find it. The second consideration is the feasibility of using that method from technical or economic standpoints. If the ideal method is considered to be not feasible, then second—and third—choice methods must be looked at and a decision reached by balancing all factors.

20. DETECTABILITY OF SPECIFIC TYPES OF DEFECTS. In view of the above discussion, let us now look at the several defects of our original classification from the standpoint: "how may they be best detected?"

21. FINE, TIGHT SURFACE CRACKS. Such cracks may be shallow or deep, but their most significant characteristic is their very small and tight surface opening. Deep cracks of this type—once well penetrated—may provide more of a reservoir of penetrant, and may therefore be easier to show than very shallow ones. The following penetrant system requirements are necessary for optimum detectability:

(a) High penetrating ability is essential. For this reason water-wash types of penetrant are less desirable than those incorporating no emulsifier in their formulation. The post-emulsification type penetrants as well as normal color-contrast penetrants meet this requirement.

(b) Maximum visibility and contrast of indications are needed in this instance. The need becomes more critical as the very fine tight cracks we are seeking to detect are less and less deep. For a given width, the shallower the crack the less

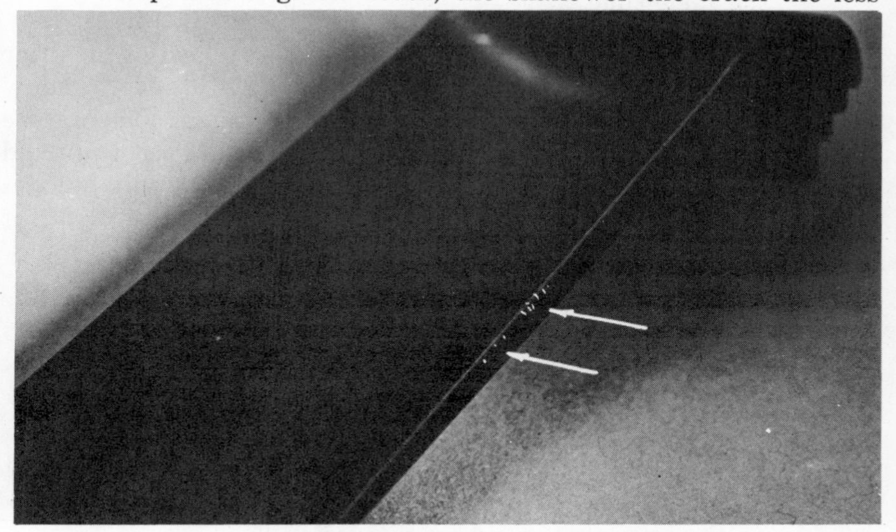

Fig. 100—Indications of very fine tight cracks.

penetrant it will hold. So the greater the fluorescing ability of whatever penetrant reappears at the crack edges, the more readily will the indication be seen. Color-contrast penetrants are practically excluded by this requirement, and the most brilliant of the post-emulsification type fluorescent penetrants would be the proper choice.

(c) Penetration time should be long in all cases, and in critical cases this may be as much as 24 hours with the part fully immersed in penetrant for the entire time. Sometimes such aids to penetration as the vacuum or the vacuum-pressure technique may be worth while (See Chap. 6, Sec. 6d) : or possibly the use of ultrasonic vibration might be helpful.

(d) Washing or cleaning should be *very* thorough in order to eliminate *all* confusing background. Over-washing of P. E. penetrants is a minimum hazard with the very fine tight cracks, since neither emulsifier or water will have much tendency to enter the fine, penetrant-filled cracks. However, neither the use of very heavy pressure spray-washing nor the use of very hot water is recommended as a means of securing a fluorescence-free background. The preferable method, if difficulty is had, as with rough surfaces, is to lengthen somewhat the emulsification time, provided of course that wide open defects are not also being sought at the same time.

(e) Drying time should not be cut short, as the heat of the drier helps to drive penetrant out of the crack. However, unduly prolonged drying may be harmful, since high temperature drives off the more volatile components of the penetrant and thereby reduces its fluidity. Whenever the minute amount of penetrant at a very fine crack loses all fluidity it cannot be picked up and spread by developer.

(f) Developer should be carefully applied so as not to produce too thick a coat. This precaution applies to both wet and dry developers. Too much developer will prevent minute amounts of penetrant from forming a visible indication. The need for a heavier developer coat, to produce an opaque white background when color-contrast penetrants are used, is another reason for not selecting the color-contrast method in the critical case we are discussing.

(g) Developer *time* should be as long as feasible—up to several hours before inspection.

(h) Black light intensity should be as high as possible, since fluorescent brilliance of an indication can be increased many times by increasing the black light radiation used to energize it.

(i) Eyes of inspectors should be fully dark-adapted before attempting any inspection.

(j) Inspection in full darkness is desirable. Indications may still be faint, even after all the above precautions, and if they are missed in the end due to less-than-optimum inspection conditions, the whole inspection has been nullified.

22. BROAD, OPEN SURFACE DEFECTS. Defects of this type may be shallow or relatively deep. Their significant characteristic is their *width,* which tends to permit penetrant to be removed in any cleaning operation. If scratches and other surface marks of similar nature are *not* significant, then the removal of penetrant from them is desirable, so as to reduce the amount of non-relevant background. But when such surface marks are the object of the inspection, all precautions must be taken to insure that penetrant is not removed during cleaning.

(a) High penetrating ability is not needed for finding the wide type of defect. Required is a penetrant or technique which permits general cleaning of the surface without removing penetrant from the significant defects. Water-wash type penetrants, with emulsifier incorporated in their formula, are *not* suitable for this purpose. Solvent cleaning is equally unusable since it will quickly dissolve the indicating substances from the broad, open defects.

The post-emulsification method was devised initially to solve the problem of reliably indicating the shallow, wide open defect, and it is the only standard technique which is generally applicable. In some special cases a wipe-off technique is practical, but smooth surfaces are essential and false indications are a hazard.

(b) *Extreme* brilliance is not necessary for most broad defects since the volume of available penetrant at an indication is usually quite large. On the other hand, in some critical parts,

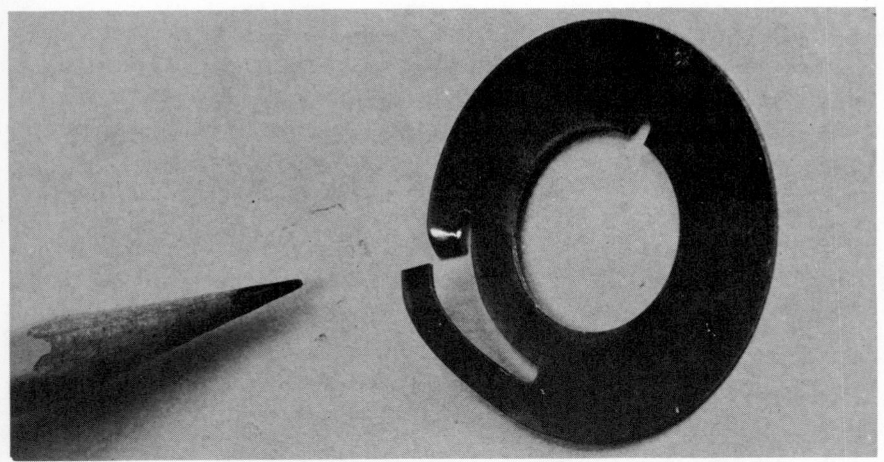

Fig. 101—Indications of broad-open defects in steel stamping.

like gas turbine blades, very fine folds and nicks are significant. In these cases the defect may be extremely minute, so that maximum brilliance again becomes a vital factor.

(c) Penetration time may be short, since there is usually no problem in penetrating this broad type of defect even if deep. However, if, as is sometimes the case, very fine tight defects are being sought at the same time, then the rules for finding such fine defects, which call for long penetration time, must be followed.

(d) Emulsification time is *critical,* and must not be prolonged beyond the *minimum* to secure a clean background surface.

(e) Drying time should also be kept to the minimum necessary to dry the surface, so as to preserve the fluidity of the penetrant in defects to as great a degree as possible.

(f) Developing time usually need not be prolonged.

(g) Black light intensity should be normal, unless very minute defects of this type are also being sought, as in gas turbine blades, in which case *extra high* intensities are desirable.

(h) Inspection conditions should be normal except that darker-than-normal inspection areas may be indicated when very minute defects are also being sought. Great care must be taken to distinguish between a real or significant indication of a defect and a non-relevant patch of penetrant remaining from poor washing.

CHAPTER 12
DETECTABLE DEFECTS

23. SURFACE CRACKS IN GENERAL. Most surface defects are neither very fine and very tight, nor are they broad and open. The defects discussed in the foregoing two sections are at the two extremes of dimensional characteristics. Actually, we are more often met with surface defects whose characteristics lie between.

What are the dimensional limits of these two types? A crack .0001″ or less wide is certainly fine and tight. At a width of .001″ it is not especially fine or tight from a penetrant inspection standpoint; and at .002″ width it is no longer in the tight class.

On the other hand, the term "broad and open" is perhaps more relative than definite in its dimensional implications. A defect .002″ wide and .01″ or more deep is not in this category; but one .002″ wide and .002″ deep certainly approaches it. Although the post-emulsification method may not be necessary in the .002″ x .002″ case, still, overwashing of a water-wash penetrant could wash out the indication. A defect .003″ or .004″ wide and .002″ deep would unquestionably be classed as "broad and open."

The determining consideration for this type of defect is therefor more a matter of *relative* width and depth, at least until width gets down to .001″ or less.

It may be safely stated, then, that most defects found with penetrants are at neither of the dimensional extremes and are therefore usually satisfactorily found by highly brilliant water-wash types of penetrant. As the finer cracks are sought, whether deep or shallow, or as the shallower but not-so-fine defects are important, the post-emulsification technique is the only safe method to use.

24. POROSITY. If porosity is wholly subsurface, it cannot be found with penetrants unless it has been exposed by machining. However, porosity often times has minute channels connecting its cavities to the surface, and this type can be readily located. This type of porosity is common in aluminum and magnesium sand castings. Sometimes it is very fine—i.e., the individual gas bubbles are very small, but they are still large in volume as compared to the volume of a fine, tight crack.

In most castings these defects are relatively clean and easily penetrated. However, in magnesium sand castings the porosity may be clogged with oxide. Some foundries clean such castings with acid before penetrant inspection, to remove the oxide. When this is done the castings should be *thoroughly* washed to remove all trace of acid, and dried preferably with heat.

(a) High penetrating ability is usually not required to locate porosity. Even though the opening to the surface often is very small, the porous cavities usually lie *close to the surface* (the condition is referred to as surface porosity), and therefore the small surface openings lead quickly into the larger reservoirs of the porous cavities themselves.

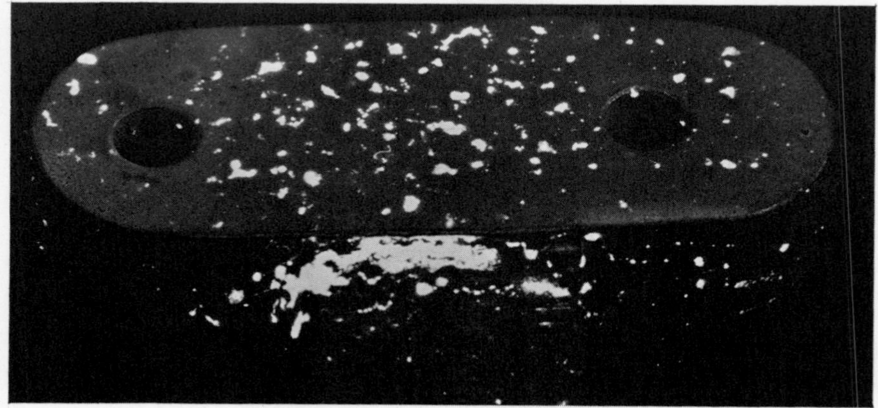

Fig. 102—Indications of surface porosity.

Normally there is no particular problem in locating this type of defect, and in nearly all cases a high-brilliance, water-wash fluorescent penetrant is satisfactory. If acid cleaning precedes the penetrant inspection the post-emulsification method may be preferable. Color-contrast penetrants also will usually perform well on all but very fine micro-porosity.

(b) Penetrating time required is usually quite short.

(c) Washing should be thorough and is usually not critical, since the reservoir of penetrant in the subsurface openings is not easily reached and removed by water through the fine surface leads.

(d) The drying time should be minimal to reduce early and rapid bleeding of penetrant from the sub-surface cavities to the surface. With very fine micro-porosity, the drying time may be longer, for not much penetrant is available to come out and cause excessive spreading due to the smallness of the cavities.

(e) Developing time should be minimal, again to reduce time for bleeding. In many cases development is almost a superfluous step, except in the instance of micro-porosity.

(f) Inspection is easy but *should be made promptly* after drying so that the indications are viewed before they have spread excessively due to bleeding of the large volume of penetrant from below the surface. If inspected promptly the definition of the indications is preserved, and interpretation as to the size and extent, as well as the exact location of the porous area, is more accurate. The extent and rapidity of the bleeding are also significant factors in judging the size and character of the defect.

25. SUBSURFACE DEFECTS. As has been said repeatedly, if discontinuities are actually completely subsurface penetrant methods are not applicable. If, however, such subsurface discontinuities are cut into during machining or are brought to the surface by some other process, then their detection with penetrant follows the same criteria as any surface discontinuity. For example, Fig. 103 shows

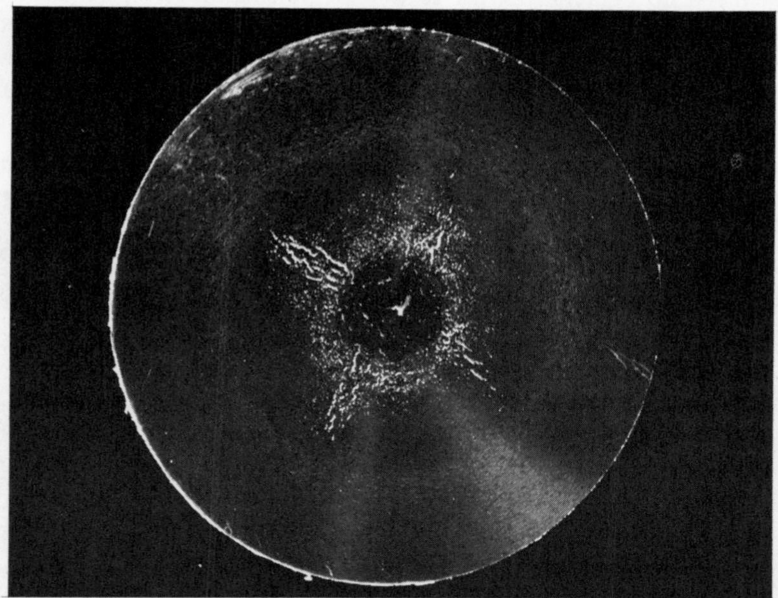

Fig. 103—Indications of bursts in stainless steel disk, 6 inches in diameter, originally wholly subsurface in the round bar.

bursts in a stainless steel disc. The disc was cut from a forged bar, the internal bursts having been produced in the forging operation. When the bar was sliced to make the discs, the defect was easily detected with penetrants.

26. THROUGH-CRACKS OR LEAKS. This classification of defects differs from the general classes of surface discontinuities only in that the crack or other opening passes completely from one surface to another. Such a defect can be found—as a surface defect—usually on *either* surface. However, when the fact that the opening does or does not pass from one surface to another becomes important (as a crack in the wall of a tank), the penetrant method provides an easy and sensitive means of demonstrating this fact. Leak detection is an important area of penetrant testing and will be discussed at length in Chapter 14. Special penetrants and special techniques are used, differing in many cases quite widely from those used in the normal search for discontinuities.

27. FALSE INDICATIONS. In any discussion of indications of defects with nondestructive testing methods, it must always be recognized that all indications are not necessarily indications of significant discontinuities or defects. There are always conditions present that may give false or pseudo-indications. Such indications may have no relation at all to actual discontinuities, or they may be caused by discontinuities entirely non-relevant to the strength or service integrity of the material or part in question. It is the old problem, common in electronic instruments, of the "signal-to-noise" ratio.

The "noise", or truly *false* indications in penetrant testing,

Fig. 104—Example of fluorescent background from poor washing.

consist of those spots of fluorescence or color which may occur on the surface of a part but are not caused by any discontinuity of any kind. Background spots of fluorescence due to poor or incomplete washing are the most prolific source of such "noise." Rough surfaces tested by the post-emulsification method may be hard to wash and such a background may be left. Persistent difficulty in washing rough surfaces may preclude use of the post-emulsification method in such instances. Penetrant on the hands of the inspector or picked up on a dirty inspection table may put fluorescent marks on a part which have no meaning whatever; or a part with a heavy indication may touch another part and leave such a mark.

The poor-wash background can and should be spotted by the operator *at the time of washing,* and the part dried and re-run at once. The accidental contamination of surfaces must be avoided by cleanliness and care on the part of the operator. Another cause of false indications not so easy to avoid, is the presence of burned-in sand or carbon on the surface, or of any other surface condition that absorbs and holds penetrants and resists washing.

Lint and dirt in the penetrant bath can be a source of false indications. Lint may attach itself to roughness of the surface or to an edge on the part being tested and may not be removed by washing. A fluorescent thread looks remarkably like an indication.

28. NON-RELEVANT INDICATIONS. The other group of indications, that must be watched for and recognized for what they are, are caused by actual non-relevant discontinuities which are present by reason of the design or construction of the part. These are true indications, but the conditions they indicate are non-relevant so far as defects that may be present are concerned.

Threads, key ways and sharp fillets may retain penetrant at their base and give indications. This is, in a sense, due only to poor washing, but does happen with the best of care. Post-emulsification techniques aggravate this tendency—so much so that it is a recognized draw-back to the use of this technique on such areas. An indication at the base of a thread or in a fillet, therefore, must be carefully examined before it is accepted as evidence of a true crack. This is all the more important because cracks—especially heat-treating cracks or fatigue cracks—often *do* occur at such locations, and are serious.

Another common non-relevant indication is caused by forced fits or other non-welded or unbrazed joints which exist where

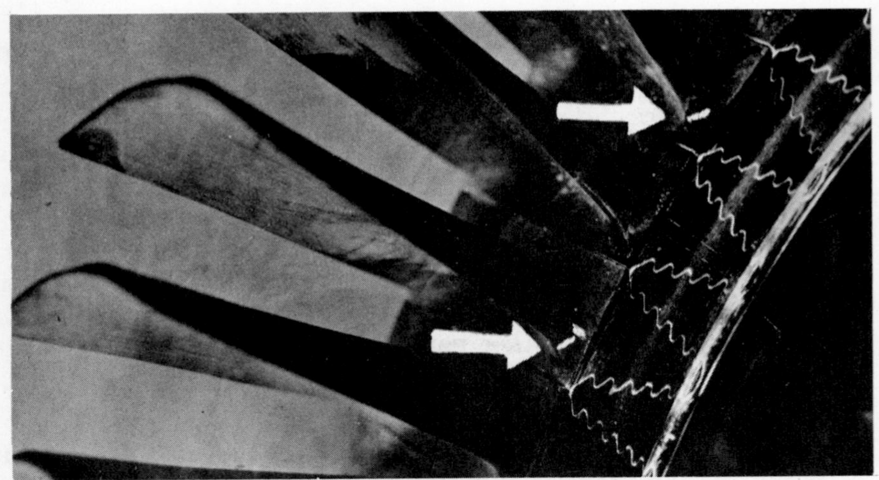

Fig. 105—Non-relevant indication of "Christmas tree" joint between jet turbine wheel and blades. Arrows point to indications of true cracks.

parts of an assembly are joined together. A gear pressed onto a shaft, or a spline or key joint, commonly provide a fine opening which penetrant can enter just as it does a crack, and good indications of the joint are produced. This type of non-relevant indication is, however, easily recognized since the construction of the part at once shows the real cause of the indication.

29. SPECIAL PROBLEMS. It has sometimes happened that cracks or other discontinuities known to be present have produced no penetrant indications. As an example, etching has revealed the presence of certain cracks in aluminum engine parts which did not show with penetrants during overhaul. If there actually is a crack present there is always a logical reason why penetrants do not show it. It has been demonstrated that penetrants can and do enter openings at least as small as 5 millionths of an inch wide, unless prevented by some circumstance. The greatest danger of failure of the method is that some material already fills the crack. In the case of the engine piston the filler was baked engine "varnish". In a forging lap the filler may be metallic oxide, in other cases acids or water may be in the crack.

Sometimes with the understanding of conditions that will prevent the formation of indications, precautions or special cleaning steps will cure the difficulty. On occasion a special technique or a special penetrant can be devised to overcome the trouble. But sometimes resort must be had to an entirely different nondestructive testing method.

CHAPTER 13

INDUSTRIAL APPLICATIONS

1. GENERAL. Up to this point we have been concerned with the penetrant testing method from the points of view of what it is, how it works and what it can do. Not much has been said as to how it is actually used in industry. To round out this discussion, it seems pertinent to describe in detail some of the many areas of industry in which penetrant inspection has proved to be particularly useful.

Nondestructive testing has become a tool of increasing value in industrial applications, and one the value of which has become increasingly appreciated by industry. Nondestructive tests are used with three different philosophies, each having a different principal objective.

One approach is to use these tests to find flaws to the end that the finished product goes to the customer and into service as free as possible from all defects that would interfere with its satisfactory performance. This objective alone would justify a large effort and expenditure for inspection and for testing equipment, and is in fact the end result desired by all who seek to supply reliable quality products. But if applied *only* to this end, much of what can be realized from the use of these methods is lost.

The second philosophy does not reject the first, but adds the concept that by applying nondestructive tests at various strategic times during processing, an actual dollar profit will result, and at the same time the original objective will still be reached. The basic principle of this second approach is to apply nondestructive testing (using whatever method may be applicable) at such times that the tests locate defective material *as soon as it becomes defective,* and permit its removal from further processing before any additional work is done on it. Thus production man-hours are devoted to producing usable product, and not to producing a product, already defective, which would be rejected as scrap on final inspection. Penetrants, along with other nondestructive tests, are used in this way in most industries.

The third philosophy, which results in substantial returns, simply makes systematic use of the information developed under the first two. By tabulating and analyzing the nature and times of occurrence of the various defects found during manufacture, raw materials may be better selected, designs improved and processes corrected to the end that the incidence of defects is reduced, production cost lowered and the service life of the product extended.

When penetrants are used to find cracks which develop in service, the prime purpose is to avoid failures during operation, with their resultant losses. But here also, by intelligent use of data as they accumulate regarding location and character of defects found, permanent improvement in materials and designs can be made if the information is fed back to the proper places.

More and more, industry is realizing the value of this return which can be had from a proper application of nondestructive tests, including penetrants, and this is reflected in the constantly growing use of these methods.

2. WHERE PENETRANTS ARE USED. Penetrant applications can be grouped in a number of ways. One grouping is by the types of product on which the method is used—such as castings, forgings, tubing, etc. (See Chapter 12.) Then, certain industries which employ these products have problems peculiar to their type of use and therefore have aplications which are special to their operations—such as aircraft overhaul, oil refining, railroad maintenance, etc. In the following sections, uses in both groupings will be listed and described. Most of the applications described are on metals, although applications on some other types of materials on which penetrant testing is used are also included.

3. CASTINGS. When metals are cast in molds and solidify from the molten state into substantially finished shape they are subject to a variety of defects which are in general peculiar to the casting process regardless of kind of metal, or size or shape of the article cast. Following are the principal defects which may occur in almost any type of casting:

Shrinkage cracks

Micro-shrinkage

Porosity

Cold shuts

Surface sand inclusion

Blows or blow-holes

Age cracking from residual stresses

Handling cracks

4. CASTING CONTROL. In addition to inspecting production castings for defects, a most important use of penetrants in the foundry is to test pilot runs to make sure sound castings can be produced from the mold. Relocation of gates and risers follows such pilot inspections, if evidences of porosity are detected—or design of the casting may be altered if the pilot run indicates proneness to shrinkage or cracking. Radiography is frequently a companion tool to penetrants in this preliminary testing program.

When the production run is started, sample testing usually is sufficient to insure a sound product, although critical castings are quite commonly inspected with penetrant, 100%. Special automated equipment has been designed and is in use to make this procedure economically feasible.

5. ALUMINUM SAND CASTINGS. These are examined to locate shrink cracks, surface porosity or micro-shrinkage, cold shuts

Fig. 106—Shrink cracks in rough-cast aluminum pressure-switch housing.

and gross porosity. Water-wash techniques are usually employed since most of these defects are clean and not too minute. In critical cases the post-emulsification method is used, primarily to secure the high brightness indications which it produces.

Figure 106 shows indications of shrink cracks around bosses

and other changes of section in a pressure switch housing in the rough-cast condition.

6. MAGNESIUM SAND CASTINGS. Magnesium castings are subject to most of the same defects as those of aluminum. Watched for are cold shuts, cracks, blows, shrinkage and dross. Micro-shrinkage is especially common in magnesium sand castings. This type of defect usually gives large indications, since the very fine surface openings communicate to larger voids immediately under the surface, which act as reservoirs to hold appreciable amounts of penetrant. Inspection techniques are usually simple and, except for cases

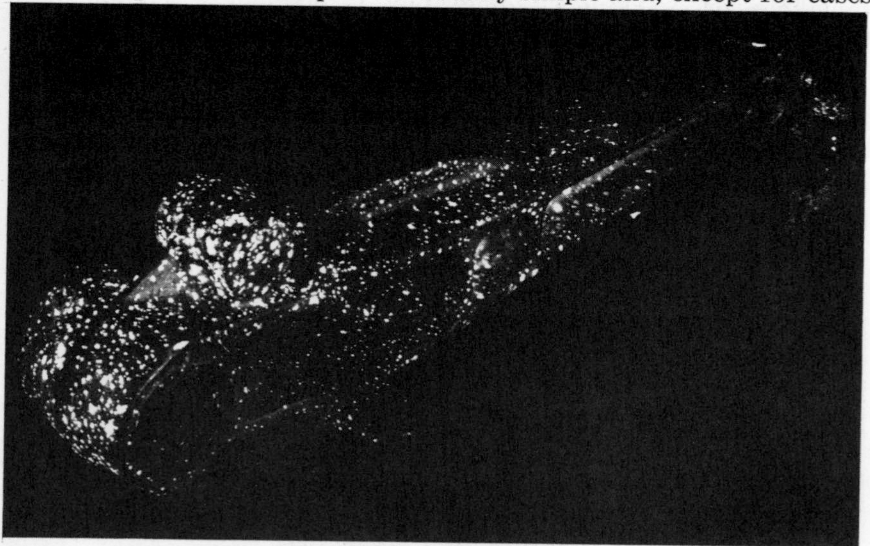

Fig. 107—Surface porosity on a magnesium sand casting.

where the micro-porosity is very critical and extremely fine, water-wash penetrants are used. (See Chapter 12, Section 24.) In some cases cold shuts can also be very tight. If important, the post-emulsification technique may be required.

Figure 107 shows the fluorescent penetrant indications of shrinkage porosity or surface porosity on a magnesium sand casting.

7. DIE CASTINGS. Precision castings in metal molds are made with aluminum, magnesium, white metal and various other alloys. The process is different from sand casting, but many of the problems are the same. Principal defects watched for are shrinkage and porosity, though the latter is much less a factor than in sand castings. Either water-wash or post-emulsification penetrants are used here, depending on whether or not the defects are large or very fine and difficult to locate.

8. INVESTMENT CASTINGS. These are precision castings often made from high-melting point heat-resistant and corrosion resistant alloys. Gas turbine blades are often cast, using this process. Defects, if present, are serious and often difficult to locate. Very fine cracks may be partially filled, which makes them difficult to find. The highest sensitivity post-emulsification penetrants are usually employed.

9. MISCELLANEOUS NON-FERROUS AND ALLOY CASTINGS. In addition to those metals already mentioned, castings are made from many other non-ferrous metals and alloys. These include copper, brass, Monel metal, beryllium, titanium and many others. Stainless steel and other corrosion resistant alloys are also often cast. Defects sought with penetrants are the usual ones, although age-cracking due to residual stresses is perhaps more prevalent in some of these alloys. Aluminum and magnesium alloys are also liable to this type of cracking. Usually water-wash penetrants are satisfactory for such inspections except in critical cases, when P.E. methods should be used.

Fig. 108 illustrates cracks found in small stainless steel investment castings.

Fig. 109 shows age-cracking found in a small cast magnesium fitting.

10. MALLEABLE IRON CASTINGS. Penetrants are sometimes used in preference to magnetic particle or other methods for the inspection of malleable iron castings. This is for the reason that the defects sought are reliably located with penetrants (which is in many cases *not* true on ferrous materials, See Chapter 2, Section 4) and on complex shapes the penetrant process is much more rapid. Fluorescent water-wash penetrants are used, with automatic equipment, for high volume inspection.

Fig. 110 shows an installation where this method is used for receiving inspection of large numbers of malleable iron castings of widely varying sizes and shapes, in a large middle-west plant, where farm equipment is manufactured. Castings may be for small levers and brake pedals up to gear case housings and other large and complex shapes. Smaller castings are automatically processed

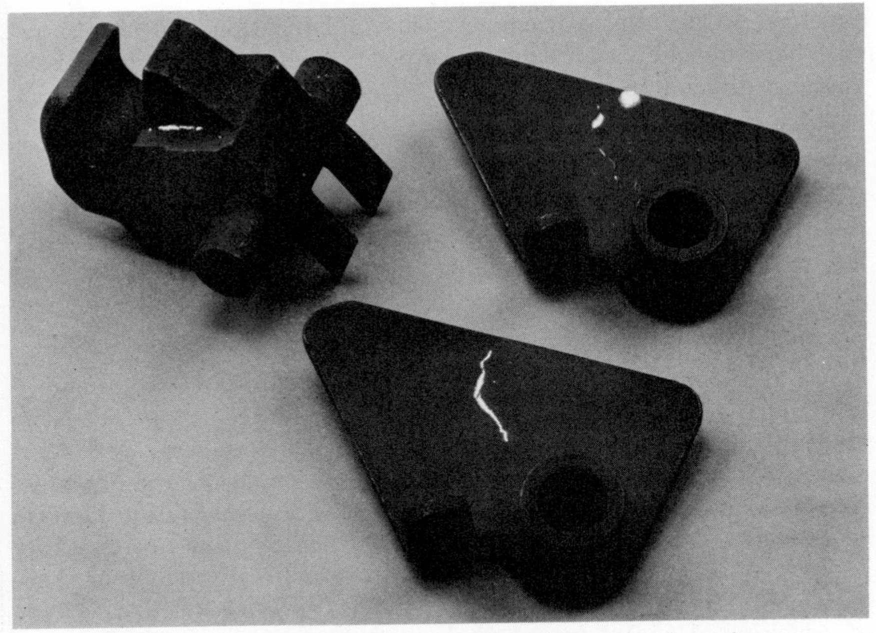

Fig. 108—Cracks in small stainless steel investment castings.

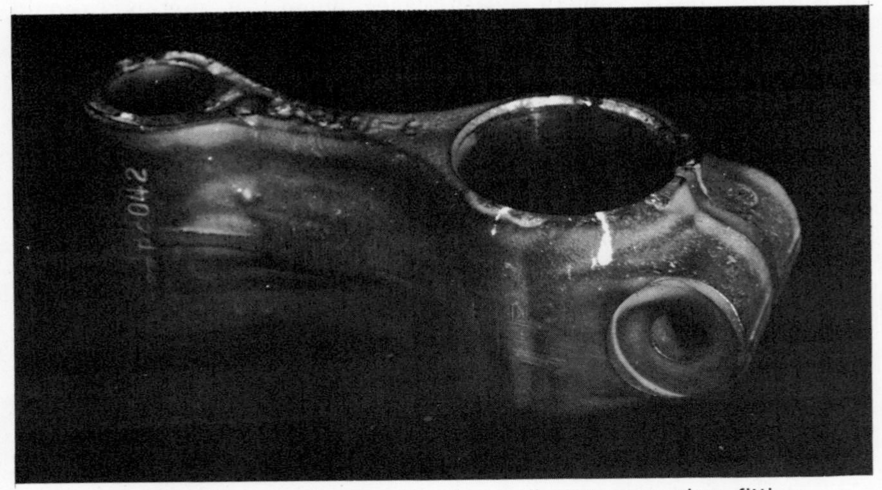

Fig. 109—Season-aging cracking in small cast magnesium fitting.

through penetrant, wash, developer and drying stations and delivered to the inspector ready for examination for indications. Large castings may be processed by hand through penetrant, wash and developer stations, then passed into the drier and on to the inspector automatically.

CHAPTER 13
INDUSTRIAL APPLICATIONS

(Courtesy Caterpillar Tractor Co., Inc.)

Fig. 110—Automatic unit for the inspection of malleable iron castings.

11. FORGINGS. Numerous non-magnetic metals and alloys are forged into a wide variety of parts, many for highly critical service in automotive, aircraft, jet engine, nuclear and space applications. Included are aluminum and magnesium alloys, stainless steel, heat resistant alloys, and alloys designed for high strength at high temperatures. Some ferrous alloys used in aircraft and missile components are not consistent or predictable in magnetic properties, so that high sensitivity fluorescent penetrants are regularly used for their inspection instead of the magnetic particle method.

12. JET TURBINE BLADES. (Also referred to as "buckets") One of the most critical parts and one which presents very difficult inspection problems is the forged jet turbine blade. The greatest problem in this instance is the detection of shallow laps, often oxide-filled and practically impossible to locate using normal water-wash

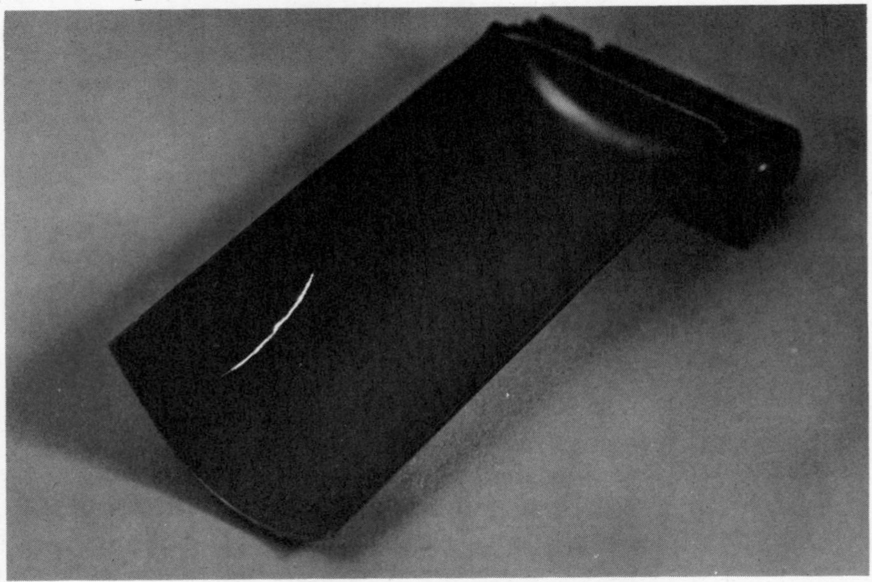

Fig. 111—Forging lap located on jet turbine blade by post-emulsification technique.

techniques. The post-emusification method for applying fluorescent penetrants was developed in order to solve this inspection problem, and such laps as well as other shallow surface blemishes—even surface nicks—are now detected by this process. (See also Section 26.)

Fig. 111 illustrates defects of this type located by the P.E. technique.

CHAPTER 13

INDUSTRIAL APPLICATIONS

13. FORGING DEFECTS. In addition to laps, other forging defects are tears, bursts, flakes, seams, laminations and pipe, the latter three originating in the blank and not in the forging process itself. Age cracking from residual stresses also may occur in some forged alloys. The P.E. technique is quite commonly used in forging inspection because of the tendency of surface flaws to be filled with

Fig. 112—Forging crack in aluminum landing gear cap for helicopter.

oxide or other foreign matter. Such conditions as flakes, laminations and pipe are, of course, not found with penetrants unless or until they have been made into surface discontinuities, as by cutting billets into blanks or by machining.

Fig. 112 shows a crack in an aluminum forging for a helicopter landing gear cap. This was detected using the P. E. method, after the surface had been anodized.

14. FORGING DIES. Although most forging dies are magnetic, and are best inspected with the magnetic particle method, many new and used dies are inspected for cracks using color-contrast penetrant. Most cracks found are either machined-into flakes, laminations or pipe, or heat treating cracks. These are usually large and open enough to be found easily with color-contrast penetrants.

15. Billet Control. Billets intended for rolling, extruding or forging into quality products are profitably examined with penetrants to locate surface defects so that such conditions can be removed before further processing. Billets or slabs of copper, aluminum, magnesium, brass, bronze and stainless steel may be inspected, using normal fluorescent water-wash penetrants. Surface cracks, seams, slivers and scabs are among the defects which occur. Elimination of seams in the billet stage, for example, assures clean strip for making of welded aluminum tubing. Such inspection on billets is a logical result of the philosophy of eliminating a defect at as early a stage in manufacture as possible.

Fig. 113—Shrink crack in copper billet.

When billets are cut up into forging blanks or extruding blanks, the cropped or cut ends are inspected for pipe or other internal discontinuities, by applying penetrant to the cut surfaces.

Fig. 113 shows shrink cracks in a copper billet which were detected with fluorescent penetrant, thus preventing the production of a defective rolled bar.

16. Rolled Products. All kinds of rolled products are inspected with penetrants for seams primarily, but also for such discontinuities as laps, slivers, laminations and pipe (the latter two on cut ends). Materials may be bars, sheets or strip, of aluminum, magnesium, copper, brass, bronze, stainless steel and many of the "modern" metals, such as titanium and beryllium.

In most cases the standard water-wash fluorescent technique is employed. For production work, where large numbers of fairly long bars must be inspected, special equipment has sometimes proved economical. Fig. 114 illustrates an automatic bar inspection unit that was installed some years ago. Handling and processing is fully

Fig. 114—Automatic bar inspection unit.

automatic, the bars being moved at a pre-determined speed through the steps of penetration, drain, wash, develop, dry and inspect. Inspection under black light is made, using an arrangement of mirrors, so that all surfaces are seen by the inspector as the bar passes before him. Push-button control enables him to sort the bars automatically according to the defects found.

Fig. 115 shows fluorescent indications of seams found in rolled copper commutator bars.

17. FERROUS BARS. Fluorescent penetrants are being used in certain cases to inspect ferrous and alloy bars. In such cases there

Fig. 115—Indications of seams in rolled copper commutator bars.

is an economic or other specific reason for substituting penetrants for the more clearly applicable magnetic particle method, and careful evaluation has demonstrated that the results with penetrants meet all requirements.

In one application penetrants are used because they will distinguish between a true seam and a rolled out inclusion in centerless-ground bars; seams break the surface of the bars and will be shown by penetrants, whereas rolled out inclusions are subsurface. Seams are objectionable, subsurface inclusions are not. In another case tool steel bars, difficult to demagnetize, are examined for seams and cracks with penetrants, thus avoiding the de-magnetization problem.

18. TUBING. Tubing, both welded and seamless, is made from a large variety of non-ferrous or non-magnetic materials. Aluminum, brass, copper and stainless steel tubing have long been used in many applications. The needs of nuclear power technology have added tubing of such metals as zirconium and beryllium or their alloys. Defects sought are seams, pinholes, tears, and various welding defects. A number of different nondestructive tests are employed in testing these products, but penetrants continue in many cases to be used as the only really satisfactory testing means for certain requirements. When it is necessary to know that there are no cracks or pinholes penetrating through the tube wall, penetrant inspection gives a positive answer.

CHAPTER 13

INDUSTRIAL APPLICATIONS

Fig. 116—Automatic unit for seamless steel tubing. Loading side at left.

The use of penetrants is dictated in many other applications by considerations of cost, economy and convenience. For example, in the inspection in production of varying sizes of non-magnetic stainless steel tubing of varying wall thicknesses, no other method has sufficient flexibility at a reasonable cost to find the defects sought.

Figures 116 and 117 show two views of such an installation in an Eastern plant. This unit automatically processes, using the P. E. method, stainless steel tubing in lengths up to 40 feet and in sizes from ½ inch to 10¾ inches O.D. Some of the larger diameter lengths weigh up to 4000 lbs. Processing takes from 3½ to 6 minutes per tube. All operations are fully automatic except the actual inspection. Tubes are conveyed through specially engineered, time-

Fig. 117—Inspection station on automatic tubing unit, showing tube with typical spiral defect.

sequenced flooding stations for penetrant, emulsifier, water-wash and wet developer, and then on through drying and finally to the hooded inspection area. Here, while the tube is power-rotated under a battery of black lights, the inspector marks all indications of seams, cracks or other defects. Run-out rollers remove the tube from the unit and the cycle is repeated on another tube.

19. MISCELLANEOUS SHAPES AND PARTS. Various processes are used to form and shape metals into useable parts. These include extruding, explosion forming, spinning, stamping, drawing and others. Metals involved are stainless steels, aluminum, brass, beryllium-copper and many others. Defects sought are seams, slivers, tears, laminations, aging cracks and pickling cracks, depending on

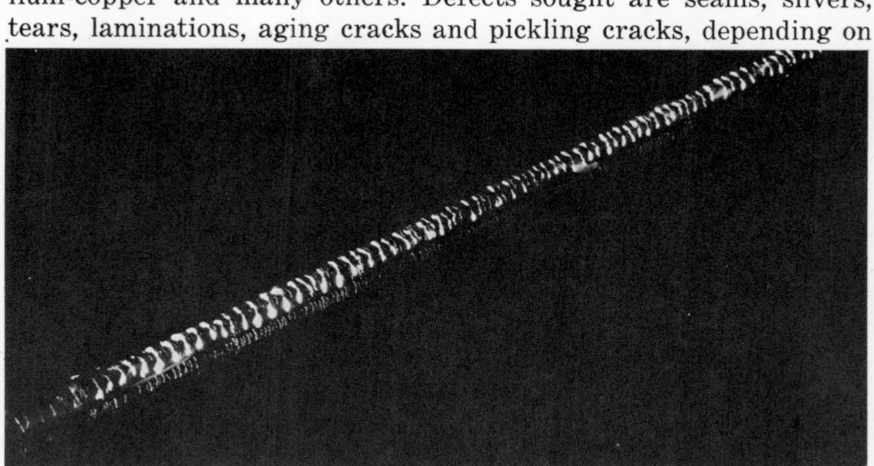

Fig. 118—Fluorescent indications of cracks in extruded aluminum bar.

the process, the metal and its intended use. Color-contrast penetrants are frequently used, as well as water-wash and P. E. fluorescent processes, depending on the sensitivity required and the kind and surface condition of the metal or part. A few examples may be interesting.

Figure 119 shows indications of cracks found in some small beryllium-copper toggle switch springs. The most sensitive fluorescent P. E. method was necessary to find these defects. The parts were immersed in the super-bright penetrant in small quantities in fine-mesh wire baskets. Penetration time was one hour. This was followed by washing with warm water. Dry fluffy developer was used and inspection conducted with maximum exclusion of white light, after a 30-minute developing period.

Cracks resulting from stamping often are wide open, but, as in the case just described, sometimes are very tight. In such cases high sensitivity penetrants offer the only reliable method of detection.

Fig. 120 shows some small stamped steel levers for an electronic communications device, having cracks which were found with fluorescent penetrant. In this case the penetrant was used instead of the magnetic particle method because it was faster and saved

Fig. 119—Cracks found with P.E. in small beryllium-copper toggle switch springs.

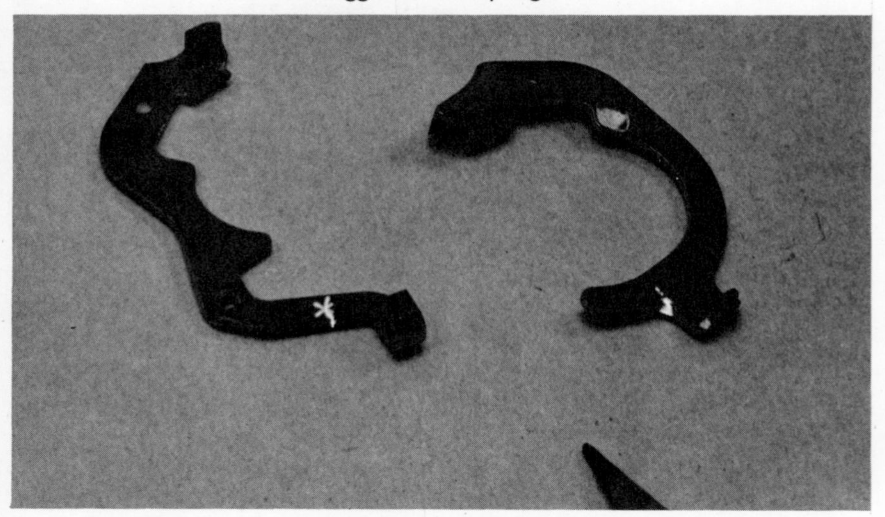

Fig. 120—Cracks in small stamped steel levers for an electronic communications device.

the handling time that would be required to magnetize each small piece. Previous evaluation had indicated that all cracks were found with the penetrant technique.

Fig. 121 shows indications of aging cracks in the rim of a stamped brass bonnet for a gas valve. The cracks are probably the result of residual stresses left from the forming operation.

INDUSTRIAL APPLICATIONS

Fig. 121—Aging cracks in rim of stamped brass bonnet for gas valve.

20. WELDS AND BRAZED JOINTS. Surface cracks or other surface discontinuities in welded joints of non-magnetic metals are most reliably located with penetrants. The same is true of brazed joints, although the metals joined by brazing may be magnetic. Aluminum, stainless steel and heat- or corrosion-resistant alloys are commonly welded, and cracks, lack of bond and surface porosity are defects that are sought.

Carbide and stellite tips are brazed to steel bases or holders, and here the integrity of the brazed joint is highly important. Cracks and lack of bond are defects to be guarded against. Lack of bond between layers of metals, as in clad sheets or strips or lined bearings, is another application of this type.

One of the earliest uses of penetrant testing using black light was for the detection of lack of bond in copper- or silver-lined aircraft engine bearings. This was the "hot oil" method. (See Chapter 1, Section 10). Some examples, taken at random from applications in the welding and brazing field are given below.

Aluminum sheet, butt-welded, is subject to cracking. Sheets may be 1/16″ or more thick, and cracks in these welds are readily located using the standard water-wash fluorescent technique.

In the case of tanks lined with a corrosion-resistant metal, in the petroleum and chemical fields, penetrants are used to locate cracks or other openings in the welded joints between sections of the lining metal, which would permit corrosive liquid to get into the space between the liner and the tank proper.

Fig. 122 shows the inspection of the welded-on corrosion resistant alloy lining in a large pressure vessel. The penetrant used is the standard water-wash type, and is sprayed over the interior of the tank. After a relatively short penetration time (up to 20 minutes), the surfaces are washed down with a hose and allowed to air-dry.

Fig. 122—Cracks and porosity in corrosion-resistant alloy lining welded to inside wall of tank.

Drying can be hastened somewhat with a hot-air blower. Dry developer is applied from a spray gun or bulb applicator, or sometimes with a soft brush, and inspection made with a hand-held "spot" type black light. Large cracks or openings in the welds cause gross indications due to the relatively large volume of penetrant that enters such a defect. Fine cracks which do not penetrate through the weld give fine indications which must be carefully watched for, as they may later progress through the weld and result in a leak.

Lead is being used increasingly as a liner for vessels to contain certain types of corrosive liquids. The joints in the lead lining, welded by a "lead burner," are subject to pinholes or porosity when new, and to cracks or corrosion discontinuities after they have been in service. Penetrant methods are commonly used to detect these defects. Color-contrast penetrants are often very satisfactory for this application. Figure 123 shows a pinhole in the welded

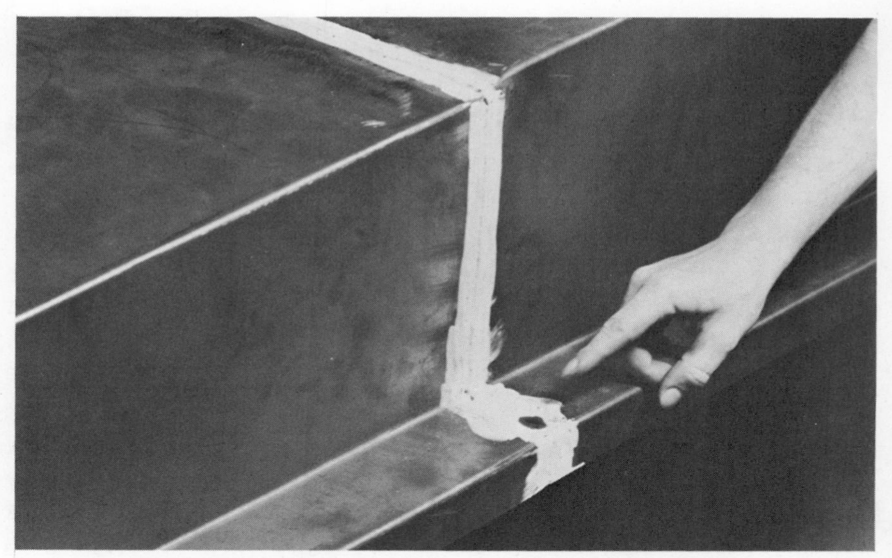

Fig. 123—Color-contrast indication of pinhole leak in seam of open welded tank.

seam of an open tank, found with color-contrast penetrant. The white streak is, of course, the developer coating applied after the excess penetrant has been removed.

Fig. 124 illustrates a number of hard-tipped tools, and shows the indications of cracks or porosity in the brazed joint between the carbide tip and the steel body of the tool. (See also Section 24, this

Fig. 124—Defects in brazed joint between steel body and carbide tip of cutting tools.

chapter.) Standard water-wash techniques are usually satisfactory for detection of defects in the brazed joint, but the post-emulsification method is preferred for cracks in the hard alloy tips.

Penetrants also are used for determining the integrity of soldered joints in such widely varied materials as costume jewelry, cutlery, and printed circuits for electronic assemblies.

21. TUNGSTEN WIRE. Tungsten lead-in wires for electronic tubes are subject to seams, longitudinal cracks, and laps. Electronic methods are being used for this type of inspection but fluorescent penetrants are still used because of their extreme sensitivity. Cracks in the lead-in wires may cause leaky or gassy tubes. (see also chapter 14, Section 11).

The wires are usually in short lengths—a few inches—and are sometimes penetrated in a vacuum. P. E. penetrants are commonly used, although standard water-wash penetrants are satisfactory if vacuum penetration is employed. Washing is done by dipping in water, the wires being held in a basket. Developer powder is poured

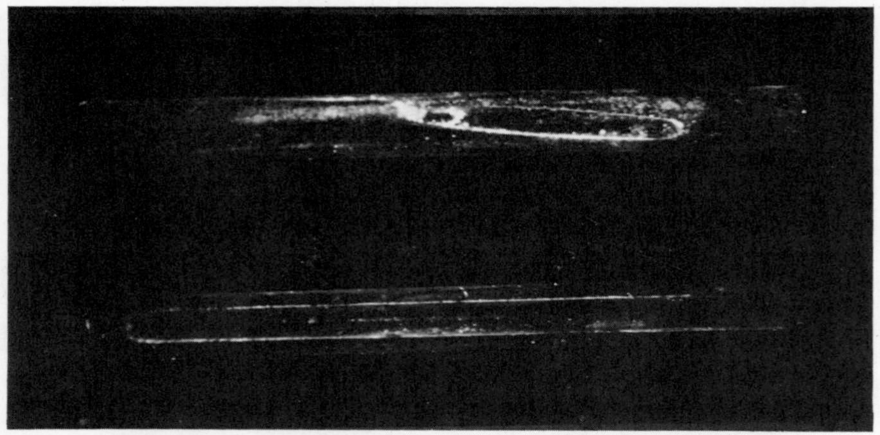

Fig. 125—Seams and laps in tungsten lead-in wires. (Enlarged)

over the wires as they are shaken in the basket, and serves as a drying agent as well as a developer. Inspection is made in a darkroom, and the wires are handled with tongs to prevent smearing of indications. Fig. 125 illustrates some of the extremely fine seams and laps that are located. The photographs are enlarged several times.

22. MISCELLANEOUS MANUFACTURED PARTS. A very large variety of large and small manufactured parts are inspected with penetrants. These may be either magnetic or non-magnetic, although the non-magnetic applications are by far the most numerous. Often, however, economics favor penetrants over magnetic particle methods, as has already been discussed. Sometimes the small portable kits, either of color-contrast or fluorescent penetrants, can be used on widely varying sizes and shapes, or such varying parts may be tested on engineered multi-purpose units.

To attempt to enumerate these applications would be a long and difficult task. Suffice it to say that the manufacturer of miscellaneous parts—frequently small and non-critical—has often improved his product and saved on production costs by an imaginative use of nondestructive testing methods. Among available methods, penetrants offer inexpensive and highly satisfactory means in a great many cases, and find wide application in this field. One manufacturer of pumps, for example, inspects 38 different component parts, including castings, forgings and fittings machined from bar stock, using fluorescent penetrant on an all-purpose unit.

A few out-of-the-ordinary uses for penetrants in this miscellaneous field may illustrate the wide variety of possible applications.

Courtesy Arwood Corp.

Fig. 126—Examples of miscellaneous precision cast parts tested for defects with penetrants.

Among them are such articles as gas pump handles and nozzles, cast white metal fittings for decorative use, die-cast aluminum camera cases and meter housings, sheet metal housings and cases, or cast shapes on which surface imperfections would result in unsightly enameled or plated surfaces. Examples of the latter group are faucets, plumbing fittings, home appliance parts and "appearance" components. The purpose is to reduce incidence of cracks or leakage, or to find surface defects that would make a good, attractive chrome plating job impossible. General hardware items, such as door locks, are often tested for cracks in parts which would cause failures, and for surface defects that would interfere with plating quality.

Even fountain pen tubes have been surface inspected with penetrants before gold-plating, and ceramic hobbyists have used the method for finding cracks in their product after firing.

23. HEAT TREATED PARTS. Small, hard, quenched or case-hardened steel parts are sometimes inspected with fluorescent penetrants. Here again economics favor the mass-handling, semi-automatic technique possible with penetrants, avoiding the need to magnetize each small piece individually as is required if magnetic particles were to be used. It is also true that fine cracks in case-hardened parts may not be well indicated with magnetic particles. Because of the low permeability of the hardened case compared to the much higher permeability of the soft core, leakage fields at fine cracks that do not penetrate beyond the case may be quite weak. Examples are case-hardened steel pins for sprocket chains, and the hardened steel teeth inserts used in large circular saws. High sensitivity penetrants may be needed to locate very fine cracks in some such applications, although normally the standard water-wash process is satisfactory. In the inspection of one type of case-hardened steel pin, however, the cracks were extremely tight at the surface. Measurements showed the surface openings to be of the order of 10^{-5} or 10^{-6} inches—10 millionths of an inch and up. Here the super-bright P. E. penetrant technique was the only effective method of indicating these cracks.

24. TOOLS. Carbide tools are commonly inspected with penetrants for cracks and poor braze. Various hard alloys such as Stellite and cermets are similarly inspected. Manufacturers check such tools for cracks in the original blanks as well as after grinding. Users inspect tools upon receipt.

INDUSTRIAL APPLICATIONS

Fig. 127 shows some very fine grinding cracks on the carbide insert of a cutting tool. Location of these required the highest sensitivity of the P. E. type penetrants.

Fig. 127—Very fine and shallow grinding cracks in carbide tip of cutting tool.

Fig. 128—Cracks in carbide inserts for multiple-head cutting tool.

In the machine shop, color-contrast (dye penetrant) kits are a common and very useful piece of equipment. All kinds of tools—both carbide and alloy steel—may become cracked in re-sharpening operations. Penetrant tests before the tools are again set up on a job may find cracks which could result in costly damage or loss of time. Forming dies can be tested at intervals for cracks without removal from the punch press. Alloy steel or carbide inserts for rotary multiple-head cutters can be similarly checked.

Many kinds of hand tools are also inspected. These are usually such impact tools as hammers and sledges, chisels, star drills, stamps, rivet sets, etc. Manufacturers of such tools are more likely to use the magnetic particle test, but users in small shops make extensive use of color-contrast kits for this purpose.

25. INDIVIDUAL INDUSTRY APPLICATIONS. In the following sections a number of applications in different industries will be described in which penetrants are used on a variety of materials and parts to locate defects which are important or peculiar to those industries.

26. JET ENGINE MANUFACTURE. This industry makes wide use of penetrant inspection in many important applications. It has already been stated that the whole system of post-emulsification penetrant inspection was devised to meet the urgent needs of the gas turbine designers and manufacturers. The turbine wheel of a jet engine revolves at tremendous speeds and stresses set up in the wheel and blades are very high. Any surface irregularity, even if only a small nick, may be a stress-raiser of sufficient severity to cause failure from fatigue. Consequently these blades and wheels are inspected repeatedly before installing in the engine, to insure absence of all surface discontinuities. These may be cracks, folds, laps, tears or porosity, or accidental nicks produced in handling. The blades may be either forged or cast from high-strength heat and corrosion-resistant alloys which are non-magnetic, and magnetic particle inspection is not applicable.

Unfortunately the penetrants available in the early years were water-wash fluorescent and solvent-removed color-contrast types. These did not reliably indicate the presence of very small, very tight cracks, and very shallow and fairly wide laps or folds. The latter are especially serious defects since they often extend below the surface to a considerable depth, but are tightly filled with oxides

CHAPTER 13

INDUSTRIAL APPLICATIONS

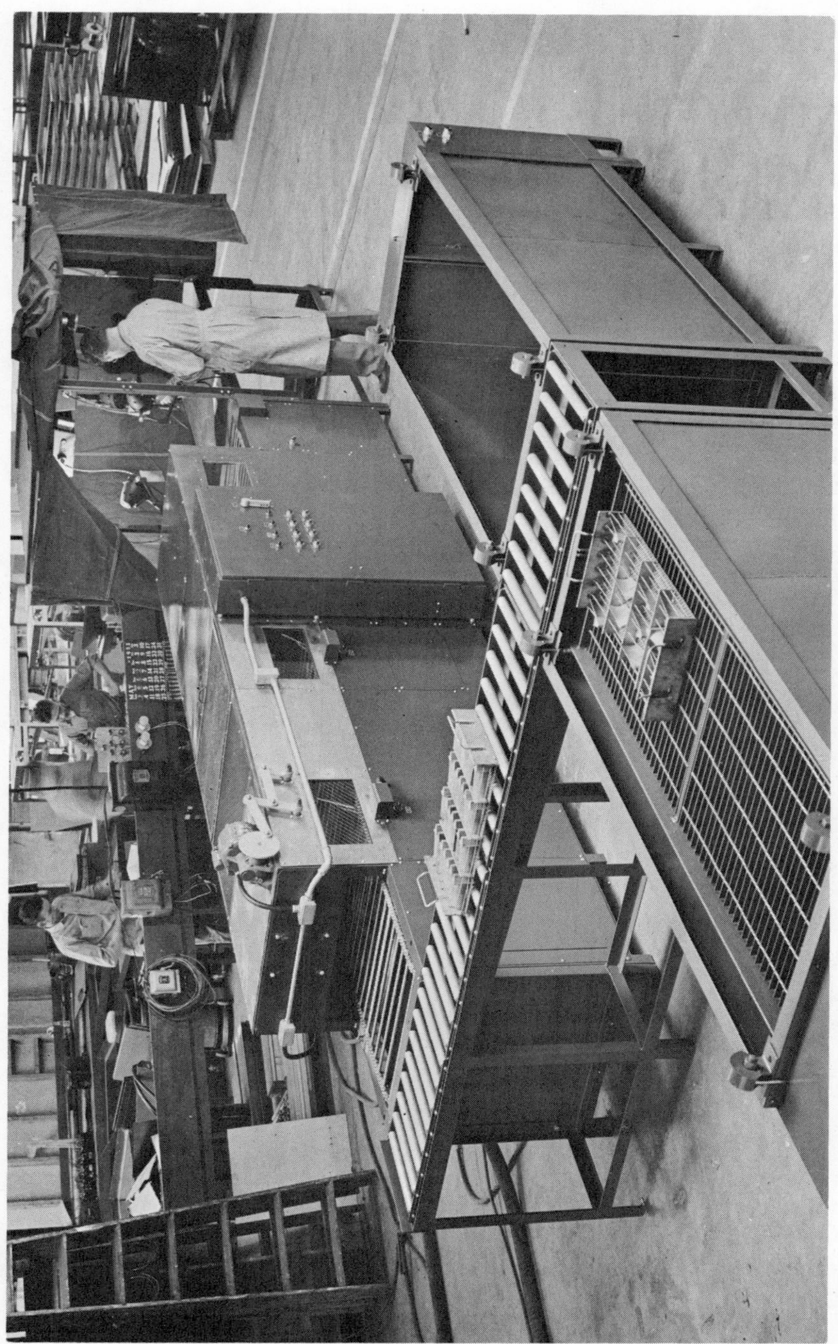

Fig. 129—Automatic unit for inspecting gas turbine blades.

or scale. Penetrants were easily washed out of such defects and at that time the only reliable way to detect them was by slow and painstaking visual inspection under a magnifying glass.

The P. E. method, devised to remedy this situation, does, when carefully and properly applied, give good indications of both the fine cracks and the broad shallow laps, (See Chapter 12) and it is almost universally used for this purpose.

Fig. 129 shows an automatic unit for carrying out this inspection using the highest sensitivity penetrant of the post-emulsification method. The blades are carried in trays on a conveyor after having been automatically dipped into the penetrant. They then pass through the emulsifier station, through a tunnel type washer, then to a station where wet developer is applied and from there into the recirculating hot-air drier. Conveyor length and speed assures optimum timing in each of these stages, so that variables due to

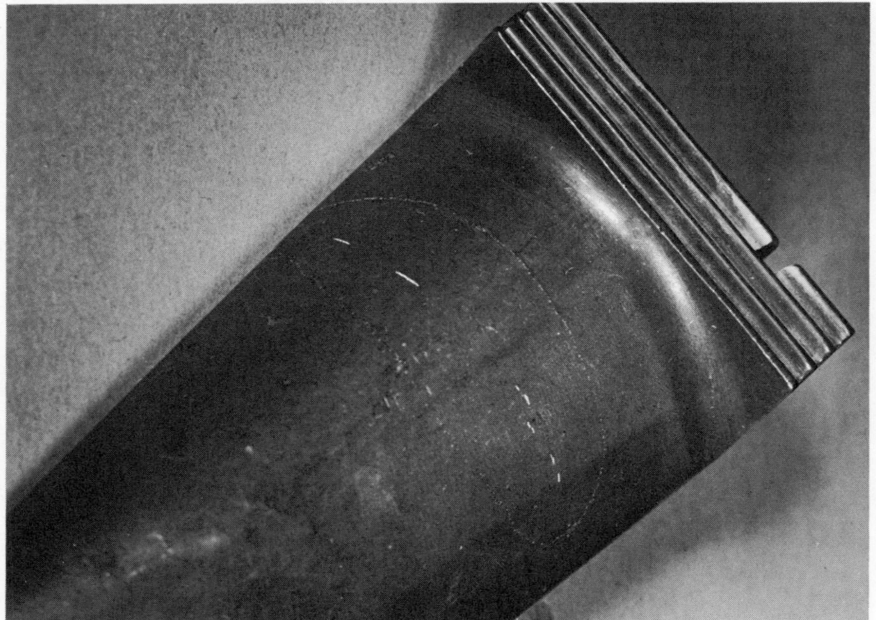

Fig. 130—Indications of very fine defects found in gas turbine blades.

the time factor, especially in the drain, emulsification, washing and drying operations are eliminated.

The processed blades are carried to the inspection station ready for examination under black light. One inspector can handle up to several hundred blades per hour—many times the best that can be done by any other process.

Assemblies of stator vanes are processed on another automatic unit through the fluorescent penetrant steps. Here the vanes themselves have already been inspected in the manner just described for blades, and the principle defects sought are in the brazed or welded joints between the vanes and shrouds, and are the usual types of brazing or welding defects. In this case only the processing up to the point of inspection is carried out on the unit itself. The parts are transferred to a separate inspection station for the very careful inspection necessary on these fabricated assemblies. Fig. 131 shows indications of some defects found at this stage.

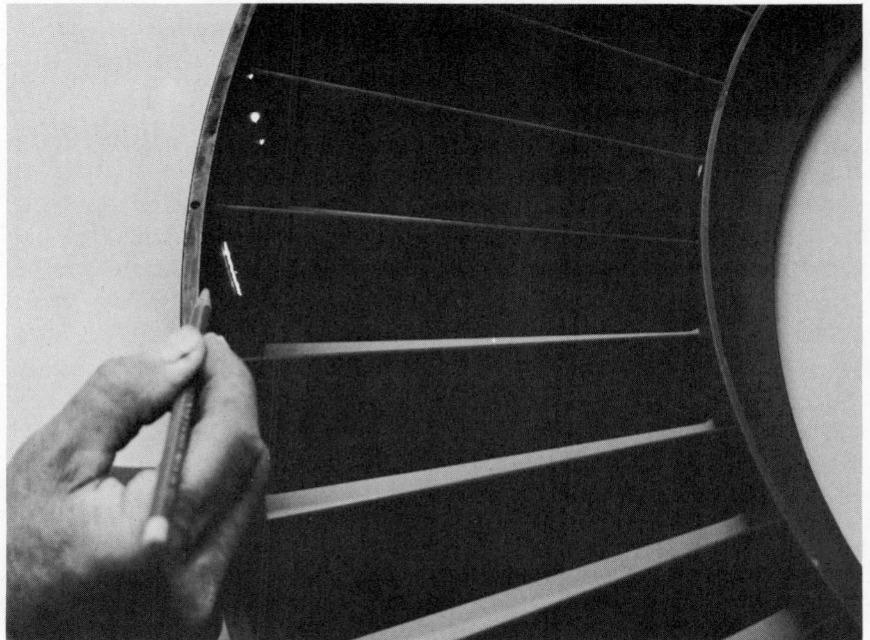

Fig. 131—Defect found in welded vanes and shrouds. (See unit shown in Fig. 75)

Fig. 132 shows an automatic unit used to inspect the turbine wheels. Here again the parts are carried through the various steps up to inspection by means of a time-sequenced conveyor to insure proper drain and development times.

In addition to the turbine wheels, blades and vanes, there are many other heat-resistant alloy parts entering into jet engine construction, and a considerable amount of welding of such materials and components. Some of these parts are diffuser rings, combustion chambers, exhaust nozzles and many others.

Control of welding is obtained in some shops by the use of pressurized cans of color-contrast or fluorescent penetrant to check welds at the point of welding. Many defects are caught here and at once corrected before the weldment leaves the shop. This reduces the rejections when these assemblies go through regular inspection, and the subsequent re-handling for reworking.

Many miscellaneous castings and forgings of aluminum and magnesium are penetrant inspected. Titanium parts and sheet metal assemblies are being quite generally used. Some compressor blades of titanium as well as bolts and fasteners of titanium are also inspected by this method. Fig. 133 shows cracks in titanium bolts found using super-bright P. E. penetrant.

27. AIRCRAFT PISTON-ENGINE MANUFACTURE. Penetrants have long played an important inspection role in the manufacture of aircraft engines. In the early days of World War II it was the great need for a method applicable to non-magnetic metals that would match the effectiveness of the magnetic particle method on iron and steel engine parts that gave penetrants their first great impetus in 1942. Aluminum, bronze, magnesium and stainless steel are extensively used in this industry. Crankcases, pistons, valves, bearings and a large variety of miscellaneous forgings, castings and fittings are penetrant inspected. For the most part the standard water-wash fluorescent technique is used, with the P. E. method being applied in special critical cases.

Receiving inspection of parts coming into the engine manufacturer's plant from sub-contractors or vendors has brought about the development of a variety of all-purpose and semi-automatic units to handle this type of work, and many penetrant inspection units that are considered standard today evolved from the inspection needs of this industry.

28. AIR-FRAME MANUFACTURE. Penetrants are also a highly important inspection tool in the manufacture of air-frames, as distinct from engines. Myriads of aluminum, magnesium and titanium parts are tested in volume. Included are wing hinges, attachment fittings, hydraulic components, welded tube assemblies, landing gear parts, magnesium landing wheels, wing spars and

Chapter 13

INDUSTRIAL APPLICATIONS

Fig. 132—Automatic unit for processing gas turbine wheels.

Fig. 133—Indications of seams and heat treat cracks in titanium bolts.

caps and many others. Leak testing of tanks and reservoirs, and hydraulic and fuel systems, is also an important application. Formerly standard water-wash fluorescent techniques were employed, but now the P. E. system is used more and more. Most of this work is done on modular general-purpose type units, since in general the number of parts of a given type and the necessary inspection rate is not sufficiently high to justify special automatic equipment.

Two interesting applications unique to the air-frame industry are worth describing.

Extruded aluminum spars and spar caps of complex cross-section and from 10′ to 110′ in length are critical components in wing construction. Flaws consist of seams, slivers, tears, and internal discontinuities exposed on machining. Penetrant inspection is the only satisfactory method for detecting such defects, but the size of the part makes it difficult to carry out the several necessary steps of the process so as to secure reliable results.

A semi-automatic unit was designed and built to solve this problem. Fig. 134 illustrates one model of this unit for handling 40′ spar caps. In this case the standard water-wash system was used, though in other versions post-emulsification penetrants were found to be justified because of the more brilliant indications obtained.

The spar-caps are dipped into the penetrant in the tank at the left and then lifted onto the rack where they are allowed to drain, excess penetrant being returned to the penetrant reservoir. The

INDUSTRIAL APPLICATIONS

(Courtesy Douglas Aircraft Co.)

Fig. 134—Semi-automatic unit for processing 40 foot spar caps.

spar-cap is then transferred to the wash station, the lid closed, and a spray washing head run the length of the tank to clean the surface of penetrant. The next station is for wet developer, into which the spar-cap is dipped. After brief draining the crane drops it into the recirculating hot air drying oven, shown closed at the right. When dry, the spar cap is placed in the special jigs to permit rotation by the inspector, who passes along the length of the cap in the moving black light inspection booth.

In P. E. versions of this application, an emulsifier station follows the penetrant dip. Because of the time needed for the spray washing head to travel the length of the part, a special step has been tried to prevent unequal emulsification times at various points along the spar-cap. When the proper emulsification time has elapsed, the cap is dipped briefly into a water bath, which tends to stop further emulsifier diffusion, and then into the wash station with its moving spray ring. The system is, however not entirely satisfactory.

In another version, penetrant is applied by spraying from a traveling head instead of by dipping. The emulsifier and wash station are combined, the emulsifier being applied by one moving spray head with the traveling spray-wash head coming along at the proper time after the emulsifier. This arrangement is very effective.

Another application involving large parts is the inspection of large milled wing-skin sections. These are machined or chem-milled out of aluminum slabs or extruded shapes which have been ultra-

Fig. 135—Fluorescent indications of defects in milled aluminum wing skin.

sonically inspected for internal voids and other defects. After milling, however, small or fine discontinuities not previously located may be exposed, and these are located with penetrants.

Fig. 135 illustrates one of these wing-skins after milling, the black light photograph showing some of the indications of defects disclosed.

Most of the miscellaneous castings, forgings and fittings entering into an air-frame assembly are supplied by outside vendors and are inspected in the receiving-inspection department of the plant. Many inspection methods are used on the non-ferrous parts as they come in, including X-ray, ultrasound and eddy currents, as well as penetrants. In most instances, however, penetrant inspection is re-applied on such parts after they are machined and finished, to insure absence of significant surface defects before they are assembled into the structure of the aircraft.

29. MISSILE AND AEROSPACE VEHICLE MANUFACTURE. Both color-contrast and fluorescent penetrant systems are used to check many components in the missile manufacturing industry. Except for the need for extraordinary care and precision, most of the applications are not peculiar to the industry but follow the normal pattern of detailed inspection of castings, forgings, extrusions and welds. Spot-checking of welds is often done using color-contrast penetrant kits. Fluorescent penetrants have generally been applied to all titanium, stainless steel, aluminum and magnesium parts.

Need to test components of liquid oxygen systems for flaws and leaks led to a demand for special penetrants for this purpose. Standard penetrants are composed of organic materials. Because of the violent reaction between liquid oxygen and any material that will burn, organic substances of all kinds must be scrupulously eliminated from liquid oxygen systems. This involves careful cleaning of the system to remove any oil or other organic substances that may be left from processes of manufacture. Such cleaning *after* penetrant testing should remove virtually all hazard involved in the use of penetrants. However, in an effort to reduce the possibility of a reaction between small amounts of penetrant which conceivably might remain, and the liquid oxygen when the system is filled, specifications have been written for impact-testing thin films of penetrant, under controlled conditions, while in contact with liquid oxygen.

Special penetrant systems have been developed which attempt to meet the requirements of this specification, so as to be available for use in testing liquid oxygen systems and components. Pumps, valves, piping and containers used in liquid oxygen systems are checked for cracks and leaks, particularly in the welds. (See Chapter 14, Section 26.) These special penetrant families are used satisfactorily on liquid hydrogen system components also.

The missile and aerospace industries use many special alloys employing unusual metals and elements. Some of these are susceptible to damage by certain elements (sulphur, halogens, etc.), and special penetrants, low in such elements, are used when inspecting these alloys.

Certain composite non-metallic materials and components are also checked with penetrants. Fig. 136 shows a crack, found with fluorescent penetrant in a glass-mica radome for a missile.

30. AUTOMOTIVE MANUFACTURING. In automotive manufacturing, penetrants have found useful application since very soon after

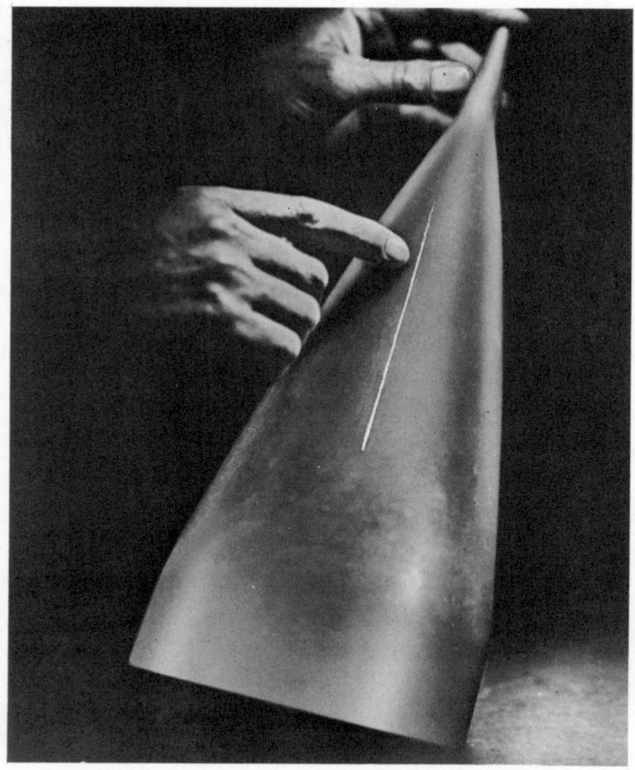

(Courtesy Micalex Corp. of America)

Fig. 136—Fluorescent indication of crack in glass-mica radome.

their introduction in the early 1940's. One of their earliest uses was to detect lack of bond between bearing-metal liner and the bronze backing of many types of bearings.

Usually penetrant inspection is applied as a quality control and cost-saving measure—as in fact it is in many other industries. Some of the items commonly tested are cast aluminum engine blocks, pistons, aluminum wheels, white metal castings, automatic transmission housings and rotors, carburetor bowls and housings, and many others. Castings are checked for thermal cracks and die castings for porosity or cracks which would become leaks. Some castings which are to be plated are checked for porous surface areas which would prevent satisfactory plating. Brazed and cast automatic transmission parts are also penetrant tested. In general, the automotive industry uses the standard water-wash technique, usually in modular multi-purpose type units.

Chapter 13
INDUSTRIAL APPLICATIONS

31. Nuclear Power. In the nuclear power field, the emphasis is on failure-free performance of moving parts such as pumps, and leak-free systems for handling "hot" or corrosive liquids often at high temperatures and under very high pressure. Inspection and testing to avoid any type of operating failure make use of every known nondestructive testing system and device. Oftentimes three, four and even more, different testing methods are applied to a single article. Pressure vessels, for instance, are frequently subjected to radiographic, ultrasonic, magnetic particle and penetrant methods to insure sound welds and a flaw-free product.

Penetrants, both fluorescent and color-contrast, are also used—among other methods—to inspect zircalloy tubing used in the manufacture of fuel elements, to detect seams and cracks. Extruded fuel rods composed of uranium elements clad with zircalloy or other metal, are examined for surface flaws and leaks using fluorescent post-emulsification methods.

Since much non-magnetic stainless steel and other corrosion-resistant alloy metal is used for components of pressure systems, penetrants find a great deal of use in the testing of such items as valve bodies, pump housings and parts, welds, and pipe and tubing. Figs. 116 and 117 illustrate an automatic unit used for inspecting the larger sizes of stainless steel tubing.

32. Maintenance Inspection. One of the most widespread, and certainly one of the most important, uses of nondestructive testing is in preventive maintenance. A very great deal of study and research has been devoted to the failures, and their causes, of equipment and structures while in service. Much has been written on this subject and the nature of these failures and the conditions which are responsible for their initiation are now quite well understood. Failures may occur in members or structures which are statically loaded, although by far the majority of service failures occur in dynamically stressed parts of moving machines or assemblies. Cracks which develop in service may require considerable time, after they are initiated, before they progress to failure. Preventive maintenance undertakes to find them in their early stages, thus avoiding actual breakage of parts.

Failures may also be caused by overloads induced by accidents or by deliberate overloading beyond design. Preventive maintenance can have little influence in avoiding such occurrences, but it may be the means for the detection and elimination of incipient cracks which would precipitate fracture at moderate overloads.

Planned preventive maintenance programs, using available crack-detecting nondestructive testing methods can and do play a major part in reducing or eliminating the occurrence of failures due to stress-corrosion cracking or to fatigue.

Stress-corrosion cracking (sometimes referred to as corrosion fatigue, though there is no real relationship to true fatigue) is caused on surfaces which are under high tensile stress and at the same time are subjected to corrosive conditions. The corrosion penetrates between the grains of the stressed metal and results in a crack which, under continued exposure, can penetrate deeply and cause eventual failure. An example of this type of failure is the "season cracking" of cold drawn yellow brass. Residual stresses remaining from the cold-drawing operation are sufficient to cause cracking in time, even under the mildly corrosive action of the atmosphere.

Fig. 137 shows indications of very fine cracks in a forged bronze steam turbine blade. These aging cracks, resulting from residual

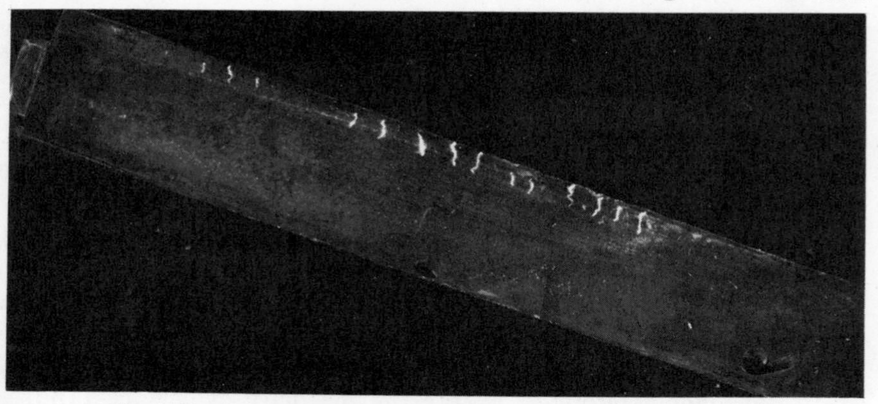

Fig. 137—Aging cracks in forged bronze steam turbine blade.

stresses, were formed during shelf storage of the blade and were found with fluorescent penetrant a considerable time after the blade was forged.

33. FATIGUE CRACKING. By far the largest cause of failures of machines and components in service is fatigue cracking. Members of machines or structures which are subject to many cycles of reversing or fluctuating stresses may, under certain circumstances, develop minute cracks. These cracks gradually enlarge and propagate through the cross section of the part until the remaining sound metal is no longer strong enough to carry the load, and breaks. Fatigue cracking is initiated at some location in stressed parts where for some reason the stress is raised locally far above the average stress for the part. Once a crack is started it usually progresses to failure unless the part is removed sooner from service.

Many conditions can cause such local high stresses. Often some feature in the design or shape of the part may be the cause. At a hole in a flat surface stressed in tension, for example, the local tensile stress at the edges of the hole may be three times the aver-

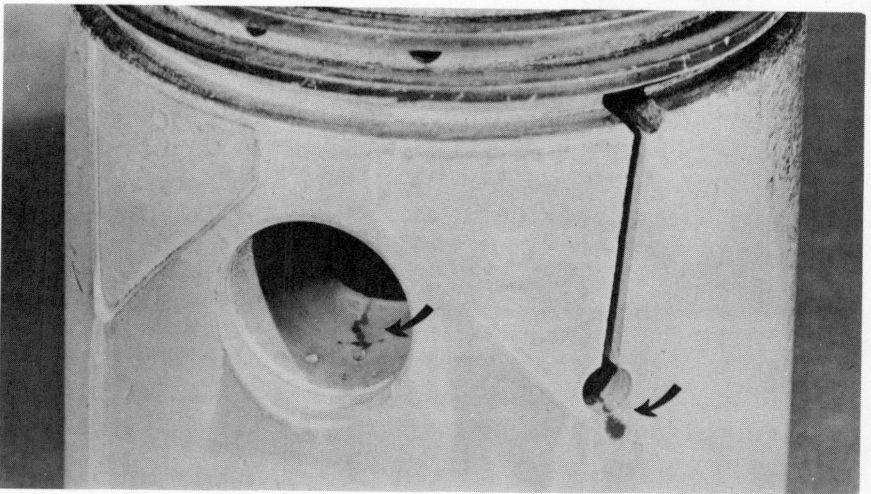

Fig. 138—Fatigue cracks in automotive piston located with color-contrast penetrant.

age for the rest of the surface. Other design features can be the cause of local high stresses resulting in fatigue cracking. Examples are sharp fillets, sharp changes of section, stiffening ribs, notches such as the roots of threads or keyways and many others.

The worst offenders, however, which the designer cannot foresee and allow for, are the surface discontinuities or cracks which occur in materials as the result of manufacturing and finishing processes. A very small grinding crack or even a small accidental nick in the surface of a part to be highly and repeatedly stressed can develop into a fatigue crack. Much, if not most, of the nondestructive testing carried out on materials and parts during manufacture is for the purpose of detecting and eliminating stress-raising flaws of this kind.

Experience has shown, however, that although most stress-raisers can be identified and avoided by design and by testing, cracking from fatigue still occurs. Therefore periodic inspection for small fatigue cracks, so that they may be found and dealt with before complete failure occurs, is a most profitable and rewarding undertaking.

Preventive maintenance inspection is perhaps of greatest importance to the transportation industries, in which failure of equipment while in operation can result in loss of life as well as property and other losses. Penetrant and magnetic particle inspection were pioneers in providing effective means for inspecting machinery for fatigue cracks in advance of failure. The operators of aircraft, railroads and automotive vehicles were some of the earliest users of nondestructive testing. Today's remarkable record of safety in flight could not have been achieved—nor could it be maintained today—without these two inspection tools. It will therefore be of interest to describe a few of the uses for penetrants in these fields.

34. RAILROAD OVERHAUL. Before the era of diesel power on the railroads, magnetic particle inspection was the mainstay of maintenance or overhaul operations starting in the middle '30's. Non-magnetic parts in critical stress locations were few and far between on a steam locomotive. Today, however, with diesel-electric power practically excluding steam from the field, the use of penetrants for overhaul inspection has become at least of equal importance to magnetic particle testing.

Diesel locomotives use many non-ferrous parts, and for these, railroad shops today are well equipped to apply penetrant inspection. One of the items universally inspected is the diesel engine valve, which is subject to fatigue cracking or heat checking on the hardened alloy face. Re-conditioned valves also may sustain grinding checks while being refinished. Fig. 139 illustrates fluorescent indications of cracks in the hardened faces of used diesel valves. The post-emulsification method is usually employed for valve inspection as the cracks may be very fine and shallow. They are also often contaminated by baked-in oil, etc. and require maximum sensitivity methods for their detection.

Other items commonly tested are bearing cages and retainers, pistons, cylinder liners (for leaks), cylinder heads, and many other non-magnetic parts. Standard water-wash penetrants are custom-

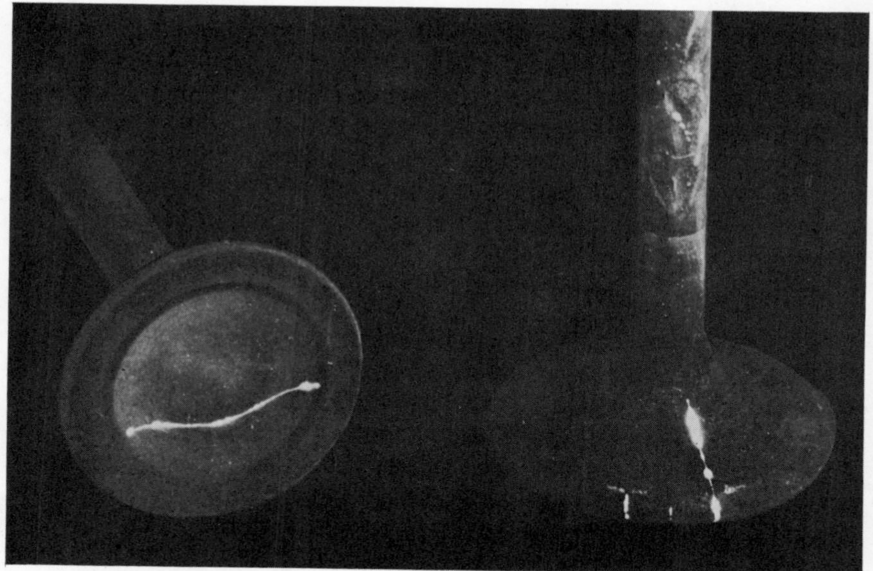

Fig. 139—Fluorescent indications of typical fatigue cracks in hard alloy face and body of diesel valves.

arily used employing one of the modular multi-purpose types of standard penetrant equipment.

Stainless steel and aluminum tank cars are examined for cracks, especially in connection with attachment lugs or fittings, or for defective welds. Tank cars are also tested for leaks with penetrants. (See Chapter 14, Section 29).

Color-contrast penetrants are often used to check hand tools and maintenance-of-way tools for service cracks. Maintenance-of-way equipment as well as off-the-road equipment is also tested in a well-planned preventive maintenance program.

35. AIRCRAFT OVERHAUL. The overhaul shops of modern commercial air lines, and of the aircraft maintenance facilities of the armed services, are masterpieces in planned preventive maintenance and repair. Every conceivable instrument and test method is available which can detect deterioration and wear of any sort in every piece of the engines or operating mechanisms of the aircraft, and of the instruments that control and monitor their operation. These shops are also a marvel of organization, by which engines and instruments are dis-assembled, inspected, repaired and re-assembled on a tight time-schedule. Before release, tests of the entire engine and control system insure that every component functions perfectly before re-installation in the aircraft.

These overhaul facilities vary in size but they are all meticulously equipped and operated, since on their effectiveness depends the flight-safety of every aircraft and its passengers and crew. Some of the large shops are able to turn out completely rebuilt engines at the rate of two to five, to ten per day. Of course, the elapsed time for each engine in the shop is a matter of days, but they come off the assembly and testing line at these rates.

Heart of the engine overhaul shop is the equipment for conducting magnetic particle and penetrant inspection of every part, from crankcase to the smallest gear and bolt, to detect the presence of fatigue cracks. When found, cracked parts are replaced by new ones unless the crack is still so small and in such a location that it can be ground out without damage to the serviceability of the part. Magnetic parts are examined using magnetic particles (usually the fluorescent type), and non-magnetic parts by means of fluorescent penetrants. Color-contrast penetrants have some applications also, but these are usually minor.

In addition to engine parts the aircraft itself is carefully inspected. Landing gear components and the hydraulic mechanisms which operate them are examined for fatigue cracks. In many instances, landing gear are given a spot inspection between major overhauls, without removal from aircraft, to guard against cracks developing in vital members as the result of rough landings. Fig. 140 illustrates the inspection of a magnesium landing wheel with color-contrast penetrant, while in place on the aircraft.

Fig. 141 illustrates another use of penetrant inspection, made on aluminum propellor blades of small aircraft, without disassembly. Stone nicks on such blades are watched for and are carefully blended out, since they act as stress-raisers which may initiate fatigue cracks. Penetrants easily detect the presence of fatigue cracks at these locations. After the nick has been blended out, a check with penetrant assures that no crack exists in the blade, before it is again operated.

36. PISTON-ENGINE MAINTENANCE. In any engine overhaul inspection with penetrants, a most important step is the pre-cleaning operation. Oil and grease, corrosion products, baked-on oil ("engine varnish"), and any other foreign material including paint,

CHAPTER 13
INDUSTRIAL APPLICATIONS

Fig. 140—Magnesium landing wheel being inspected in place with color-contrast penetrant.

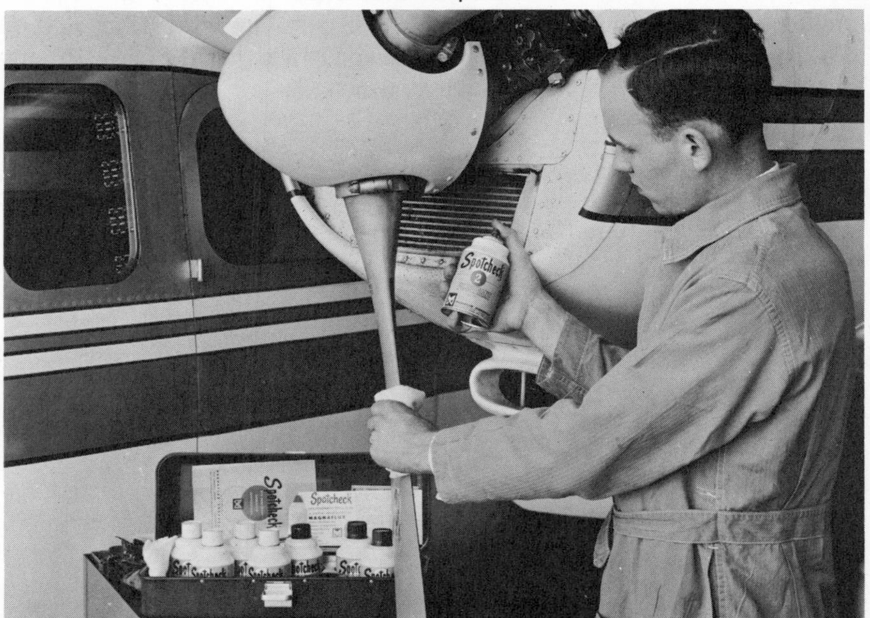

Fig. 141—Checking aluminum propeller blades for possible fatigue cracks.

must be completely and painstakingly removed. Solvent guns, vapor degreasers, chemical baths and other washing and cleaning processes must be applied. This need is especially difficult to meet properly on those parts of the piston engine which have been subjected to heat over prolonged periods of operation.

Pistons and cylinder heads, customarily made of aluminum alloy, must be most carefully watched from this point of view, since it is sometimes practically impossible to clean these baked-in contaminants out of fine, small cracks. Power-recovery turbine wheels present a somewhat similar problem.

Post-emulsification fluorescent penetrants and techniques are used for inspection of most piston-engine parts. In addition to pistons and cylinder heads, some of the other parts inspected are crankcases, bearings, and numerous aluminum, stainless steel and bronze fittings and miscellaneous small parts. Valves are carefully examined for cracks which occur on the hardened valve surface as a result of heat and wear.

37. JET ENGINE OVERHAUL. A typical overhaul shop for the inspection with penetrants of jet engine parts consists of two complete lines of equipment, one for the larger parts, which are relatively few per engine, and one for the large number of small parts including blades and minor fittings. The post-emulsification method is normally used. The installation consists in general of the following stations arranged in the order named:

1. Degreaser
2. Penetrant dip station
3. Drain station
4. Emulsifier dip station
5. Drain station
6. Wash station
7. Drying unit
8. Dry developer booth
   (with dust collector)
9. Developer rest station.
10. Inspection booth
11. Post-inspection wash station

CHAPTER 13

INDUSTRIAL APPLICATIONS

(Courtesy Pan American World Airways)

Fig. 142—View of large jet engine overhaul shop of a commercial airline.

Large parts are handled through these stations on an overhead mono-rail conveyor. Small parts may be handled in groups in baskets moved along on a roller conveyor in a separate line.

The large parts requiring penetrant inspection include the turbine wheels, case, vanes and shrouding, and various parts of the combustion chambers and nozzle assemblies. These are handled by conveyor, the washing booth being semi-automatic for rotating the part under black light while washing with a hand-held hydro-wash gun. The part is similarly handled in the developer station, with the dry powder developer being applied by air pressure from a hose, the dust collector removing the excess powder from the booth.

On the small-parts line the most numerous items are the non-magnetic compressor blades and the heat-resistant alloy turbine blades. There may be as many as 500 to 1000 of these in a single engine. This line is therefore equipped with automatic washing and other devices to speed up and control the processing and inspection.

38. AIRFRAMES AND COMPONENTS. Color-contrast and fluores-

(Courtesy Pan American World Airways)

Fig. 143—Inspection of aluminum attachment of nose-gear outer cylinder, using fluorescent penetrant portable field kit.

cent penetrant portable kits are extensively used in spot checking various areas of the fuselage and wing asemblies where cracking is suspected. Fail-safe points should also be examined. Landing gear cylinder parts and wheels are given on-the-line checks of this type, especially after known hard landings. Some types are given an inspection after every 100 hours of operation or after a specified number of landings. These methods are also freely used in apprais-ing damage to various parts and assemblies after severe landings. Cracks due to overstressing resulting from such landings are usually wide open and easy to find.

Helicopter engines and parts are also most carefully tested with penetrants at specified intervals. Non-ferrous engine parts, part of the rotor hub assembly, transmission housings, and landing gear

(Courtesy Naval Air Station, Jacksonville)

Fig. 144—Inspecting helicopter part for crack indications with black light.

parts are examples. Line maintenance checks are made on known critical areas which are readily accessible. Penetrants—usually high-brilliance fluorescent—are applied by means of pressurized cans from the portable kits.

39. ARMED SERVICES MAINTENANCE USES. All aircraft and engines used by any of the branches of the Armed Services are care-fully and frequently inspected along the lines just described. In addition, maintenance of vehicles, weapons, weapon carriers and all the machinery of defense includes penetrant inspection of critical non-magnetic parts. Field units are equipped with kits of both color-contrast and fluorescent penetrants for in-the-field checking of equipment. More extensive production testing equipment is installed in all overhaul and repair bases.

40. AUTOMOTIVE MAINTENANCE. Bus and truck overhaul on a planned preventive maintenance basis has been a growing and profitable practice especially over the past ten or fifteen years. Regular timed teardown of engines, based on mileage, is in many cases carried out in a manner comparable to aircraft engines, though automotive engines are far less complex or critical. The business of rebuilding automotive engines on a commercial basis has become a large industry, which employs nondestructive testing means extensively, including both color-contrast and fluorescent penetrants.

Penetrant inspection of all non-ferrous components is usually done, using standard water-wash fluorescent materials and techniques. Color-contrast penetrants are also used for such purposes in many shops, especially the smaller ones that handle relatively few engines. Parts tested include such items as pistons, exhaust valves, parts of automatic transmissions, carburetor bowls, aluminum truck

(Courtesy Trio Auto Parts, Inc.)

Fig. 145—Inspection of fluid torque-converter housing for leaks, using fluorescent penetrant.

wheels and cast aluminum blocks. Fuel tanks are also tested for leaks after repair. On the vehicle itself such things as spring hangers, axle housings and frame members are tested, often with color-contrast kits. On these parts, which are especially greasy and dirty, great care must be exercised to secure thorough pre-cleaning else reliable results cannot be obtained.

Penetrants are extensively used at the Indianapolis Motor Speedway in inspecting non-magnetic parts of racing cars and motors, in preparation for the annual 500 mile race. Racing and sport car drivers in all parts of the country also avail themselves of this testing process to insure that defective equipment does not add to the hazards of their profession. Fig. 146 shows a crack found at the Indianapolis track in a magnesium wheel from a racing car.

Fig. 146—Fatigue crack in magnesium wheel of a racing car. Located with fluorescent penetrant at Indianapolis Speedway.

41. OIL REFINERY AND CHEMICAL PLANT MAINTENANCE. Present-day processes in the oil refining and petro-chemical, as well as other chemical manufacturing industries have tended toward high pressures, high temperatures and the use of highly corrosive reacting chemicals. As a result, processing equipment is heavier and very often made of corrosion-resistant materials, such as stainless steel and other alloys, as well as lead, alloy, glass or ceramic liners. Preventive maintenance inspections at planned shut-down periods are here very effective.

Non-magnetic parts and welds are inspected for flaws with penetrants during manufacture and installation, and are also periodically inspected for service cracks especially where suspected of stress- or corrosion-fatigue. Parts which may be inspected include cracking tubes, return bends, pump parts, valves and fittings, and welds. Fluorescent and color-contrast kits are extensively used in this work.

42. UTILITY MAINTENANCE. Penetrant testing finds use in the steam power generating field in many ways. With the use of high pressures and temperatures in modern steam plants, much of the equipment and piping is made of high strength heat- and corrosion-resistant alloys. In modern intsallations these are often of non-magnetic types and so do not lend themselves to magnetic particle inspection. Welds, pipes, valves and fittings are consequently examined periodically for surface cracks using portable kits and equipment. Both fluorescent and color-contrast penetrants are used for such inspections.

The high-pressure blades of steam turbines were formerly often made of non-magnetic alloys, and these were carefully gone over with fluorescent penetrants at the time of general tear-down. Most non-magnetic alloys have now been replaced with alloy steels which may be examined for fatigue cracks with magnetic particles. However, in many turbines, the last three low-pressure stages are fitted with blading on which the leading edges have been protected from erosion by means of welded-on hard-alloy strips. These tend to develop cracks, and when the turbine is down and the rest of the blades are inspected with magnetic particles, these strips are tested with fluorescent penetrant.

The inspection is usually carried out on the turbine floor of the plant, the spindle being mounted on blocks so that it can be rotated. A canvas shield is built around it, as illustrated in Fig. 147. The blades are thoroughly cleaned and are then sprayed with water-wash type fluorescent penetrant. After a short penetration time (up to 20 minutes) the blades are washed off with a low pressure hose and dried with an air blast. Developer is applied as a powder from a hand applicator bulb and inspection for cracks carried out after several hours with a hand held spot-type black light.

An interesting part that requires inspection is the stainless steel steam-strainer, intended to prevent any solid articles from entering

CHAPTER 13

INDUSTRIAL APPLICATIONS

Fig. 147—Temporary enclosure around steam turbine spindle for purpose of fluorescent penetrant inspection of low pressure blades.

(Courtesy Consolidated Edison Co., New York)

Fig. 148—Inspecting steam basket strainer with black light after processing with fluorescent penetrant.

the turbine with the steam. These strainers develop cracks, between the holes, which can progress so far that whole sections of the strainer can break out and be carried into the turbine, resulting in very serious damage to the blading of the first stages. Water-wash fluorescent penetrant is used for this inspection.

Condensers are tested for leaks by filling the water-side with water to which a fluorescent concentrate has been added, the steam side of the tubes then being examined for leaks with black light. Hold-down bolts that hold the turbine and cover to the base are often inspected for cracks with penetrants, since magnetization for use of the magnetic particle test is sometimes difficult or inconvenient. The penetrant test is much quicker and simpler.

In nuclear power generating stations penetrants are an important adjunct to maintenance, since much of the equipment, such as valves, piping, etc., is made of non-magnetic materials.

Many small co-op and stand-by generating plants are diesel powered. When these are overhauled the diesel engine receives major tests of critical parts to detect any fatigue cracks from thousands of hours of service.

43. MISCELLANEOUS PLANT EQUIPMENT. In addition to the many specific maintenance and overhaul applications which have been described, penetrants perform a very useful function in any plant in which moving machinery is operated. Such machinery is subject to fatigue and can break at awkward times and result in costly down-time and repairs. Examples are cranks of punch presses, parts of forging hammers, hydraulic pump parts, and many similar machine parts. Color-contrast penetrants in portable spray-can kits are very serviceable and convenient for such inspections.

In many plants the maintenance foreman has learned the value of this inspection tool, and has set up periodic inspections at pre-arranged times of shut-down. Many cracks found in such a program can be eliminated without scrapping the part and before an actual failure causes secondary damage. Color-contrast kits are used in this way even on ferrous parts, because of the extreme availability and convenience which they provide.

44. PLASTICS. In the testing of non-metallic materials, penetrants have found many uses. Molded plastics are subject to cracks resulting from stresses set up in the molding process or on cooling. No special techniques are required in most plastics applications,

INDUSTRIAL APPLICATIONS

Fig. 149—Punch press crank shaft with fatigue crack indicated with color-contrast penetrant.

except that care must be taken that the plastic in question is not attacked by the liquids used in the particular penetrant system being considered.

Normally, water-wash fluorescent penetrants have been satisfactory for use with plastics, though several special formulations have been made in those cases where the standard penetrant and the plastic are incompatible. Water-base penetrants also perform well in this application and are usually inert to plastics. Color-contrast penetrants, too, are successfully used in many cases. Cracks that occur in plastics are usually clean and easy to find with penetrants.

Molded phenolic resin parts for electrical components such as distributor caps, switch housings and parts, etc., are examined for cracks using the standard water-wash penetrant formula, since this type of plastic is unaffected by most liquids. Fig. 150 is a good example, showing a complex molded "clam shell," inspected with water-wash fluorescent penetrant. Indications are of minute molding cracks.

An interesting type of molded product is made by hot-pressing a mixture of powdered mica and glass. Complex parts, many for

Fig. 150—Fluorescent penetrant indications of cracks in molded plastic "clam shell" used in electronic assembly.

Fig. 151—Fluorescent indications of molding cracks in insulator made of glass-bonded mica.

electrical insulating purposes, are precision molded of this material. Tube sockets and coil forms are examples. The material lends itself readily to penetrant inspection. Fig. 151 shows such a part with fluorescent indications of cracks.

Color-contrast penetrants are used to test sheets of "Teflon" resin for surface imperfections such as porosity. Lack of bond between inserts or reinforcements in molded plastics is another use in this field. An example of this is the inspection of the edges of thick canvas-phenolic resin sheets for lack of bond between resin and reinforcement.

Some of the newest reinforced plastics may be found to be too porous for the use of penetrants. On these filtered particle tests (Partek)* are used.

45. CERAMICS. Closely allied to the inspection of plastics is the use of penetrants on ceramic parts. Among the early uses of fluorescent penetrants was the finding of cracks in fired ceramic articles. On hard-fired or vitrified parts, such as most insulators, the method works exceptionally well. The spark plug industry has long used this means for eliminating defective insulator bodies. Fig. 152 shows a group of spark plug insulators containing cracks revealed

Fig. 152—Fluorescent penetrant indications of firing cracks in spark plug insulators, and pores and cracks in electric-porcelain bushings.

by the normal water-wash fluorescent penetrants. The test is widely used on high-dielectric electronic insulators for capacitors, etc.

Color-contrast penetrants also perform well on most materials of this type, though fluorescent indications give faster results where high inspection rates are required, because they are easier to see and scanning of parts for defects is more rapid. Water-base penetrants have also solved some problems in the inspection of ceramic articles.

*Partek. Trademark registered in the U. S. Patent Office. Property of Magnaflux Corporation. Also registered in Canada and Great Britain.

Some ceramics are quite porous in the fired state, and these may not always give good results due to difficulty of getting a clean-washed surface. Special techniques have on occasion been worked out to permit satisfactory inspection of this type of article. However, in some cases the filtered particle (Partek) method has worked more satisfactorily than penetrants.

Color-contrast penetrants have found some application for detecting cracks on glazed tile and on decorative floor or wall tile.

46. GLASS. Penetrants work well on glass, and will find most cracks in glass articles even though some are very fine indeed. In many cases, with very fine cracks, there is no advantage in the penetrant approach, since the Electrified Particle method (Statiflux)* gives much heavier and more easily readable indications on such small cracks. When, however, the question of leakage is involved, penetrants give a direct and positive answer as to whether a leak exists or not. These applications will be discussed in the following chapter, including the important field of glass-to-metal seal testing.

47. MISCELLANEOUS AND UNUSUAL APPLICATIONS. There are many applications of penetrant testing that are interesting in themselves but which may have no widespread industrial significance. A few of these seem worth including in this discussion.

48. ORTHOPEDIC IMPLANTS. These are metallic members used to replace missing bones in the human body or to strengthen bones that are weak. They are made of various metals that are inert to the fluids of the body, and include stainless steel, titanium, tantalum, silver and other metals. Since these artificial bone replacements often must take an appreciable amount of load, and are very difficult to replace, it is important that they be sound and free from flaws before they are put in place.

Manufacturers of these devices have for some years used penetrants to insure that such articles are free from cracks. Fig. 153a shows an Eicher type prosthesis, or artificial hip ball-joint. The material in this case is stainless steel. The fluorescent indication shows the presence of a serious crack just under the upset flat base under the ball. The indication was developed using standard water-wash techniques although the P.E. method is very often

*Statiflux. Trademark registered in the U. S. Patent Office. Property of Magnaflux Corporation. Also registered in Canada and Great Britain.

employed. Straightening and grinding cracks are looked for in these products, which are usually cast of metals not easily machined.

Recent experiments have shown the feasibility of implanting an artificial valve in the heart. This is called the Starr-Edwards mitral prosthesis. The valve body is a precision investment casting

Fig. 153a—Indication of crack in Eicher type prosthesis (hip ball joint) made of stainless steel.

Fig. 153b—Starr-Edwards mitral prosthesis (heart valve).

of stainless steel. Penetrant testing is employed to locate cracks and porosity in the casting. Fig. 153b shows this heart valve. The ball is of Silicone rubber and Teflon fabric is used to make the junction with the heart tissue.

49. STONE. Stone slabs are sometimes checked with penetrants for cracks before cutting into shapes and sizes for fabrication. Soapstone for laboratory tables and sinks, marble for architectural and ornamental work are examples. Penetrants offer a reliable method for showing the presence of such cracks. Standard water-wash penetrants have been successfully used. The penetrant must not leave a permanent stain to discolor stone intended for ornamental work.

50. SPINELS. A "spinel" is an ornamental or semi-precious stone used for making jewelry. Some of these stones contain cracks which reduce their value as jewelry, and it is important to eliminate such defective stones before they are mounted. In some of the more expensive mountings the back of the stone is given a metal flash coating. Invisible cracks interfere with the application of this coating. Fluorescent penetrants offer an easy and quick answer to these problems.

51. FOOD PROCESSING CONTAINERS. Metal tanks and kettles in which food or milk is conveyed, stored, or processed are subject to cracking and to leaks in welds. Penetrants provide a means for testing for cracks or leaks as in any other tank or vessel. In this case, however, it is important that the penetrant fluid and the dye used be completely non-toxic and also that no odor or taste remain after cleaning, to contaminate the food.

Penetrants have been formulated for this purpose using potable liquids and approved dyes such as are used for food coloring or marking. Since most of these dyes do not fluoresce, these penetrants are necessarily of the color-contrast variety.

52. DENTISTRY. An interesting corollary to the application of penetrants to ceramics is their use in finding cracks in artificial teeth and other dental components. In the case of teeth, color-contrast penetrants work excellently, and the test can be applied in the dentist's laboratory before the teeth are mounted in a denture. Fig. 154 illustrates this application. The same method can be applied to plastic teeth and to metal investment castings.

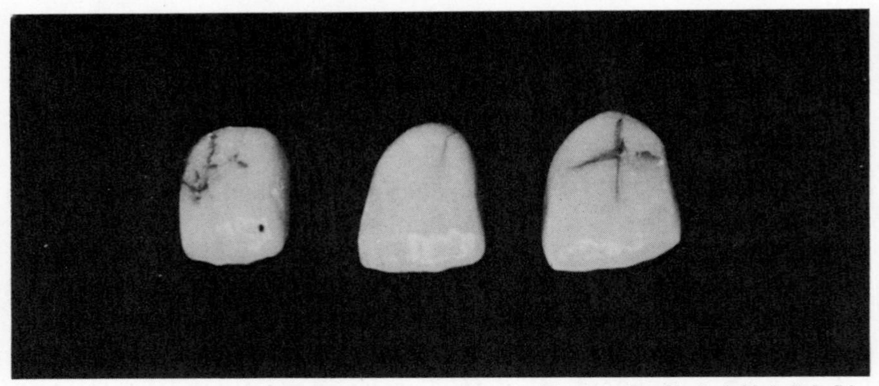

(Courtesy Dr. M. J. Saklad, D.D.S.)

Fig. 154—Color-contrast indications of cracks in dental porcelain jacket crowns.

53. VERIFYING CRACKS. As an aid in calibrating and correlating other nondestructive testing methods, as for example, eddy current or ultrasonic, penetrants are reliable and well used to study and verify the presence of cracks, seams and other surface discontinuities, evidence of which are indicated by such other methods.

Penetrants are more easily used for this purpose and give more positive results than etching, which method is sometimes used. In the case of magnetic particle indications, it is sometimes important to know whether the discontinuity actually breaks the surface. Penetrants give a conclusive answer to this question, since no penetrant indication will be obtained, if no break in the surface exists.

CHAPTER 14

DETECTION OF LEAKS WITH PENETRANTS

1. GENERAL. Leaks are a special type of flaw of tremendous importance where they have any significance at all. A vessel constructed to contain a fluid or to act as a barrier to exclude a fluid, whether liquid or gaseous, fails of its purpose if it leaks. In some circumstances fine leaks, though undesirable, may be tolerated where gross leaks may not be—as for instance in very large crude-oil storage tanks. In other circumstances the most minute leak renders the vessel wholly unsuitable for its intended purpose, as in the case of evacuated electronic devices.

Therefore, the detection of leaks has become a major problem in many industries and many special applications. Much technical ingenuity has gone into the development of methods of leak detection having adequate sensitivity to satisfy the requirements for various purposes. Leak detection is vital in a wide variety of operations and components, ranging all the way from the closed systems of nuclear power generators to the miniature encapsulated semi-conductor devices used by the million in modern electronic circuits. Other examples include the pipe, tank and processing complexes of the oil refining and chemical industries, storage and transmission systems for oil and gas, hydraulic sytems used for controls in aircraft and other types of machinery, water mains, refrigeration equipment, tank cars and countless others.

2. APPLICATIONS FOR LEAK DETECTION METHODS. Leak detection methods find application under two quite distinct groupings, the conditions of which to a large degree determine which methods may be used. Penetrant methods are applicable in both categories. The groups are:

(a) Leaks in closed systems.

  (1) Under pressure. These may be either liquid-filled or gas-filled systems.

  (2) Under vacuum. These are usually concerned with gaseous leakage into the system.

(b) Open tanks or vessels for liquids, or open sub-assemblies of closed systems.

CHAPTER 14
DETECTION OF LEAKS WITH PENETRANTS

3. AVAILABLE METHODS. A considerable number of methods have been devised and are in use for leak detection. Some of these are relatively crude and not particularly sensitive, while some, especially those for detecting passage of gases through leaks, are amazingly sensitive. Each of these has its own special area of application, although each has some peculiar advantages and limitations. There is also considerable overlapping of usefulness, and this is especially true of penetrant methods which, although having specific limitations which will be discussed, are useable in practically every field of leak detection.

Some of these methods are extremely effective for determining whether or not a leak exists, but have little value in pin-pointing the exact location of the leak. Other of the methods will, with varying degrees of sensitivity to the size of the leak, indicate its exact location. Penetrants in most instances have a relatively high degree of sensitivity, and also have the merit that they always point accurately to the location of the leak.

4. AIR PRESSURE TESTS. A very simple, though not highly sensitive leak test, is to subject the vessel or system to air pressure, using as high a pressure as circumstances warrant. If the vessel can be submerged in water, the leak is indicated by air bubbles escaping under the water. This method may be used provided the vessel is closed, or may be temporarily closed to take the air pressure for the purposes of the test. The escaping air usually gives the location of the leak and, by the volume of air escaping, indicates its approximate magnitude. The test has the advantage of being an all-over test, scanning the entire surface of the vessel at one time. However, air at moderate pressures may fail to indicate very fine leaks. Higher pressures make the test more effective, but many systems, not designed for high pressures, are not strong enough to permit this method of increasing sensitivity with safety.

5. SOAP BUBBLE TEST. A much-used variant of the air pressure test does not involve the need for immersion of the vessel. Instead, the exterior surface, either in its entirety or locally, is coated with a soap or detergent solution. Escaping air from a leak produces bubbles which are easily detected and which give the location and some idea as to the magnitude of the leak.

Weaknesses of the test lie in the fact that air will pass through a fine leak insufficient in amount to produce a conspicuous indication, and also that a very meticulous covering of the surface is requried, first, to keep it wet with soap solution long enough to allow bubbles to form, and then to scan carefully for the appearance of bubbles. It is a useful test in many circumstances but has little value for very fine leaks, and none for testing of open vessels.

6. HYDRAULIC PRESSURE TESTS. Filling a closed system or vessel with water or other liquid under pressure is another quite simple method for leak testing. Kerosene is preferable to water for this purpose if circumstances permit its use, as it will find its way through finer openings than will water. This method is not particularly sensitive for small leaks, since a small damp spot is not always easily seen, and small leaks may thus be missed. Gross leaks are, of course, readily located.

Sometimes closed systems are checked for leaks simply by pumping up pressure to operating levels or above, and observing the pressure gauge over a period of time to see whether it holds or drops. The *fact* of leakage is clearly indicated by dropping pressure although this drop may be very slow with very small leaks. The *location* of the leak, however, must be determined by scanning the system either visually for appearance of liquid or by use of one of the other systems for making small leaks easily visible. The principle of fluorescence is extremely useful for this purpose.

In the case of hydraulic systems filled with fluid which is naturally fluorescent, this test is made effective by inspecting the outside surfaces of the system with black light. If the surfaces were carefully cleaned before the test to remove all fluorescent oil or other substances, the black light will reveal indications of very fine leaks. The method may be made even more sensitive by adding a highly fluorescent dye to the hydraulic fluid. (See Section 15.)

7. WATER MAIN LEAKS. Detection of leaks in water mains is sometimes a very serious problem. One method is to use a sensitive microphone and amplifier. This device may be used first to locate the buried pipe, and then, once the pipe is found and uncovered, to amplify the sound of the leak by making contact directly on the surface of the pipe. The frequency response of these devices may be adjusted so as to filter out low notes and hear only the high notes produced by high-pressure leaks. Conversely, it may be adjusted to favor the low frequencies which characterize low-pressure leaks.

8. GAS PIPE-LINE LEAKS. Leaks in natural gas pipe lines traversing many miles of rural territory present a problem in detection. Air patrols of pipe lines will reveal the lethal effect of the escaping gas on vegetation in the vicinity of a leak. A combustible gas indicator or sniffer can then be used in this area to locate the leak more accurately. This instrument makes use of the heating effect of the combustible gas on a platinum wire which is part of a bridge circuit, and presence and amount of combustible gas is read on a meter. Addition of an odorous substance to natural gas is another widespread practice to call attention to leaks by the presence of a distinctive and usually disagreeable odor.

9. HALOGEN GAS DETECTORS. Copper chloride as well as the other halogen compounds of copper have the ability to color a flame green. This phenomenon is made use of in the Halogen Gas Detector. A flame is impinged on a brass plate and a stream of the suspected gas or air is directed to the heated area under the flame. In the presence of one of the halogen gases the copper compound is formed and imparts the characteristic green color to the flame. In its simplest form, an ordinary L. P. gas torch with a brass shield around the flame is all that is needed. In looking for Freon leaks in an air-conditioning system, such a torch need only be passed in the vicinity of a suspected tube or fitting. If a leak exists, the flame is colored green.

Another halogen type of leak detector makes use of the fact that the positive ion emission from a heated platinum surface is substantially increased in the presence of gases which contain chlorine, fluorine, bromine or iodine. An audible signal is produced and this can be adjusted for sensitivity. As gases used in refrigeration systems frequently contain fluorine or chlorine, this instrument is particularly suited to testing leaks in such units. The sensitivity of this instrument, when the system tested is filled with Freon 12, is one part of Freon per million of air.

10. MASS SPECTROMETER. Another approach for detecting very fine leaks is to test for the presence of small amounts of gas not normally present in the atmosphere, but which can be introduced into closed vessels or systems. Very small amounts of such a gas issuing from a leak can be detected.

A commonly used device of this type uses mass spectrography to detect minute amounts of helium. Containers to be tested may be charged with helium and then placed inside a vessel that can be evacuated. If helium leaks into the evacuated space it is indicated by the mass-spectrometer. Alternatively, the vessel to be tested for leaks can be put in a helium atmosphere and a vacuum drawn inside the vessel and tested for helium. The sensitivity of this method is very high, and a leak rate of 5×10^{-9} standard cubic centimeters of gas per second can be detected, corresponding to less than one part of helium in one million parts of air.

11. LEAKS IN EVACUATED GLASS VESSELS. Glass vacuum tubes or other evacuated glass vessels can be tested for leaks using a spark coil. If a leak or crack exists in the glass, the high voltage spark enters the glass envelope and lights up its interior. The electrified particle method is also excellent for finding cracks in such glass envelopes. Neither of these methods, however, will find leaks between metal electrodes and the glass. Penetrant methods are excellent for this purpose (Section 31).

12. TESTS OF OPEN TANKS. All the methods so far described require that the vessel or system can be closed so that pressure or vacuum can be applied. Many large vessels and tanks cannot be so sealed, and it is customary to test these for leaks by filling them with a liquid and examining all accessible outside seams for leaks. For this purpose water is almost exclusively used because of cost and availabilty. Gross leaks are readily found, but leaks in seams not accessible for inspection are, of course, not located. This includes all the welded seams in the bottom, for example, of large oil storage tanks. Penetrants applied at the time of welding not only permit detection of leaks but allow immediate repair. (See Section 19 below.)

13. PENETRANTS. As has been stated, penetrants have applications in practically every type of leak detection, and although the penetrant methods have limitations of their own, they frequently offer the best and least expensive method for a given purpose. They do not necessarily have the ultimate sensitivity of the helium mass spectrometer technique and may not always be quite as simple as the air-pressure soap-bubble method, but in a great majority of cases they offer advantages in either sensitivity or cost, or both, over other available methods. The following sections will detail leak detection techniques with penetrants and describe typical applications.

CHAPTER 14

DETECTION OF LEAKS WITH PENETRANTS

14. SPECIAL PENETRANTS FOR LEAK DETECTION. The standard penetrants are for the most part excellent for most leak-detection purposes. There is usually no need for water-washability in this application and, of the fluorescent types, the post-emulsification penetrants are often preferred over those incorporating emulsifier in their composition, because of somewhat better penetrating ability. From this standpoint the standard solvent-removal color-contrast types are also excellent.

One of the most commonly used penetrants for leak detection is a Type 3 liquid (Table XV) in which the dye fluoresces red. This has the advantage that the red color differs completely from any fluorescence likely to be picked up around equipment being tested. Since oils and greases fluoresce with a blue-white to blue-green color, the appearance of a red fluorescing spot is very conspicuous.

Following is a list of the penetrants and additives commercially available for leak detection purposes, in addition to the usual types of penetrants.

TABLE XV

SPECIAL FLUORESCENT PENETRANTS AND ADDITIVES FOR LEAK DETECTION

Type	Fluorescent Color	Characteristics
3	Red	Complete liquid penetrant
4	Yellow	Liquid—oil-free
5	Yellow	Powder—water soluble
6	Yellow	Powder—water soluble, with added wetting agent
7	Yellow	Powder—oil soluble
8	Red	Powder—soluble in water or alcohol
10	Blue	Powder—water soluble

Additives in powder form are convenient and cheap to use when making up a considerable volume of fluid for many kinds of leak tests. For example, the water used for a fill-test can be made fluorescent by this means; or a normally non-fluorescent or weakly fluorescent fluid used in a system can be made strongly fluorescent using one of the powders having suitable solubility.

15. USE OF PENETRANTS FOR LEAK-DETECTION IN CLOSED PRESSURE SYSTEMS. The procedure followed is the same as outlined in Section 6. If the liquid filling the system is itself fluorescent, all exterior surfaces and joints are examined with a black light for signs of leaking fluorescent fluid. When a spot is found, it is wiped off and watched for re-appearance of leaking fluid.

If the fluid normally used in a system is not fluorescent, a fluorescent additive can be used as described in the previous section. Sometimes the system may be filled with a light petroleum or other solvent, or water, to which one of the available fluorescent penetrant components has been added.

Care must be taken after the test to flush out the penetrant used with suitable solvents so as not to contaminate the operating fluid if the penetrant is other than the normal fluid for which the system is intended. In some cases, however, a fluorescent additive may be permanently incorporated in, say, a hydraulic fluid, or a transformer oil, making leak detection at any time during its operating life only a matter of black-light inspection.

16. USE OF PENETRANTS FOR LEAK DETECTION IN VACUUM SYSTEMS. In testing systems designed to operate at lower than atmospheric pressure, the exact procedure in applying penetrants for leak detection may be varied to suit the circumstances which exist. In some cases it may be feasible to fill the system with penetrant and examine the outside for evidence of leaks, as in the case of pressure systems. This is the only possible approach with penetrants in cases where the inside surfaces of the system are not accessible for examination.

If inside surfaces are accessible, penetrant may be applied over the outer surface while pressure is reduced on the inside. After a suitable time, the inside surfaces are examined with a black light for the appearance of penetrant coming through any leaks. In the case of transparent glass systems, penetrant is applied to the outer surface and after removal of excess, black light examination is carried out from the outside, since any leaking penetrant in a leak or crack can be seen through the glass. Electronic tubes and similar evacuated glass containers are inspected in this manner.

Chapter 14

DETECTION OF LEAKS WITH PENETRANTS

17. Use of Penetrants for Leak-Detection in Open Vessels. As has already been stated, the simple fill-test on a finished vessel is made much more effective by use of fluorescent additives in the filling liquid and use of a black light in looking at the outside of seams for leaks. With large tanks, however, the filling operation even with water is an expensive and time-consuming matter, and if leaks are found it must often be repeated after repair. It is therefore much more desirable to test for leaks during fabrication so that the finished tank, when fill-tested, is not likely to show any leaks. The penetrant method makes this possible with a high assurance that no leaks will exist when the final acceptance test is made.

18. Testing for Leaks During Fabrication. Location of leaks with penetrants is a simple process. In the case of small closed vessels, a small amount of fluorescent penetrant is introduced into the vessel and sloshed about until all interior surfaces are covered. Black light inspection on the outside after a period, from minutes

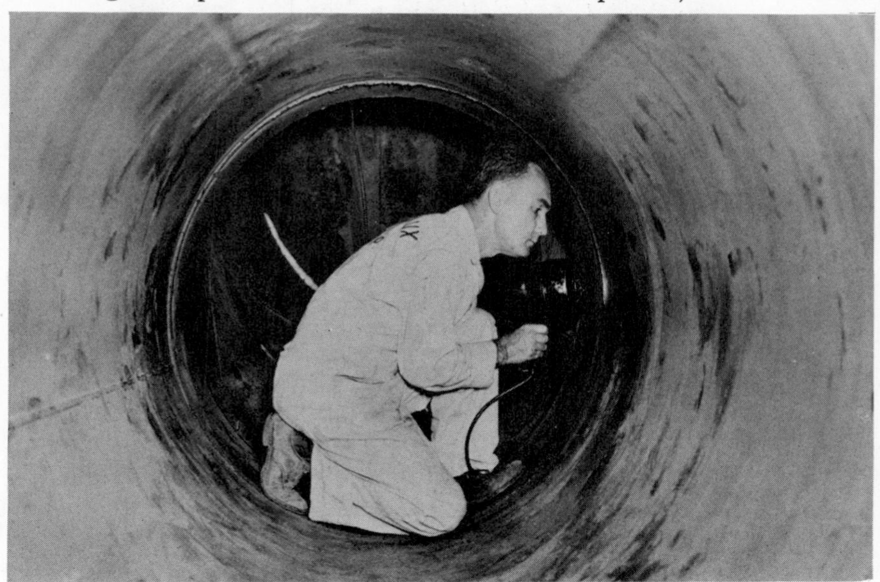

Fig. 155—Looking for indications of leaks in welded joint on interior of large pipe.

to hours for penetration, reveals any leaks, and these may then be repaired. On larger vessels or piping assemblies, penetrant is usually painted or sprayed on the outside seams and black light inspection conducted on the inside. Fig. 155 illustrates the use of black light to find leaks in the welded seams of a large pipe which

Fig. 156—Outside view of welded pipe line of large utility generating station.

is part of the main water-supply line to a new generating station. The outside view of this weldment is shown in Fig. 156.

For small light tanks or cases, the welder can easily be his own inspector and repair any leaks found before the article leaves the welding area. Figs. 157 and 158 show the use of fluorescent penetrant in pressure spray cans for this purpose. After spraying, and a penetration time which may be 2 to 5 minutes for thin sheet and up to an hour or more on thicker sections, the outside of the seam is examined with black light. During the penetration time, the welder is free to continue fabrication of other work. For the longer penetration times, it is usually best to reapply penetrant after a half hour or so. Heavier welds mean longer leak passages and additional penetrant insures sufficient supply to allow penetration completely to the opposite side.

19. Leak-Testing From One Side Only. In some applications both sides of a welded seam which must be free of leaks are not accessible for examination. In this case, inspection of the seam from one side only with penetrants, gives a very high assurance that leaks do not exist. Obviously the most convincing evidence

CHAPTER 14

DETECTION OF LEAKS WITH PENETRANTS

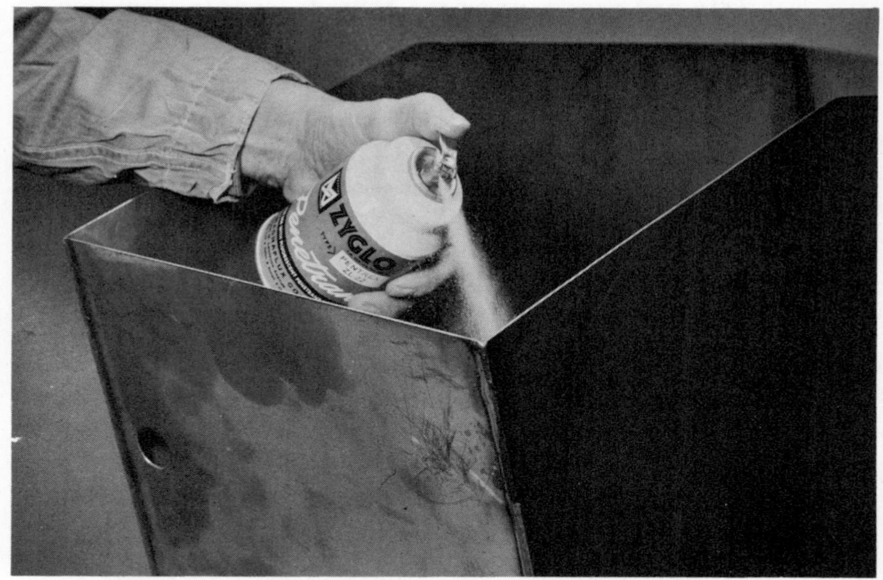

Fig. 157—Applying fluorescent penetrant to inside of welded seam of small tank, from a spray can.

Fig. 158—Indication of leak on outside of welded seam.

of a leak is to find penetrant on the opposite surface from that on which it is applied, a procedure which is of course impossible if both sides are not open to examination. Examples of one-side testing are the welded seams in the *bottom* of large storage tanks, and the welded-on corrosion resistant liners of many processing vessels in the petroleum refinery and chemical manufacture fields. (See Section 27 below.)

In such cases, normal penetrant techniques for crack-finding are used. Penetrant is applied liberally and then washed off. Water-wash penetrants are usually used, since cracks are usually fairly large and clean. After a relatively short penetration time, the surface is washed with water and allowed to air-dry. Developer should be used if small leaks are important, but very often this is not necessary because most leaks will hold a considerable amount of penetrant and quite a bit of penetrant will bleed back out, causing a fairly large and spreading indication. (See Fig. 122 P. 312)

Leaks or cracks, if found, can be chipped out and re-welded. It is not critical at this stage whether or not a crack penetrates through the section to constitute an actual leak.

20. USE OF SPECIAL PENETRANTS. The liquids used in making standard or available penetrants may in some cases be incompatible with the materials of which a vessel or system under test is constructed. For example, oil or petroleum solvents soften and deteriorate articles made of rubber. Many plastics are soluble in certain liquids and these liquids must not be present in penetrants used for testing such plastic materials.

Use of water as the base liquid is often a solution to such a problem, although for various reasons water and the materials incorporated to give water good penetrating properties may in some cases be undesirable. Alcohol or some other organic solvent may provide an answer in many cases. Usually a satisfactory penetrant can be formulated for any special situation.

21. USE OF DEVELOPERS IN LEAK DETECTION. Developers may or may not be required in leak-detection work, depending on the type of penetrant used, the vessel or system being tested and the size of leaks which are sought. When color-contrast penetrants are used the developer is almost always desirable to provide the contrasting background against which to observe the indications. Color-contrast penetrants are widely used for leak-detection in the smaller welding shops because they are so simple to use and have good sensitivity, especially on thin gauge material.

When fluorescent penetrants are used, developers are usually not necessary since there is a continuing supply of penetrant moving through the leak to enlarge the indication, and the test is not dependent on being able to see the very small amount of penetrant reissuing from a crack. However, developer is sometimes a help for very fine leaks. When welded seams are being inspected from one side only, the procedure is no different from the usual crack-finding techniques, and developer here is quite often desirable.

22. SPECIFIC APPLICATIONS OF LEAK DETECTION. To illustrate the use of penetrants in leak detection and to give a more specific idea of how these applications are implemented, a number of typical and interesting uses by various industries will be described and discussed in the following sections.

23. TRANSFORMER CASES. A very interesting production use of fluorescent penetrant leak testing is in the manufacture of pole-transformer cases. These tanks are welded out of 13-gauge sheet, with the bottom put on as the last step by a rolling forming operation. Tanks are from 20 inches to 50 inches in length and from 12 inches to 22 inches in diameter.

(Courtesy Westinghouse Electric Corp.)

Fig. 159—Automatic unit for inspecting transformer cases for leaks with fluorescent penetrant. Tank in foreground is at the penetrant spray station.

Immediately after the bottom is rolled in, the tanks move on a conveyor, open end down, to the penetrant leak testing station. Fluorescent penetrant is automatically sprayed over the interior surface. The standard water-wash type of penetrant is used. The conveyor is paced to permit about three minutes for penetration time, after which the tank reaches the inspection station. Fig. 159 shows a tank on the conveyor at the penetrant spray position. At the inspection station—Fig. 160—the operator, with push button control, seals the inverted top with a clamping head and applies 20 lbs. of air pressure. He then rotates the tank before a battery of black lights and locates and marks any fluorescent indication of leaks.

Cases showing leaks are shunted to a repair bench, and after repair are again sent down the inspection line. Inspection rate is about one case per minute. Effectiveness of leak detection by this process is reported to be better than 99.5%.

24. GAS FURNACE MANIFOLDS. Fig. 161 illustrates another automatic unit for leak detection. It is designed to test gas furnace manifolds for leaks, using fluorescent penetrant. The manifolds are of pipe, from 3/8″ to 1 1/4″ inside diameter, and are swedged closed at one end, which closure must not leak. They are from 6″ to 60″ in length. Fixtures on the unit will accommodate all these sizes.

The manifolds are carried on an intermittent-motion magnetic conveyor. Penetrant is automatically pumped into the tubes, which are then inverted, and drain as they move to the inspection station. They are inspected with black light for indication of leaks and defective pieces lifted from the magnetic fixture. Good tubes move to the end of the unit and are automatically stripped off.

Inspection rate is up to 2500 pieces per hour. Results are far superior to the air-pressure test previously used, and the method achieves a very substantial saving in cost over the older method.

25. AIRCRAFT FUEL TANKS. Aluminum fuel tanks or disposable pod tanks for small aircraft are inspected for leaks with fluorescent penetrant. In this case a few ounces of penetrant are sloshed about the interior of the tank and after a few minutes the outside is examined with a black light. Dry powder developer is used in this operation. Rubber or plastic-lined tanks have been similarly inspected, sometimes using the actual fuel as the liquid and adding a fluorescent material to it in the tank. When testing rubber or

Chapter 14

DETECTION OF LEAKS WITH PENETRANTS

(Courtesy Westinghouse Electric Corp.)

Fig. 160—Inspection station on automatic transformer case leak test unit.

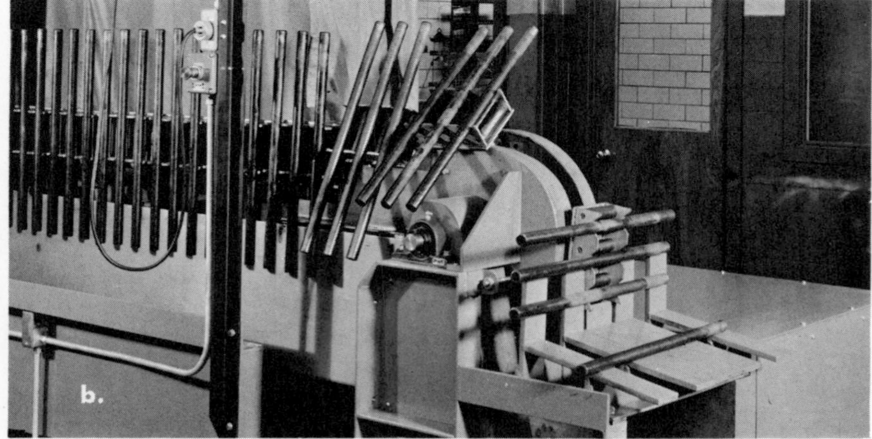

Fig. 161—Automatic unit for testing gas furnace manifolds for leaks. a) Loading and penetrant end. b) Inspection and automatic unloading end.

synthetic rubber tanks it must be first established that the penetrant liquid used does not soften or in any way affect the tank material.

26. LIQUID OXYGEN SYSTEMS. The use of liquid oxygen as part of the fuel for aero-space vehicles has created a leak-testing problem requiring the development of special penetrants. It is, of course, essential that all parts of the liquid oxygen system be free of leaks, as well as any other defect that might cause failure under the pressures involved. Because of the high reactivity of oxygen with any combustible substance, ordinary penetrants are not satisfactory, since even small amounts of most organic materials, penetrant or emulsifier, would cause trouble if not completely removed from the system after testing.

Penetrants having a water base and a minimum of organic components were developed for this purpose and after extensive tests have had limited use in inspecting components of liquid oxygen systems. Although not absolutely free of organic substances (such as fluorescent dyes, and the necessary wetting agents) these materials were present in small enough proportion that the amounts likely to come in contact with the liquid oxygen after careful cleaning were minute. A fully acceptable penetrant for this purpose should be entirely non-combustible.

27. CORROSION RESISTANT LINERS. (See Chapter 13, Section 20). An important area of leak-testing with penetrants is in the inspection of corrosion-resistant liners applied to various types of containers or processing vessels designed to contain corrosive liquids. These vessels are usually constructed of steel and are then lined by the application of alloy or other metal to the inner surface. Sometimes relatively small plates of alloy are key-welded to the inner surface of the vessel, and also seam-welded to each other to produce a continuous corrosion-resistant surface. In another application, sheet lead is applied over the inner surface, and welded or "burned" to form a continuous sheet. It is important that no cracks or pinholes remain in these protective surfaces that would permit corrosive liquids to get through and attack the base material of the vessel.

This is an outstanding example of inspection for leaks from one side only. The techniques employed and illustrations of the process have already been detailed in the preceding chapter.

28. INSPECTION OF WELDED SEAMS WHILE HOT. When conducting in-process inspection of welded seams for leaks, it is sometimes desirable to make the test at the point of welding with a minimum of delay. If cracks that are not leaks are not a problem, through leaks may be detected by applying to one side of the welded seam a water soluble penetrant component that will be fluid at the temperature involved (600°). Water is then applied to the other side. This cools the weld, but also dissolves and spreads any of the penetrant that has come through any opening from the other surface. Black light inspection then reveals the presence of any leak.

29. Leak Testing on the Railroads. Several applications for leak testing have been found in the railroad field. Welded tank cars for carrying liquids or gases are tested for leaks with penetrants. If the liquid is oil, leaks can be revealed by black light inspection of the exterior while the tank car is full, relying on the slight natural fluorescence of most oils.

Sometimes the tank is filled with water in which one of the fluorescent additives has been dissolved, followed by black light inspection of the outside surfaces. If the tanks are made of heavy gauge metal the full-tank technique has the advantage that a sufficient reservoir of penetrant under some head is present to insure that the liquid will pass completely through any leak-passage which may be long and devious.

Tests are also made by the usual method of applying penetrant to one surface and inspecting the other, and this is an entirely satisfactory approach except on thick plate sections. Penetrants moving by their own forces may not get through a long leak path unless time and a sufficient reservoir of penetrant are provided.

Leaks in fuel lines of diesel locomotives, as well as in transmissions, torque converters, speed-reducers, etc., can be detected by the use of black light alone.

Diesel engine cylinder liners are sometimes inspected for leaks during overhaul. Leaks are the result of pitting due to corrosion on the outer surface of the liner, and if present admit water into the cylinder. Such a leak is difficult to detect by ordinary inspection and may be very serious if the leaking liner is re-assembled into an engine. Water in the cylinder breaks down lubrication and piston-seizure while on the road can wreck an engine.

The liners are easily tested. A tube about one third larger in diameter and a few inches longer than the liner is placed in the penetrant tank. The bottom of the liner is then sealed with a rubber-gasketed cap and lowered into the tube sealed end down, causing the penetrant to rise to the top of the liner but not overflow it. Leaks show up practically at once, and can be seen by directing the black light into the interior of the liner.

30. Die Castings. Many die castings are made to contain fluids so they must be leak-free. One example is an aluminum gear housing which must hold oil or grease. Fig. 162 shows a die-cast splice case for communications cable. Telephone and other cables en-

DETECTION OF LEAKS WITH PENETRANTS

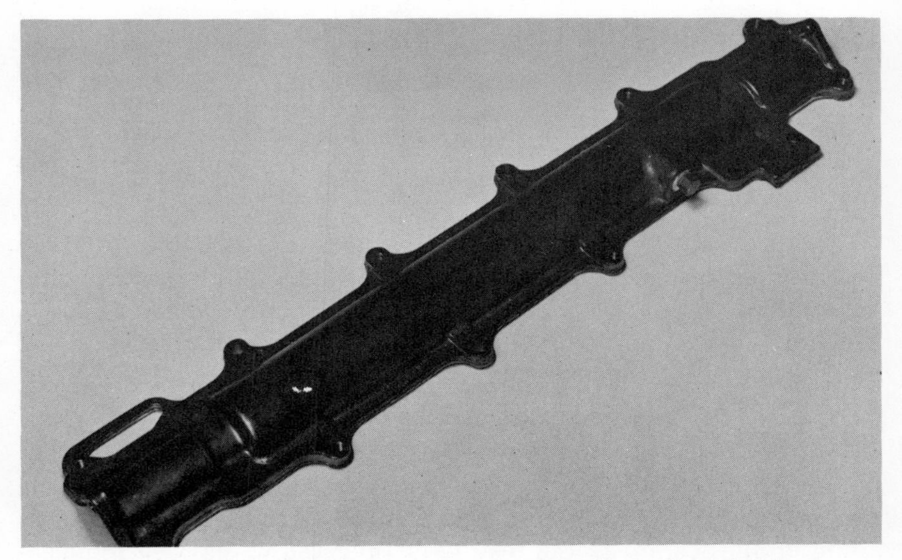

Fig. 162—Communications cable splice-case die casting showing fluorescent indication of leak.

closing multiple wire circuits are customarily kept under a small positive pressure of dry nitrogen to prevent air and moisture from entering the cable. Splices are enclosed and sealed by means of these die-cast cases which must, of course, be gas tight.

Hydrostatic pressure tests are used on these castings but set-up time is long, and rejections are not made until all machining has been completed — machining being necessary before the pressure test can be made. Fluorescent leaker tests are simple—the inside of the half casing is painted with penetrant and fifteen to thirty minutes later the outside is inspected with black light. The illustration shows a leak indication near one end of the case.

Leak testing of die castings with penetrants must be accepted with reservation, since these castings are prone to porosity associated with leaks. Large internal reservoirs or voids may occur as part of the leak path, and penetrants in all instances may not be able to fill these and move on to show on the opposite surface. In the splice cases the penetrant test finds a high proportion of the leakers in the unmachined state and saves the cost of machining these pieces. It does not avoid the need to apply a pressure test to those which are machined, and except for the cost saved by eliminating most leakers before machining, would probably not be justified.

31. TUBS FOR AUTOMATIC WASHERS. This case history is interesting because the leaker test is applied on a production basis, as with the transformer cases. (Section 23). The leaks occur in the seam welds. The type 3 leaker penetrant (red) is used. It is brushed onto the inside of the seams and leaks looked for with a black light on the outside. Production rate is in thousands per week.

Another manufacturer who makes industrial laundry machines tests the finished washer assembly for leaks by filling it with water into which a fluorescent additive has been incorporated. (Type 5, yellow). The machine is then operated and all pumps, plumbing and tank connections and seams are tested for leaks at one time. Black light inspection of all parts of the unit is conducted while it is operating.

32. GLASS-TO-METAL SEALS. This is an important application and one in which fluorescent penetrants were put to early use. In Chapter 13, Section 21 the testing of tungsten wires used for lead-in connections for electronic tubes was described. Seams or cracks in these wires result in leaky seals which spoil a tube. However, even if defective wires have been eliminated by earlier tests, defective tubes can still be produced due to cracking of the glass at the point at which the wire is sealed in.

A bead of glass is usually fused to the wire in advance at the point where the seal is to be made, and then this bead of glass is fused to the glass envelope or base. Cracks or pores may occur between the bead and the wire, or in the seal to the envelope. Fluorescent penetrants can be applied to the sub-assembly of lead-in wires and base. Water-wash penetrants are used and, after washing, cracks between glass and wire are readily seen under black light. Alternatively, the finished tube after evacuation can be tested, the vacuum helping to draw the penetrant into the crack.

Small diodes, transistors and capacitors are similarly tested. The devices are immersed in water-wash penetrant, washed thoroughly with water and examined with black light. One manufacturer prefers color-contrast penetrants for this purpose.

33. DUAL PANE GLASS WINDOWS. Thermal windows are composed of two panes of glass sealed on all edges with an air space between the two panes. In some cases the seal consists of a metal solder strip, and in some the seal is made of fused glass. In either case success of the window depends on a perfect and permanent

CHAPTER 14

DETECTION OF LEAKS WITH PENETRANTS

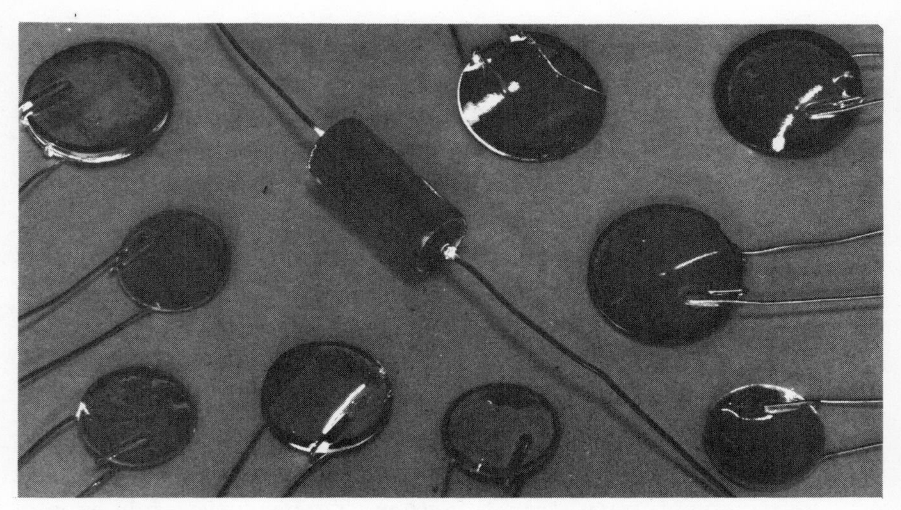

Fig. 163—Leaks in glass-to-metal seals of electronic capacitors shown by fluorescent penetrant.

seal. If this does not exist the air space will "breathe," moisture will be drawn in and will condense on the window glass and obscure vision through it.

These windows are checked 100% with fluorescent penetrant at the manufacturer's plant. An automatic test unit has been designed and built for this purpose, which applies penetrant to all edges,

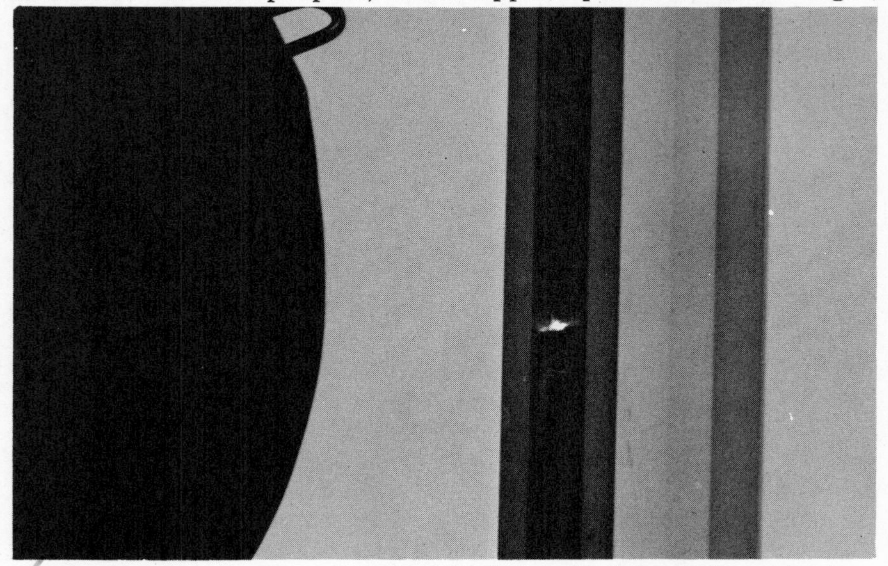

Fig. 164—Testing thermal windows for leaks with fluorescent penetrant.

and after a brief penetration time washes off the excess. Inspection with black light detects even very minute leaks. Defective seals are reworked and reinspected. Experience has shown that the method is almost 100% effective in eliminating leaky windows. Fig. 164 illustrates this testing operation.

34. PRECAUTIONS. In conducting leak tests with penetrants there are a few points that should be understood if dependable results are to be obtained.

(a) Penetrant tests for leaks are very sensitive and almost infallible when the leak occurs in thin material. Here a crack or other opening is a short and direct passage from one surface to the other which penetrants easily pass through.

(b) In thick material the leak path is necessarily longer and penetrant must travel farther. To be successful, enough penetrant must be supplied to "feed" the leak, and enough time allowed for it to get through to the opposite surface. Filling the tank with penetrant is the optimum method of application in such instances, just as complete immersion of a part in penetrant for the full penetration time is optimum for finding extremely fine cracks.

(c) Castings, some welds, and brazed or rolled seams may have porosity as part of the leak path, so that the openings from one surface to the other may be quite far apart. The porosity may provide a large reservoir which may be difficult or impossible for the penetrant to fill, so that even though a through-leak exists, penetrant may not show it.

(d) When penetrants are applied on one surface and inspection made on the opposite surface, *only* through leaks will be indicated. This is definitely an advantage in most instances. It should be remembered, however, that in welds, for example, cracks that do not penetrate completely through the section at the time of test may propagate and later become leaks. In important applications the usual inspection for cracks should not be omitted in favor of the leak test on opposite surfaces.

CHAPTER 15

INTERPRETATION OF RESULTS

1. GENERAL. All nondestructive testing methods produce indirect indications of conditions, but do not of themselves tell exactly what these conditions are. The indications must be correctly interpreted before they give any useful information as to the actual conditions that exist in the material. In radiography, spots or lines or only a vague variation in density appearing on the film mean nothing until a trained radiographer interprets their significance. A pip or pips on a cathode ray screen or a variation in audible pitch in ultrasonic inspection give warning of some variation from homogeneity, but a person trained in the method must interpret what he sees or hears. Similarly, traces on a chart or movement of a needle, or a pattern on a cathode ray screen or record tape in eddy current testing have significance only to the trained operator.

Magnetic particle and penetrant tests alone among the major nondestructive test methods produce, directly on the surface of the part being tested, indications which are clearly related to the size and shape of the discontinuity causing the indications. Filtered particle, electrified particle and thermographic methods also do this, though their fields of application are much more restricted than those of the five major methods. The task of interpretation with magnetic particles and penetrants is made somewhat easier for the inspector because of this characteristic of the methods, since the size and direction of the indication often give him some direct clue to its cause.

Actually, however, none of these indications *of themselves* tell the observer what he has to deal with. They must therefore be interpreted

2. INTERPRETATION VS. EVALUATION. There is often a tendency on the part of an inspector to confuse the terms "interpretation" and "evaluation," and to fail to recognize that there is a significant distinction between them. Actually, the terms refer to two entirely different steps in the inspection process and require entirely different categories of knowledge and experience on the part of the inspector.

To "interpret" an indication means to give a decision as to what the condition is that is causing it. It may be a crack from whatever cause, porosity, lack of bond, or merely some surface discontinuity which results from the assembly of parts, such as a forced fit. "Evaluation" then follows "interpretation." If it has been decided that a crack of given size and direction exists, the extent of its effect on the usefulness of the part must be *evaluated* before the part can be disposed of—either accepted as is, reworked, or scrapped.

3. EXPERIENCE NEEDED FOR INTERPRETATION. To interpret indications correctly, the inspector must first of all be thoroughly familiar with the test method he is using. He must know that inspection-processing has been correct. In the case of fluorescent penetrants, for example, he must be certain that washing has been thorough, so that the indication he sees can be accepted as that of a bonafide discontinuity. He must further be able to derive all possible significant information from the appearance of the indication itself (see Sections 13 & 14), and from this he may be able to declare that a crack or porosity or some non-relevant condition is present.

His task, however, becomes easier and his declaration more authoritative if he has a background of knowledge regarding the part he is testing. He should know the material, the process by which it is made, and the various processes it has been through subsequently. He should know the kinds of defects characteristic of the material and should be aware of what defects various processes are likely to introduce. If the part has been in service, he should know enough about how metals fail to know where fatigue cracks are most likely to occur. In other words, he should have enough background knowledge regarding a given part to know in advance what defects are likely to be present, and about where he should look for them. In addition, of course, he must be familiar, from past experience, with the appearance of indications of defects of these types on similar parts or material.

4. EXPERIENCE NEEDED FOR EVALUATION. Once it is known that a crack or porosity or other defect of given size or direction is present, a decision as to the disposition of the parts depends on an evaluation of the significance of the defect to the serviceability of the part. This is a question of stress and stress distribution, and calls for the knowledge of the designer and engineer who are responsible for the performance of the part. For a given service a defect in one direction may be harmless, but the same defect in another direction which may be at right angles to the tensile stress may be highly objectionable. In the same way, a defect in one location on a part may be in an area of low stress and perhaps can be tolerated, but if a similar defect occurs in an area of high stress it would cause rejection of the part.

The usual way of expressing this idea is that "a discontinuity is only a *defect* when it will interfere with the usefulness of the part in service." To make the decision as to whether a part should be used or scrapped, therefore, requires the knowledge and experience to interpret the indication *plus* a knowledge of the service requirements of the part. This latter has basically no relationship with the nondestructive testing method which has revealed the presence and character of the defect, and sometimes calls for the judgment of several persons. These may be (in addition to the inspector), the metallurgist, design engineer, quality control manager and possibly others. This group is sometimes designated the "salvage committee."

5. IMPORTANCE OF THE INSPECTOR. Since correct evaluation depends on accurate interpretation, the inspector is the key man in the inspection process. In some mass inspection operations, the man who operates the test equipment merely segregates the parts which show indications and others pass on their disposition. In most cases, however, the inspector, who first sees the indication, is also expected to interpret it. Actually, if he has any of the qualifying background, he is the one best able to do this since he is most familiar with all kinds of indications as they occur on the parts he handles. Also he is best able, because he is the man who made the tests, to know that the process has been properly carried out or to know of and assess any variations from normal behavior during the test.

The inspector therefore must be a thoroughly honest and dependable individual. He must be alert at all times and not become bored with his job if he finds few defective parts. He must be fully alive to the importance of the work he is doing. If incidence of indications becomes greater or less than normal he must take immediate action to determine the cause. He must check his own operation—equipment, material, technique—to make sure that the deviation from normal is real. Then the information should be passed on without delay to those who are in a position to check processes and sources of material.

6. INTERPRETATION OF PENETRANT INDICATIONS. Actually, the interpretation of penetrant indications is relatively simple. Since penetrants cannot indicate any but *surface* discontinuities, *any* indication can be caused by only two things:

(a) An actual discontinuity in the surface, or

(b) Penetrant remaining on the surface from some non-relevant cause, such as poor washing or accidental contamination from some external source.

7. FALSE INDICATIONS. Penetrant inspection is liable to the production of wholly false indications—that is, fluorescent or colored spots or areas which are present entirely independent of any kind of surface discontinuity.

8. POOR WASHING. The most common source of false indications is poor washing. If the excess of penetrant is not completely removed from the surface after penetration is complete, it remains to show at the time of inspection and may be very confusing. Use of black light to follow the washing process with fluorescent penetrant is therefore highly important, because an experienced operator can tell whether a good rinse is being obtained or whether patches of fluorescence are being left behind.

Usually such fluorescent patches are due to dye which has not been carried away by the emulsifier and water, and is fixed pretty tightly to the surface. Wet or dry developer tends to reduce the brilliance of such patches, since there is little or no fluid penetrant for the developer to pick up and spread, and so it tends simply to cover up the patches. However, since the amount of developer coating must be light, such masking is really not much protection. See Fig. 104, Chapter 12.

In the case of color-contrast penetrants, this is not a real problem since the usual cleaning method is with solvents and cleaning is much more likely to be thorough. In any case the developer layer is heavy enough to cover unremoved penetrant and at worst the developer solvent will pick up remaining dye and color the developer layer pink. Of course, patches of unwashed dye could remain where water-wash color-contrast penetrant is used, but again, the developer would pick them up.

9. OUTSIDE CONTAMINATION. To guard against the confusion resulting from fluorescent or color spots other than true indications great care must be taken that there is no chance of penetrant from outside sources reaching the surface of the part. Some of the sources of such contamination are:

(a) Spots of penetrant on the inspection table.

(b) Penetrant on the hands of the inspector.

(c) Contamination of dry or wet developer with penetrant.

(d) Penetrant rubbing off from an indication on one part to a clean portion of the surface on another.

The inspector must practice constant cleanliness in the inspection area and use great care in handling parts to avoid contamination of parts from such sources. This cleanliness should also be observed with respect to the tanks of penetrant and other materials, to

Fig. 165—Example of bad housekeeping in fluorescent penetrant inspection booth.

exclude dirt, etc. Stray lint from wiping cloths may be held on surfaces of parts and result in deceptive but meaningless indications. Fig. 165 is a horrible example of bad housekeeping in an inspection booth.

10. NON-RELEVANT INDICATIONS. Outside the realm of truly false indications there is a category of non-relevant indications which the inspector must be able to recognize. These are true indications in that they are caused by surface discontinuities, but the discontinuities are there by design and are in no way defects. The most common source of this type of non-relevant indication is the opening between parts which are fitted together as by a forced fit, a keyed or splined connection, or two parts riveted or spot welded together. Fig. 105 (P. 294) shows indications of the "christmas tree" joints where blades are attached to the wheel of a gas turbine.

Such non-relevant indications are usually quite easy to recognize, since they can be related directly to some feature of the assembly that accounts for their presence. Forced fits may be so tight that a complete outline of their presence may not be indicated, but if the operator knows that such a joint exists he will be able to interpret the cause of an indication at such a location correctly.

11. SURFACE CONDITIONS. Sometimes castings may have rough surfaces due to burned in sand, or may have loosely adherent scale. These will hold penetrant that will show up on inspection. The indications of these conditions are not due to poor washing, but rather to inability to produce a clean-washed surface. Nevertheless, this type of indication interferes with easy, correct interpretation and the inspector must watch for it. In many cases this type of non-relevant indication can be avoided by proper initial pre-cleaning.

12. TRUE DEFECTS. Indications of true defects ordinarily take one of two forms:

(a) Linear indications which are caused by cracks or other crack-like discontinuities, or

(b) Irregular or spotty indications which are caused by porosity.

These may vary widely in size and extent but practically all penetrant indications will fall in one class or the other.

13. WHAT AN INDICATION CAN DISCLOSE. In addition to the significance of the shape of an indication, its size, intensity and amount of spreading give useful information regarding a defect. Very fine cracks and very fine porosity give faint indications whether the defects are isolated or in groups. The wider or deeper the crack or the larger the porosity cavities, the more penetrant is available to form the indication, so that larger, brighter, and more rapidly spreading indications are produced.

Thus the intensity and spread of the indication gives information as to the size and severity of the sub-surface portion of the defect—depth in the case of a crack, or volume in the case of porosity. Similarly, the *speed* with which an indication forms is a clue to the volume of penetrant available in the defect. Large defects form indications immediately and do not require developer—fine defects may require long developing time before the indication is visible at all.

Fig. 166 shows fluorescent indications of fatigue cracks in an aircraft engine piston. In the center is a very bright indication showing considerable spread. At both sides are very fine indica-

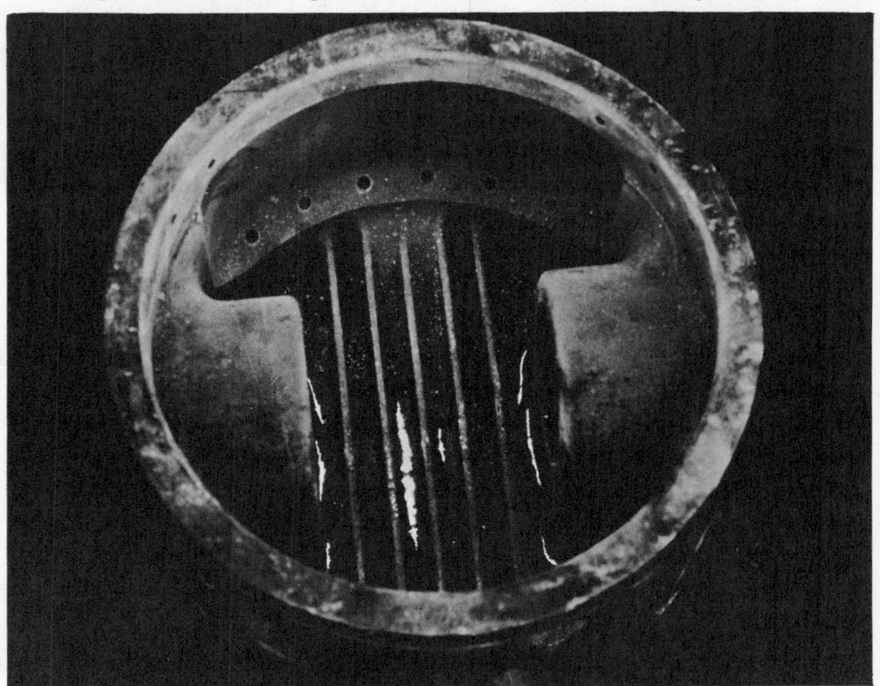

Fig. 166—Fluorescent penetrant indication of fatigue cracks in aircraft engine piston, showing difference in appearance at fine and large cracks.

tions. Obviously, all are indications of cracks (or crack-like openings) but the great difference in their width and depth is equally apparent.

Fig 167 shows indications of surface porosity. Again the difference in the indications clearly shows that some are produced from

Fig. 167—Indications of porosity in aircraft magnesium casting, showing some fine and some gross porosity.

very fine openings, whereas, in other areas the porosity is much more gross.

14. Spreading of Indications. Although all indications tend to spread with elapsed time, a good penetrant is designed to limit the speed of spreading. This gives better delineation of a discontinuity. Indication of a large crack may spread so fast that the exact location of the crack may be hidden under an area of fluorescence or color, and the crack-like shape of the indication may be masked before the inspector sees it. Of course, it would still be obvious that a large discontinuity was present, but interpretation would be hampered.

Conversely, if the formation of the indication is watched, the speed with which the indication forms and spreads is another clue to size. Also, the indication may be wiped off—possibly with a little solvent—and the location observed to see whether and how rapidly an indication re-forms. Discontinuities with large penetrant-holding capacity will reappear rapidly.

15. Cracks. Cracks may be short or long, shallow or deep, single or in families. Unless masked by excessive spreading, indications of cracks all have a linear appearance—they are long but have little width in relation to their length. These are therefore much easier to see and indentify, in an area of background fluorescence or color, than are the spotty indications of porosity.

16. POROSITY. Porosity varies widely in character, and may be fine or gross, relatively isolated or spread over large areas. Micro-shrinkage in aluminum and magnesium sand castings is similar to

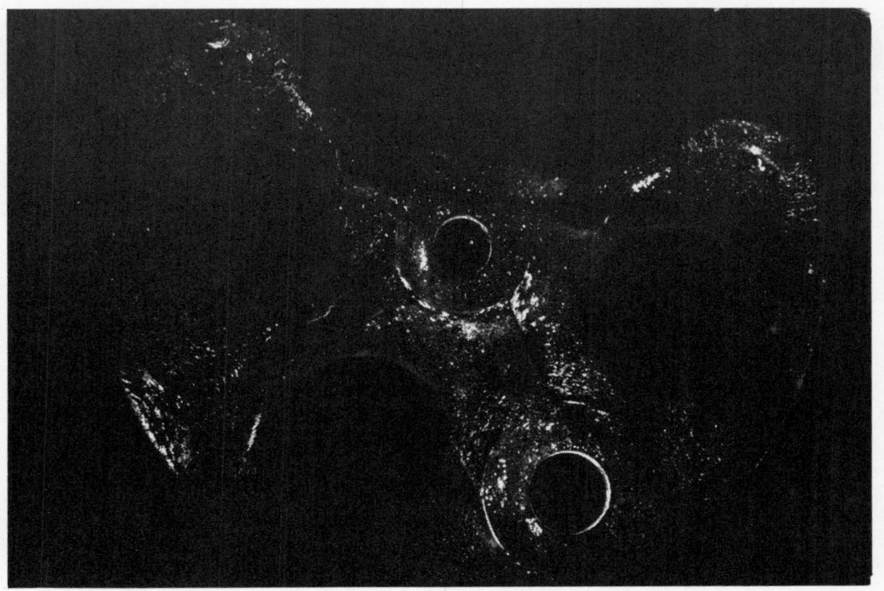

Fig. 168—Indications of microshrinkage in magnesium casting.

porosity, and gives similar indications. Figure 168 is an example of micro-shrinkage in a magnesium sand casting, the indications being produced with fluorescent penetrant.

17. SUPPLEMENTAL TESTS. A crack is a crack no matter what its origin, and the fact that the discontinuity is a crack may be clearly revealed by the shape and other characteristics of the indication. Sometimes a few additional tests may give a knowledgeable inspector a better lead to the reason for its occurrence. Cleaning off the surface with very fine emery paper will often make the crack visible in white light, either directly or with the help of a magnifying glass. Sometimes a light etch of the cleaned surface will reveal more details of the exact appearance of the crack.

Fracture of the part through the crack exposes its face and again may give information regarding it. Sometimes a section taken across the crack is polished and examined under the metallurgical microscope. Such tests are often very valuable and worthwhile to build up an inspector's experience with defects and indications. They are especially valuable if a metallurgist or other competent person is available to guide such tests and explain the significance of the information revealed.

18. BACKGROUND KNOWLEDGE. We therefore come again to the importance of broad knowledge and experience on the part of the inspector, for proper interpretation of penetrant (or any other type of nondestructive testing) indications. Familiarity with the part—how and of what it was made and what processes it has been through—tells the inspector, if he has such knowledge, what defects are likely to be present, and what kinds cannot be. It tells him "what to look for and where to look for it," and makes for more dependable inspection as well as for more accurate interpretation.

CHAPTER 16

STANDARDS AND SPECIFICATIONS FOR PENETRANT INSPECTION

1. GENERAL. Flaw detection with penetrants is an art and not a science. This is necessarily true unless or until some successful means is evolved which can automatically see and accurately interpret penetrant indications. In the meantime, the inspector must be relied upon to perform these functions, and skill and proficiency in developing and then interpreting indications must be acquired by experience. A skilled and experienced inspector can add greatly to the inherent effectiveness of this method of inspection.

The tendency today is to try to eliminate this factor of human skill—or rather the effect of the lack of it—by substituting, at least for the purpose of seeing the indication, some mechanical or electronic means more reliable than the human eye. There is the further tendency to describe and prescribe or standardize every step in the complete inspection process, so that the operator need bring to his job as little thought and skill as possible.

This tendency may be looked upon as having some very desirable objectives, as well as some effects that seem less desirable. By reducing all activities with regard to the inspection either to automatic processes or to processes governed by rules and standards the following desirable results are presumably achieved:

(a) Overall reliability of the inspection is increased.

(b) More uniform results are obtained.

(c) Operators not having a high level of education and experience may be used.

(d) Training of operators is minimized.

(e) Time of skilled and experienced inspectors is conserved.

Some less desirable effects may be:

(a) Tendency to relieve operator of the necessity for thinking and developing skills.

(b) De-emphasizing the importance of watching for abnormalities in materials and processes that may affect the inspection.

(c) Tendency to make the inspection more perfunctory (which it should *never* be).

Still, the balance of weight is definitely on the desirable side, and standards and specifications are indeed important and necessary for reliable inspection. Therefore, much has been written and proposed to provide guides and controls in all phases of penetrant inspection technology.

2. TYPES OF SPECIFICATIONS. Specifications and standards which are applicable to penetrant inspection may be divided into two broad classes:

(a) Those dealing with methods and techniques.

(b) Those dealing with materials.

Each of these groups can be further broken down. Some of the sub-groups are:

(A) METHODS AND TECHNIQUES.

(1) Broad procedural guides—general.

(2) Company procedural guides.

(3) Procedural guides for specific types of products, or for industries.

(4) Procedures for testing specific articles—specified by a purchaser or by a company internally—process specifications.

(5) Procedures specified for overhaul inspection of a company's products.

(6) Specifications for certification of operators.

(7) Standards for acceptance or rejection, set up by buyer, or by company for quality control.

(8) Repair Station requirements.

(9) Equipment specifications.

(10) Instructions for operating specific types of equipment or individual special units.

(B) MATERIALS

(1) Specifications designed for use in purchasing penetrants and other materials.

(2) Specifications designed for testing and evaluating performance of penetrants and other materials.

3. BROAD PROCEDURAL GUIDES. A number of technical societies have prepared broad procedural guides for the use of their members who wish to learn about or use penetrant nondestructive testing. These consist, for the most part, of a very general description of penetrant testing. They are intended to be informative, and give the reader an idea of how the method works and the steps by which it is properly applied. Usually, examples of applications are given, often with some illustrations of typical indications.

The sections on penetrant testing in the Handbook of the Society for Nondestructive Testing constitute by far the most complete presentation of this type. Some of the other societies whose handbooks include a section on penetrant testing are the Society of Automotive Engineers, American Society of Mechanical Engineers, American Welding Society, American Society of Tool Engineers and the American Society for Metals. In addition, there are various books, both here and abroad, dealing with nondestructive testing, that include similar more or less complete descriptions of the method.

4. COMPANY PROCEDURAL GUIDES. Many large companies that make extensive use of penetrant testing have prepared their own versions of the procedures which are to be used within their plants. These are also rather broad in their approach, except that they may be limited to those specific procedures applicable to their products. As an example, if post-emulsification penetrants are not used in their plant, no guide for the use of this process need be included. Also the procedure specified may be written around the particular equipment used in that plant.

Such manuals are used in training new operators and for the guidance of those regularly using the method. Included in this type of specification or manual are those issued by various facilities of the Armed Services prescribing the materials and techniques which are approved for use. Such Technical Orders (T.O's) are issued by the U. S. Air Force, for example, for the use of inspectors engaged in testing aircraft parts on overhaul. These T.O.'s are usually very complete and cover all types and phases of penetrant testing.

5. PRODUCT OR INDUSTRY SPECIFICATIONS. Some method specifications have been written from the point of view of a single industry or type of product. For example, the description of penetrant testing which appears in the handbook of the American Welding Society is directed toward its use for the inspection of welds and weldments. The U. S. Air Force technical order is, of course, written for use in the inspection of aircraft and aircraft engine parts. A company that makes only castings would prepare a specification to cover the inspection only of castings, and this would be no broader than necessary for this single purpose. The U. S. Air Force has issued a specification limited to the inspection of castings as a class.

6. PROCESS SPECIFICATIONS. A much narrower type of specification is that drawn up to prescribe the exact method of testing for a specific article. These are usually prepared by the quality control department and, in addition to calling for an exact testing procedure, usually also include a definition of indications which may be tolerated and of those for which the article must be rejected. Such process specifications may refer to or make use of the broad method description of a company-prepared or handbook-type of procedural guide, but should be specific with regard to those factors which will insure proper inspection of the specific part to which the process specification refers.

Some of the factors that should be covered are:

(a) Cleaning or pre-inspection preparation (paint stripping, degreasing, etc.)

(b) Specific penetrant and method technique to be employed.

(c) Penetration time.

(d) Emulsification time (if P. E. method is specified).

(e) Type of developer.

(f) Developing time.

(g) Black light source or intensity.

(h) Inspection environment (degree of light exclusion when critical).

(i) Post-cleaning, when required for following processes.

(j) Surface protection (corrosion preventives and packaging).

In addition, critical areas are usually defined, and indications described which may or may not be accepted, so that disposition of questionable parts may be expedited. Length, direction and frequency of indications and their location with regard to the critical areas are usually the means for classifying acceptable and rejectable indications. The advent of fluorescent printing inks has made possible fluorescent reproductions of actual photographic records of acceptable and rejectable indications of defects of specific types. Sheets containing these printed indications may be kept in the inspection booth by the inspector and referred to by simply holding the sheet under the black light.

These process specifications are an excellent device for insuring good inspection. They must be prepared with care by engineers who are fully aware of the service requirements of the part, the directions and amounts of stresses and location of stress concentration areas. Those preparing the specifications should also be thoroughly familiar with the various techniques of penetrant inspection and the degrees of sensitivity attainable.

Similar specifications and acceptance standards may be agreed upon in advance between buyer and manufacturer to cover the inspection and the acceptance and rejection limits for a specific purchased part.

7. MAINTENANCE OR OVERHAUL INSPECTION. Manufacturers of complex and critical products (as, for example, aircraft engines) frequently include a section in their maintenance manuals in which recommended inspection procedures for use on overhaul are given. Such a procedural guide is broad enough to cover general techniques and equipment, but is specific with respect to the inspection of critical parts and components. Such guides are of great value, since they tend to assure in advance that the inspection for maintenance purposes that will be performed by the user will be suitable and proper for the specific items involved. The chance that the inspector responsible may not be sufficiently experienced to perform the inspection properly is minimized. Advice is often included in such manuals as to where to look for trouble and how to judge the significance of an indication when found.

8. CERTIFICATION OF OPERATORS. The U. S. Air Force and other government departments that make regular use of these methods long ago recognized the danger of poor inspection results if operators and inspectors are not properly trained and experienced. For this reason a system of operator qualification has long been in use, and specifications have been issued under which operators must be qualified. Inspections may not be performed on Government procurement or overhaul of aircraft or parts unless the operator is so certified.

Usually such certification is limited to certain types of inspection on specific types of equipment, and even to certain specified locations. If the operator changes jobs he may need new certification tests in order to qualify for the new work. Operators and inspectors in vendors' plants must be so certified, as must those who are directly employed by government agencies. Responsibility for certification of operators now rests in the prime contractor for a given government project. Tests are given in accordance with government specifications, and include written examinations on materials and techniques as well as actual demonstration of ability to find defects in actual parts.

9. STANDARDS FOR ACCEPTANCE OR REJECTION. Over the years there has been an insistent demand for standards to govern acceptance and rejection of parts on the basis of indications produced by this (or other) inspection method. Users complain that they are told how to use a method of inspection but are not told what to do about indications of defects that are disclosed. A little reflection should make it readily apparent that any broad standards for this purpose are impossible.

Whether or not a given discontinuity warrants rejection of a given part depends entirely upon factors that have no relation whatever to the inspection method that produces the indication of its presence. The service requirements of the part are the controlling factors. Nature of the stresses in service, stress concentrations, critical nature of the function of the part—even location and orientation of the defect on the specific part—must all enter into a decision as to acceptance or rejection. These considerations cannot be generalized, but must be applied by those possessing the information to each specific case. A given defect in one part for one type of service may warrant rejection, but may have no significance if present in another part for a different type of service.

The preparation of standards for acceptance or rejection are the responsibility of the designers of the part and of the quality control department, and are most effectively included in process specifications. If such standards are not available and the individual judging the results of the inspection does not possess the necessary knowledge, he must seek it from those responsible for the design and service performance of the part. He should not *expect* broad standards to be available. However, knowledge of the material and its expected service, as well as of defects in general and their effect on strength and performance, often allow an inspector, with the use of common sense, to arrive at an intelligent decision regarding acceptance or rejection.

10. REPAIR STATION REQUIREMENTS. Another type of specification bearing on the use of penetrant (and other) inspection methods is that setting forth the requirements for repair stations for aircraft and aircraft engines. The Federal Aeronautic Administration (F.A.A.), which has jurisdiction over the approval of shops or stations for repair and overhaul, specifies the extent and type of equipment and other facilities necessary to insure satisfactory inspection of all parts before they may be reused. Penetrant inspection facilities are a requirement for a fully authorized repair station for aircraft and engines.

11. EQUIPMENT SPECIFICATIONS. Specifications for standard equipment for applying the penetrant inspection methods have been prepared and are used for procurement of such equipment by the U. S. Air Force and by other agencies.

12. OPERATING INSTRUCTIONS. Manuals or operating instructions are prepared by the manufacturers of equipment to guide the user in its proper use. These are not specifications in the usual sense of the term, but may include method procedures and techniques as applied to the use of the specific piece of equipment.

For large pieces of equipment, where automatic handling is involved, these manuals become lengthy and complex. Larger reservoirs for penetrants, emulsifiers and developer require more complicated controls, and maintenance of proper levels and concentration is important. Successful operation of a large unit such as the one for stainless steel tubing described in Chapter 13, Section 18, would be difficult if not impossible without the specific instruction furnished in such a manual.

13. PURCHASE SPECIFICATIONS FOR MATERIALS. The practice of procurement by competitive bidding by government and other users of penetrants has emphasized the need for a specification under which bids can be prepared and submitted. Awarding of purchase contracts to the lowest bidder is a satisfactory method of purchase of such a critical material as penetrant *only* if the purchaser can in some manner be assured that the material he receives is of satisfactory quality and suitable for his application. Every purchaser and user of materials of all kinds knows that the cheapest product in price is not always—or even often—the best.

A definite specification that pins down the essential properties of the desired material and also provides tests and procedures for verifying the compliance of materials actually delivered is needed. Proper use of such a specification and tests is the only means by which the purchaser can be assured that acceptance of a low bid will result in his receiving material of satisfactory quality. In the case of penetrants, the writing of such a specification has proven to be an extremely difficult undertaking.

In the early days of penetrant inspection, Magnaflux Corporation was the sole supplier of fluorescent penetrants, since the process and materials had been largely developed by and were proprietary with it. The company realized its responsibility to furnish to all users of the penetrant methods only the highest quality materials which its development of the art was able to produce. Great effort was and is expended to insure uniformity and to maintain quality in every shipment. Early purchasers under competitive bidding recognized these materials as the only available standards, and used the questionable "or equal" device when buying.

The difficulty here arises from the fact that the physical properties and chemical composition of penetrants—which *can* be defined—are of far less importance than the ability of the penetrant to find defects of a wide variety of kinds in a wide variety of materials under widely varying circumstances. Many attempts to write performance specifications for this purpose have been signally unsatisfactory.

There are many properties and characteristics of penetrants that should and can be specified. These are mostly of the type to insure uniformity once defect-finding ability has been defined and satisfactorily achieved. Such properties and the tests used to measure them will be covered in the following chapter (17). These properties and tests—at least many of them—do and should have a place in purchase specifications. But alone they do not and cannot assure the principal requirement—that of satisfactory crack-finding ability.

14. MEASUREMENT OF CRACK-FINDING ABILITY. In Chapter 4 the attempts to measure performance of penetrants have been fully discussed. Various cracked test specimens have been devised and proposed as a means for evaluating performance. These are at best useful for *comparing* two or more penetrants in their ability to find those particular types and sizes of cracks which the test pieces present. As a means for defining performance quality, a reference standard of proven sensitivity must be available for comparison. All attempts to devise tests which take into account all the variables which affect performance and sensitivity and also assign a numerical value for overall performance without use of reference standards have so far been unsuccessful.

15. GOVERNMENT PROCUREMENT SPECIFICATIONS. The several branches of the Department of Defense have great interest in developing a satisfactory specification by which purchase of penetrants and associated materials can be made satisfactorily under the competitive bidding system. Some years of effort have been spent and many proposed specifications have been written and even used. These have been less than satisfactory to either Government facilities or suppliers, since they have provided neither acceptable definitions of properties and performance nor tests by which such characteristics can be verified in delivered materials.

Ideally, such a specification should be based primarily on performance. Limits for specific characteristics such as flash point, viscosity, fluorescent brightness, etc. would then be used to assure consistent quality and uniformity. The core of the difficulty lies in the apparent impossibility, to date at least, of defining performance in absolute terms. The best currently proposed specifications therefore rely on reference standards of several types of penetrant materials, the satisfactory performance of which have been demonstrated over long periods of actual use. Tests are specified to assure that delivered families of penetrant materials measure up to the standards in quality, although here performance comparisons are limited to one or more types of artificially prepared cracked specimens. Additional assurance is derived, however, from various other tests—flash point, washing characteristics, fluorescent brightness, etc.—which bear on performance and quality when compared to the reference standards.

Use of such a specification involves much testing which is time-consuming and expensive. It is justified because of the critical importance of securing the best possible inspection of vital aircraft and missile parts as well as wide varieties of other important equipment and materials.

16. EMULSIFIERS AND DEVELOPERS. Procurement of penetrants also requires, to assure satisfactory performance, procurement of emulsifiers and developers which will work well with the given penetrant being purchased, and enable it to perform at its maximum capability. Here, however, the problem is somewhat simpler, since the manufacturer of the penetrant has devised emulsifier and developer to bring out the best possible crack-finding abilities of every given penetrant. Specifications for emulsifier and developer need therefore be little more than a means for assuring quality and uniformity, and use of the correct product.

The close inter-dependence, for maximum performance, of penetrant, emulsifier and developer is widely recognized, so that procurement from the same supplier, of a "family" of these materials which experience has shown to work well together, is today accepted procedure.

17. ACCEPTANCE TESTS. Procurement specifications define desired properties and give limits for these properties for acceptable materials. However, the tests and methods by which these properties are to be determined must also be defined and described. Such method specifications are usually made a part of the procurement specification, but may also be used for purposes other than procurement.

18. SPECIFICATIONS FOR TESTS AND TEST METHODS. A large number of tests have been devised by the manufacturers of penetrants and allied materials for use in their own processes of evaluation and quality control. Users of penetrant families also make use of such tests in evaluating or qualifying a penetrant for a specific application.

Some of the tests specified may be standard for other materials, such as the A.S.T.M. test for flash point or viscosity. Some of the tests have been devised to measure properties which are peculiar to penetrants and their performance. To insure uniform results among various users of these tests, all details must be carefully described—not only the method of making the test, but also the equipment to be used.

Detailed discussion and description of many such tests are given in the following Chapter (17).

19. LIST OF GOVERNMENT SPECIFICATIONS. Following is a list of Government Specifications currently in force, which bear in one way or another on the application of penetrant nondestructive testing to Government material and equipment:

Inspection, Penetrant Method of
Mil—I—6866

Inspection, Penetrants, Nondestructitve Testing
Mil—I—19684

Inspection Materials, Penetrant
Mil—I—25135

Qualification of Inspection Personnel—
Magnetic Particle and Penetrant
Mil—Std—410

Nondestructive Testing Requirement for Metals
Mil—Std. 271

NavShips 250—1500 (Welding Handbook)

Air Force Manual, Inspection of Material,
Fluorescent & Dye Penetrant Methods.
T. O. 33B1—2—1—2.

Inspection Unit, Fluorescent Penetrant,
General Spec. for
Mil—I—9445

Inspection Unit, Fluorescent Penetrant, Type MA-2
Mil—I—25105

Inspection Unit, Fluorescent Penetrant, Type MA-3
Mil—I—25106

Inspection Kit, Penetrant, Naval Shipboard
Mil—I—19867

Inspection Requirements, Nondestructive, for
Aircraft Material & Parts.
Mil—I—6870

Penetrant Inspection, CAA Quality Control
Digest No. 2 Nov. 1958

These specifications are subject to frequent change or modification. Some are undergoing such revision at the time this is written. The list is given to indicate the scope which existing specifications cover at this date.

CHAPTER 17

TESTS FOR EVALUATION AND CONTROL OF PENETRANTS, EMULSIFIERS AND DEVELOPERS

1. TYPES OF TESTS. Tests that are performed on penetrants and related materials are of four types and have four different objectives.

(a) EVALUATION OR PERFORMANCE TESTS. These tests are intended to give information as to the quality, and probable performance in use, of penetrants and related materials. For the most part they are tests which compare such materials in various significant aspects with standards selected for their known and proven excellence over a period of actual use.

Such tests may be used in several ways. First, they may be made part of an acceptance specification to determine that delivered materials are equivalent in important performance characteristics with the specified comparison standards. Second, they may be used to compare the characteristics of new materials of unknown properties with others of known satisfactory performance, or with each other. Third, they may also be used as control tests by the manufacturer to verify quality and uniformity of batches of material, in relation to comparison standards.

(b) TESTS FOR PHYSICAL PROPERTIES. The second group of tests determine measureable abstract physical properties which in themselves have little or no bearing on actual crack-finding performance. Their prime purpose is to establish conformity with certain physical parameters which may have been established for a certain type of material. As acceptance and control tests they indicate the uniformity of a penetrant or emulsifier, from batch to batch or shipment to shipment. The acceptable limits of the properties measured—such as flash point, viscosity, etc.—are set up from experience with similar materials that have proven satisfactory in use. Such limits may also be set up from practical considerations, such as safety and health hazards, or economic factors not necessarily related to crack-finding performance.

(c) OPERATING CONTROL TESTS. This group comprises tests devised to be used to determine the continuing suitability of penetrants, emulsifiers and developers as they are being used for actual inspections. They include tests for contaminants or other types of deterioration that would impair the effective performance of these materials, to determine that no significant deviation from optimum values has occurred. Some of these tests are identical to those of the two previous groups, though the information they produce is sought for a different purpose.

(d) MANUFACTURING CONTROL TESTS. These tests are of no interest to the users of the penetrant methods except as their use assures uniformity in quality and performance from shipment to shipment of each type of penetrant or other material purchased. Some of the tests of this group are the same as those of group (a) and (b), but some are specially designed for control purposes. These tests will not be listed or described in this chapter.

2. COMPARISON OR REFERENCE STANDARDS. Since many of the tests used are comparison tests, the first requirement is to determine upon and have available a reference standard. Government specifications define the standards and provide for their selection and renewal. Usually the standard is a sizeable amount of penetrant of a given type (or developer or emulsifier) withdrawn from a shipment of satisfactory quality. Industrial users follow the same procedure—simply preserve a sufficient amount from the last previous satisfactory shipment, and use it to compare with the next shipment to be tested.

Standards should be kept in sealed containers in a cool dark storage space, where they will not deteriorate from the effect of heat, light or evaporation. Standards should be renewed at intervals of two to three years, or more frequently if there is any reason to suspect deterioration of any sort from any cause.

3. SAMPLING. The results of any tests intended to give information regarding a given lot of material are of no value and the tests are futile unless the samples on which the tests are performed are truly representative of the lot. This should be self evident, but the taking of samples for testing purposes is too often given insufficient thought and attention. Correct sampling procedures vary widely for different types of product. For liquids the prime requirement is that each container from which a sample is drawn be thoroughly agitated so that the liquid is well mixed. If several containers of similar size are involved, a sample should be withdrawn from each. These samples should be of equal quantity and should be combined and mixed for testing. When large numbers of small containers are to be sampled, a sufficient number (10% or more) of the total should be opened for sampling.

For dry materials, the procedures are similar except that effective mixing of the several sample increments is far more critical, to insure a representative lot. A.S.T.M. specifications and standards give details of approved sampling procedures for a variety of solid and liquid materials. For a general discussion of sampling theories and methods the reader is referred to A.S.T.M. Symposium on Usefulness and Limitations of Samples, published in A.S.T.M. Proceedings Vol. 48 P. 857.

4. EVALUATION TESTS. The following tests are listed under this heading and will be described:

(a) Fluorescent Brightness.

(b) Stability of Fluorescence under Black Light.

(c) Stability of Fluorescence on Hot Metal Surfaces.

(d) Spot or Meniscus Test for Thin Film Fluorescence of Penetrants.

(e) Sensitivity of Penetrants on Cracked Aluminum Blocks.

(f) Sensitivity of Penetrants on Cracked Plated Strips.

(g) Water Washability of Penetrants—Water Wash Type.

(h) Water Washability of Penetrants—Post Emulsification Type.

(i) Tolerance of Water Wash Penetrants and Emulsifiers to Contamination with Water.

(j) Water Drop-Through Test for Post-Emulsification Penetrants.

(k) Compatability of Post-Emulsification Penetrants and Emulsifiers.

(l) Stability of Penetrants to High Temperatures.

(m) Stability of Penetrants to Low Temperatures.

(n) Dispersibility of Wet Developers.

(o) Wetting Ability of Wet Developers.

(p) Removability of Wet Developers.

(q) Surface Uniformity of Wet Developers.

(r) Corrosion Test for Wet Developers.

5. TESTS FOR PHYSICAL PROPERTIES. The following tests are listed and described (or referenced) under this heading:

(a) Specific Gravity.

(b) Viscosity.

(c) Flash Point.

(d) Water Content.

(e) Sulphur Content.

(f) Chlorine Content.

6. OPERATING CONTROL TESTS. The following tests are listed and described or referenced under this heading:

(a) Sensitivity Tests for Penetrants.

(b) Fluorescent Brightness of Penetrants.

(c) Water Contamination Test for Penetrants.

(d) Glycerine Breakdown Test for Water-Wash Penetrants.

(e) Emulsifier Sensitivity Tests.

(f) Fluorescence of Emulsifiers.

(g) Emulsifier Water Content.

(h) Wet Developer Concentration Control Tests.

(i) Developer Fluorescence.

(j) Developer Coating.

(k) Developer Wetting Ability.

CHAPTER 17

TESTS FOR EVALUATION AND CONTROL

Evaluation Tests

7. FLUORESCENT BRIGHTNESS OF PENETRANTS.* It seems obvious that one of the most important characteristics to be evaluated in a fluorescent penetrant is the brightness with which indications produced by it will fluoresce under black light. To measure this characteristic is not easy and requires the use of rather expensive instruments. Actually, in applying such a test, we are usually less interested in the quantitative value of the light emitted under given circumstances, than we are in the *relative* emission as among several penetrants or as between a given penetrant and a reference standard.

Quantitative values for the emitted light can be obtained by the use of the spectrophotometer, and this is undoubtedly the best and most accurate method of evaluating this property and for making comparisons among penetrants. One advantage of the spectrophotometer is that it analyzes the emitted light over the entire spectrum and gives information as to color, dominant wave length and purity which, in addition to actual overall brightness, are factors in the effectiveness of fluorescent penetrants in actual flaw-finding applications. If color differences — as opposed to mere brightness — are to be measured, the spectrophotometer instrument is the only one that can give this result with accuracy.

However, for many purposes we are more interested in the overall brightness of a given penetrant in comparison to that of other penetrants or of a reference standard. This can be quickly and easily determined by the use of the simple filter-photometer. The instrument is less expensive than the spectro-photometer, and tests are less costly and time-consuming to make.

For this purpose the Coleman Model 12-C Photofluorometer is satisfactory,** although other instruments may be used. Some of the instruments may require some modification, depending on type of penetrant specimen to be used. A filter-paper disc (or other

*For a more complete discussion of the measurement of this property the reader is referred to the paper "Brightness of Fluorescent Penetrants, Its Measurement and Influence in Detecting Defects" by D. W. Parker and J. T. Schmidt in Nondestructive Testing Nov.-Dec. 1957. Also to the discussion of color measurement in "Handbook of Colorimetry" by Arthur C. Hardy, published by Technology Press, M.I.T. 1936, and to a good physics text such as "Principles of Physics" Vol. 3, "Optics" by Francis W. Sears.

**Other instruments of this type that may be used are: Aminco Light Scattering Microphotometer, Farrand Photoelectric Fluorometer; Fisher Nefluoro-Photometer; Photovolt Multiplier Photometer; Turner Photometer—Model 110.

shape to fit the sample holder of the instrument being used) saturated with diluted penetrant offers a simple specimen which approaches the condition of penetrant at an indication dispersed on a white developer. There is some difference of opinion as to the most dependable type of sample to use for this test. Instead of the filter paper specimens, a thin film of penetrant or diluted penetrant in a glass cell has been proposed. When the emphasis is on thin film fluorescence this type of specimen offers advantages. The spot or meniscus test also gives useful information from the standpoint of thin films. However, both the latter techniques are affected by the passage of the fluorescent light (and incident black light) through a film of penetrant liquid, whereas at an indication the fluorescent light is *reflected* from the specimen or developer surface. Fluorescent light transmitted through a film of penetrant will be affected by the light-absorbing properties of the liquid of the penetrant itself. (See Section 13, this Chapter).

At this time the filter paper test specimens have had extensive use over a period of years, and it is felt that for most purposes the results obtained by their use with the photofluorometer or the spectrophotometer give reliable comparison data for various penetrants. They will be described here.

8. PREPARATION OF FILTER PAPER SPECIMENS. Five ml. of the penetrant to be tested and five ml. of the reference standard are pipetted into two 50 ml. stoppered glass cylinders, and diluted to the 50 ml. mark with methylene chloride. After thorough mixing the dilutions are transferred to 4 oz. open-mouth jars.

Six pieces of Munktell's No. 5 filter paper of suitable shape and size are immersed, one after the other, into the diluted penetrant and six others into the diluted reference standard. Excess penetrant is drained off by touching the edge of the jar for four seconds. The filter papers are then placed in a horizontal position on a clean metal screen to air-dry for 5 minutes. They are then placed in an oven and dried at 225°F for a further 5 minutes.

Measurement in the photofluorometer should be made promptly on the filter paper specimens after they have been dried.

9. THE COLEMAN 12C PHOTOFLUOROMETER. Two modifications of the instrument are necessary to make the desired measurements on the filter paper specimens.

TESTS FOR EVALUATION AND CONTROL

Fig. 169—Preparation of filter paper specimens for fluorescent brightness determination.

(a) A black light filter (B-1-S) made from Corning 5874 glass may be obtained with the instrument and is satisfactory for filtering the incident light. The photo-tube, however, must be fitted with a filter modifying its sensitivity to correspond more closely with response of the human eye. This can be done by means of a Corning CS 3-132 filter, which can be mounted in a spare filter holder obtainable with the instrument.

(b) The sample holder of the instrument must be modified for measurement of the reflected light of the filter paper specimens. This is done with the sample holder shown in Fig.

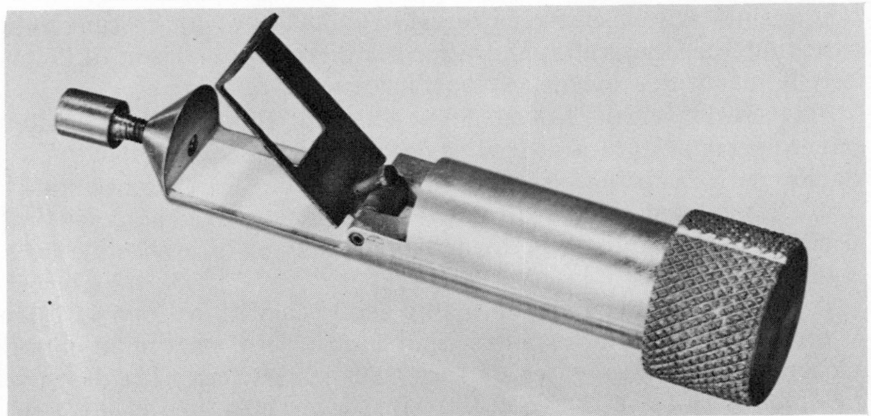

Fig. 170—Filter paper sample holder for Coleman photofluorometer (modified).

170. (Details for this modification can be obtained from Magnaflux Corporation).

With the instrument and specimens properly set up, readings are made on at least 4 of the specimens from each penetrant and the results averaged. When the specimens are mounted in the holder

Fig. 171—Coleman Model 12C Photofluorometer with special sample holder in place.

they should be backed with a piece of similar paper, untreated. The results are measured in terms of quantity of fluorescent light reaching the phototube, and afford a direct comparison of fluorescent brightness of the various specimens.*

10. STABILITY OF FLUORESCENCE UNDER BLACK LIGHT. Filter paper specimens are prepared as described in Section 8 above. Two papers each from the test penetrant and from the reference standard are mounted on a clean flat test panel supported in a vertical position. The four papers are mounted tangent to each other in a square pattern.

A CH 4 mercury vapor spot lamp equipped with a Kopp 41 filter is directed at the filter papers so that the center of maximum illumination falls at the center of the "square" pattern. The lamp is mounted with filter 12″ from the panel. Exposure time is one hour, and the panel is rotated one quarter turn at 15 minute intervals,

*Here see Appendix III for a further discussion of brightness measurement.

so that each paper receives the same light pattern for the same period of time.

After exposure, the papers are measured for fluorescent brightness in the photofluorometer and compared with the values obtained on the unexposed papers. The difference is expressed in percentage of the original, and indicates the relative stability toward black light of the fluorescent materials involved.

11. STABILITY OF FLUORESCENCE ON HOT METAL SURFACES. Some fluorescent dyes tend to fade when subjected to heat in a thin film on a metal surface. Stability under these conditions is of practical importance in a penetrant, since there should be no loss of fluorescence during the drying operation in the hot air drier.

The test is made on stainless steel panels prepared as described in the following Section 12, and is a comparison test between the reference standard and the penetrant under test. Two spots are marked on the panel two inches apart, and 0.05 ml. of penetrant and of standard is pipetted onto these spots. The panel is placed horizontally in an oven and held at 200°F for 5 minutes. The fluorescence of the spots is then compared visually under black light. The apparent luminance of the sample penetrant should not be less than that of the standard.

12. PREPARATION OF STAINLESS STEEL TEST PANELS. Stainless steel test panels are used in the test for stability on hot metal surfaces, and also in the water washability test. They are prepared as follows:

Panels 4 x 4 inches square are cut from type 310 stainless steel sheet of about 20 gauge. The panels are sandblasted on one side only, using grit of average 100-mesh size, using 60 pounds of air pressure with the gun held 18 inches from the panel. Panels are then slip-sheeted and wrapped in Kraft or other non-oily and non-waxed paper for storage. Before using, the panels are heated to 225°F and then cooled to room temperature in a desiccator. The sand blasted side is used in all tests.

After each use, the panels must be degreased and resandblasted.

13. SPOT OR MENISCUS TEST FOR FLUORESCENCE IN THIN FILMS. This test was first proposed by James R. Alberger* as a means of

*"Theory and Applications of Liquid Tracers" by James R. Alberger, SNT Journal, Vol. XX (1962) No. 2 p. 91.

measuring the relative sensitivity of penetrants. For this purpose it is inadequate since it measures only one factor of many that enter into the matter of sensitivity. (See Chapter 4, Sections 24 to 42 incl.) The test, however offers a method of estimating the relative ability of penetrants to fluoresce in thin films. A plano-convex lens of 1.06 meters radius is placed upon an optical flat. The thickness of the space between lens and flat can be calculated for any distance out from the point of contact. Penetrant is introduced into this space and the assembly viewed with black light.

The film of penetrant will fluoresce with the exception of an area immediately surrounding the point of contact between lens and flat, where the thickness of the film approaches zero. The smaller the diameter of this dark spot or bull's eye, the greater the thin film fluorescing ability of the penetrant. This ability is a function of the concentration of dye in the penetrant, of the fluorescing activity of the dye and of the intensity of the black light employed. The ability to fluoresce in thin films does not seem to be directly related to fluorescent brightness as measured in the photospectrometer. It is a property, however, which is of interest in comparing the performance of various penetrants.

The theoretical expression for thin film fluorescence is the following:

$$I_f = I_o \cdot K \cdot Q \; (1 - 10^{-ecl})$$

where:

I_f = fluorescent light intensity given off by the film.

I_o = Intensity of black light that energizes the film.

K = a constant based on the means used for viewing the film (phototube, the human eye, etc.)

Q = The quantum efficiency of the dye.

e = the molor extinction coefficient of the dye.

c = the concentration of the dye in the liquid.

l = the optical path length—i.e., the thickness of the film.

For a given dye and a given viewing means, K, Q and e are constant. The variables are:

I_o = the incident black light intensity.

c = the concentration of the dye.

l = the film thickness.

Fig. 172 illustrates the effect on the diameter of the black spot when the incident fluorescent light intensity, I_o, is varied. In (a)

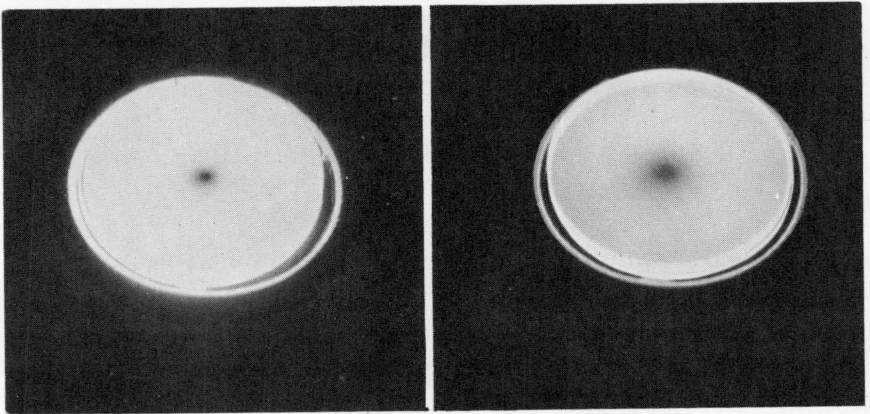

Fig. 172—Photographs with different black light illumination of the same meniscus test spot. a) High illumination (Lamp 2½″ above specimen). b) Low illumination (Lamp 5″ above specimen).

the spot is small when I_o is high. The same specimen exhibits a larger spot (b) when I_o is reduced.

If we *fix* the intensity of incident black light, the *emitted* fluorescent light intensity will vary with c and l; i.e., the fluorescent light is reduced as film thickness (l) becomes less, and is increased as dye concentration (c) becomes greater.

If then, we choose a dye and fix a level of incident black light intensity, emitted fluorescent light intensity for *any given film thickness* is a function of "c", the concentration of dye in the penetrant. Thus, for a given dye, the meniscus test is an approximate measure of the *amount* of dye present. Conversely, *at a given dye concentration* the spot diameter will vary with the values of "Q" and "e" for the dyes used.

The meniscus test may therefore give information of interest in comparing the performance of various penetrants, but must be better defined and standardized before it can be very useful. Furthermore, it gives information regarding only *one* item in the list of properties bearing on penetrant performance.

One of the principal drawbacks of the method is the difficulty in defining accurately the conditions of test, especially with respect to the measurement of the diameter of the black spot. Assuming that the variable of black light intensity can be measured and controlled, there still seems to be no precise method of determining the diameter of the bull's eye. This is largely because there is no sharp line of extinction—instead the intensity of emitted light falls off at a varying rate, and the diameter of the dark spot varies with the means adopted to measure it, and with the operator.

Measurement of the diameter of the spot may be made.

(a) Visually, using the naked eye and a pair of dividers and ruler.

(b) Photographically.

(c) Electronically, by scanning with a photo-tube through a slit traversing the diameter.

None of these methods is satisfactory. Visual scanning is dependent too much on the eye of the observer. The photographic approach depends on illumination, type of film and time of exposure. The phototube scanning is affected by mechanical and optical limitations. For these reasons, although the test basically is capable of giving useful information, much work must be done to so define the equipment and conditions of test that reliable comparisons and reproducible results by different operators can be obtained.*

14. SENSITIVITY OF PENETRANTS ON CRACKED ALUMINUM BLOCKS. Cracked aluminum blocks have had wide use over a number of years as a means of comparing the performance of penetrants in actual crack-finding use. They have the advantage of providing an easily prepared test specimen containing cracks of varying size, from large to fine, and of varying depth. Comparisons are necessarily visual, but are made under actual use conditions. They can be used for either fluorescent or color-contrast penetrants. However, in making thorough evaluation tests other types of cracked specimens should also be employed, such as one or more of the cracked plated specimens, as well as actual defective parts of various shapes and compositions. This test is not very satisfactory for comparing some of the modern high sensitivity penetrants.

15. PREPARING THE CRACKED ALUMINUM BLOCKS. These blocks are cut from ⅜″ thick aluminum alloy (Type 2024 - T - 3) sheet or strip. They are 3 x 2 inches with 3″ dimensions in the direction of rolling. Thermal cracks are produced in the blocks by heating and then quenching in cold water.

The heating is done over a gas flame with the blocks horizontal and the flame of the burner or torch impinging on the center of the

*Here see Appendix III for further information regarding this test.

underside. On the center of the top side a mark about the size of a penny is made with a 950° to 980° F. Tempilstik applied with a circular motion. The heating is done at a rate to cause the Tempilstik mark to melt in approximately 4 minutes' time, when the panel is immediately quenched in cold water. The heating and quenching is then repeated on the other side of the block.

A center groove about 1/16″ wide and 1/16″ deep is then cut in the 2-inch direction across each flat side of the block. This forms two similar specimen areas on each face of the block and permits side-by-side treatment with two penetrants without allowing the two to come together across the groove.

Figures 173 and 174 show the steps in the block preparation.

16. TEST PROCEDURE ON ALUMINUM BLOCKS. For critical comparisons new blocks should be used. However, reuse is permissible provided the blocks have been carefully cleaned as described in the following section (17). Blocks should ordinarily be used only three or four times, because the cracks tend to become enlarged in the cleaning operation. Before re-use blocks should be checked with black light to make sure no residual fluorescence is present.

Fig. 173—Heating and applying Tempilstik on aluminum block.

Fig. 174—Quenching hot aluminum block in cold water.

Fig. 175—Cracked aluminum block ready for tests.

The comparison tests are made using the entire sequence of steps and materials as are used in actual inspections for flaws, and in the way prescribed for the family of materials being tested. The test family is applied to one-half of one face of the block and the reference standard family to the other half. Recommended washing, drying, and developing procedures must be followed exactly. The

CHAPTER 17

TESTS FOR EVALUATION AND CONTROL

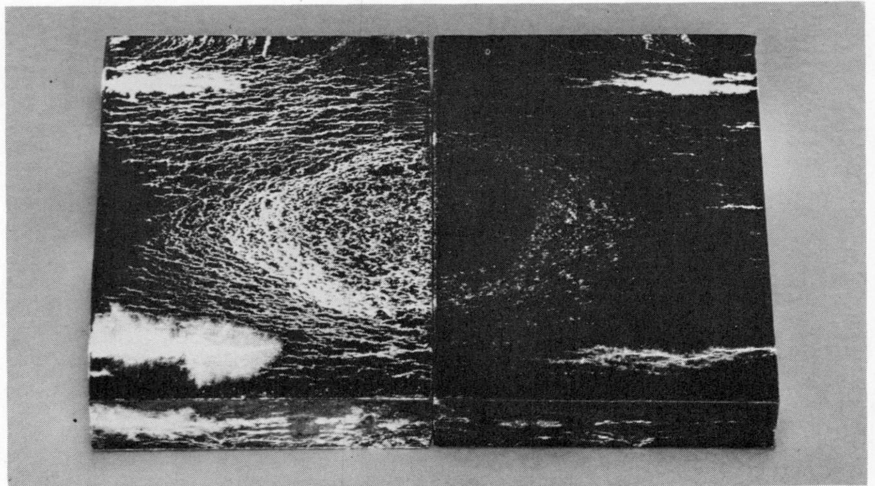

Fig. 176—Black light photograph of indications of two penetrants on cracked aluminum block.

block is then examined under black light and careful comparison made of the number, size and brightness of the indications produced on the two sides. At least 3 blocks should be used for each test.

17. CLEANING BLOCKS FOR RE-USE. To prepare test blocks for re-use they should be heated slowly with a gas burner to 800° F. as determined by an 800° Tempilstik, and then quenched in cold water. The blocks should then be dried for 15 minutes at 225° F. to drive out any water in the cracks. After this treatment, the blocks should be cleaned by scrubbing with a bristle brush and a solvent such as naphtha, and then exposed in a vapor degreaser. Just before using, the blocks should be oven-heated for 15 minutes at 225° F and cooled to room temperature. The reheating and quenching operation, necessary to drive all penetrant out of the cracks, acts to enlarge the cracks and also tends to clog cracks somewhat with non-volatile components of the penetrant. After three or four such reheatings the blocks are no longer very suitable for comparison tests.

18. SENSITIVITY COMPARISONS ON CRACKED PLATED STRIPS.* By plating a coating of brittle metal onto a strip of steel that can be bent, a cracked specimen can be produced in which the depth of the crack can be known and its width controlled over a wide range. Thickness of the brittle coating determines the depth of crack,

*Here see Appendix III for description of this test made on cracked chrome-plated strips.

which may be from a few micro-inches up to .0025″ or more. Width or tightness of the cracks is controlled by the method of bending. The strips are cracked by bending just before use, so that cracks are clean and fresh. Amount of bending should be sufficient to insure that cracks extend to the bottom of the brittle layer.

The test strips are 3″ x 1½″ pieces cut from 16 gage hot-rolled steel. The coating usually used is iron, plated under conditions to insure that it will be brittle. The plating procedure is quite complicated and the several variables of composition of bath, temperature and current density must be carefully controlled. Details for applying this coating may be obtained from Magnaflux Corporation. Instead of iron, a chromium coating has been proposed which may be equally satisfactory.

Plated strips are dried, and stored in a desiccator until they are used. Strips may be cleaned and reused as often as 10 or 12 times, following the cleaning method described below (Section 20).

19. TEST PROCEDURE ON PLATED STRIPS. Plated strips are withdrawn from the dessicator and bent just before use. One strip is bent on a jig having a cylindrical surface with a radius of 4½ inches. Another is bent as a cantilever by clamping one end and depressing the other over a contoured jig. The former produces a pattern of uniformly spaced cracks, the latter a pattern of decreasing frequency out from the clamping point. Fig. 177 illustrates the bending jigs and the cracked patterns produced. Both of these strips are used for the test.

The cracks produced by the above procedure are relatively wide open. In order to close them so as to provide cracks of very fine widths, the strips are replaced in the jigs and bent in the opposite direction. The cracks located on the concave side after this second bend are the ones used for the test. The cracks on the cantilever specimen will vary in tightness, the narrowest being at the clamped end. Cracks on the radius-bend specimen will be of uniform opening.

To prevent cross-contamination of the penetrants being compared, a saw slot is cut down the middle of the specimen after bending, as shown in Fig. 177.

To make the test, the penetrant family to be evaluated is applied to one-half of the panel (on the concave side) and the comparison standard family is applied to the other half. The panels are

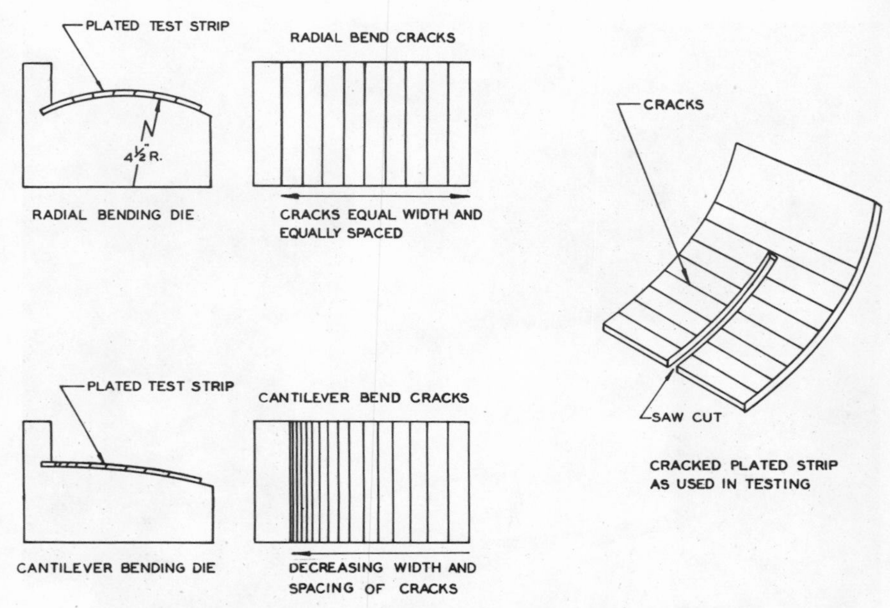

Fig. 177—Drawing of plated test strip, bending jigs and crack patterns produced.

processed through the various steps recommended for the penetrants involved, exactly as they would be in an actual inspection. After developing, the panels are examined under black light and the indications compared visually for number, size and brightness. At least two panels of each type should be used for each comparison test.

20. CLEANING CRACKED PLATED STRIPS FOR REUSE. To clean the cracked panels for reuse they are first scrubbed with a bristle brush and detergent solutions, thoroughly rinsed with water, and dried in an oven at 225° F for 15 minutes. They are soaked for 24 hours in acetone and then vapor-degreased. They should be kept in a desiccator until used. Some users prefer to cut the panels completely in two instead of extending the saw cut only the length of the cracked zone. On cleaning, such strips should be kept together as a matched pair.

21. WATER WASHABILITY TEST—EQUIPMENT. The sandblasted stainless steel panels prepared as described in Section 12 above, are used for the various washability tests. A special fixture has been devised for these tests capable of flowing an even curtain of water for a definite length of time over the surface of the panel at a controlled low pressure. Fig. 178 illustrates this washing

Fig. 178—Wash test fixture with panel in place.

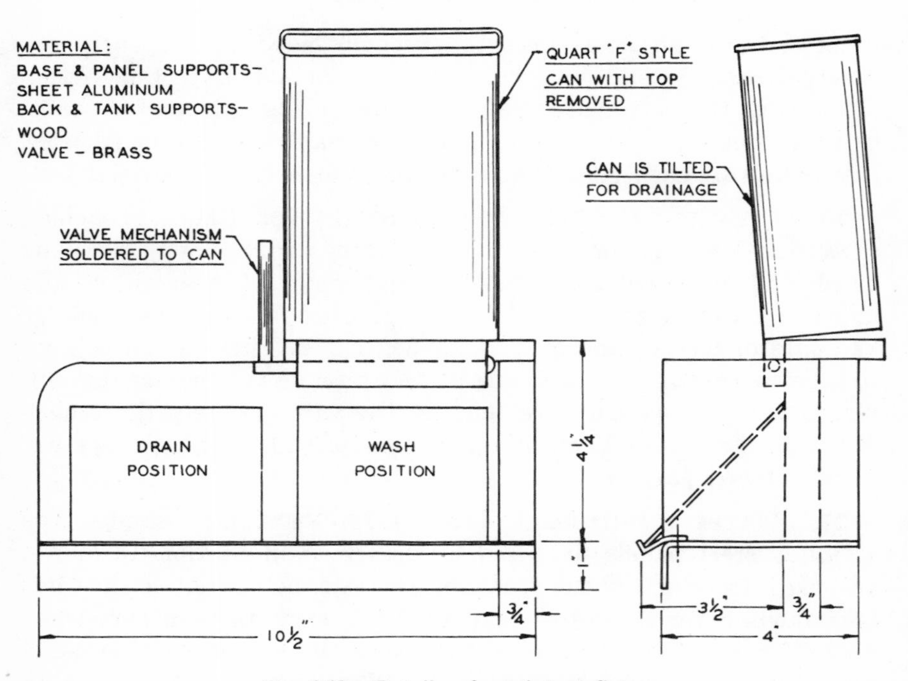

Fig. 179—Details of wash-test fixture.

fixture with one of the panels in place. The drawings of Figs. 179 and 180 give the details for making this fixture and the valve mechanism for it. The fixture provides a location where the panel can be held at 45° for draining and then moved to a similar position under the water openings for washing.

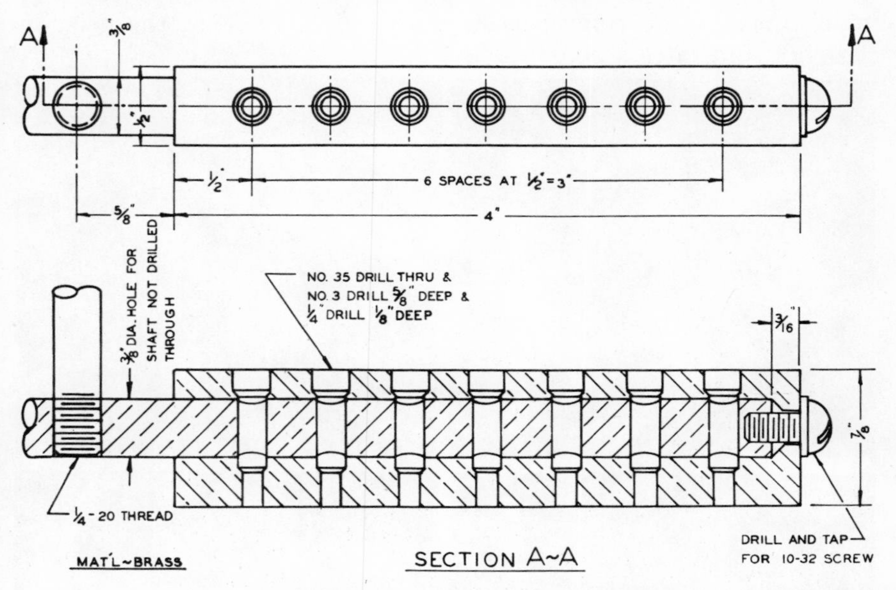

Fig. 180—Details of valve for wash-test fixture.

22. WASH TEST PROCEDURE—WATER-WASH PENETRANTS. This test is an absolute one—i.e., a penetrant can be tested alone for washing characteristics or the test can be used for comparisons, two water-wash penetrants being tested side by side on the same panel. The procedure is as follows:

Two spots are marked on the sandblasted side of the test panel, located 1 inch from the top edge and 1 inch from each side edge. The reservoir of the test fixture is filled with one liter of water at 65°F ± 5°. The panel is placed in the drain position on the fixture and 2 or 3 ml. of each of the two penetrants being compared are poured onto the panel at the two marked locations. The panels should be at 45° in both the drain and wash positions of the fixture. Draining is allowed for 5 minutes and then the panel is moved to the wash position and the valve of the reservoir fully opened. After washing the panel is examined in a darkened area with black light.

Figure 181 shows the several steps in this operation. The bright outer edge of the test areas are disregarded, but the entire area within the halo marking the original spots covered by penetrant should be evaluated for degree of freedom from residual fluorescence, and a comparison drawn between the two samples (one of which may be the reference standard). In Fig. 181d the spot on the right indicates a poor wash.

Fig. 181—Steps in the washability test. a) Applying penetrant. b) Drain. c) Wash. d) Examination.

23. Wash Test Procedure — Post-Emulsification Penetrants. These tests are made with the same type of panel and the same fixture as used for water wash penetrants. The spots marked on the panels should be 1½ inches from the top edge, however, to allow room for the complete covering of the penetrant spots with emulsifier. Two or three ml. of the penetrants are poured on the spots and 5 minutes drainage time allowed. The emulsifier intended for use with each of the penetrants should be used. Then 5 ml. of the proper emulsifiers are poured over the penetrant spots, taking care that the entire area covered by each penetrant is blanketed with emulsifier, even if in draining the emulsifiers come in contact with each other. Three minutes drain time is allowed and then the panel is moved to the wash station and washed.

The spots are examined under black light in a darkened area, and compared for residual fluorescence. The bright halo around the penetrant spots may be ignored for this comparison.

24. TOLERANCE OF WATER-WASH PENETRANTS AND EMULSIFIERS TO CONTAMINATION WITH WATER. The penetrant is tested in a 100-ml. graduated stoppered cylinder, and temperature of the test materials should be maintained at 80° F ± 2° F. Forty ml. of penetrant are placed in the cylinder and water added from a burette in ½ ml. increments. After each addition the material is mixed by stoppering the cylinder and inverting several times. The end-point is reached when the sample turns cloudy, separates or gels. The percent water-tolerance of the sample is calculated by dividing the ml. of water added by the volume of sample plus water in ml. at the end of the test and multiplying by 100. The better water-wash penetrants have high tolerance to contamination with water. Emulsifiers are tested similarly.*

25. WATER DROP-THROUGH TEST FOR POST-EMULSIFICATION PENETRANTS. Post-emulsification penetrants are designed to be immiscible with water, so that water washing of unemulsified penetrant will not remove the penetrant from shallow defects. This test is intended to determine the degree to which water does or does not mix with the penetrant when water gets into the penetrant bath. It is the converse of the water-tolerance test of Section 24. Usually a reference standard is used in this test for comparison.

Twenty ml. portions of the reference standard and of the penetrant under test are placed into separate 100-ml. graduated cylinders by pouring down the inside wall. Samples should be at 75° F. Four ml. portions of water at 75° F are then added to each cylinder by pouring down the inside wall with the cylinders inclined 30° to the vertical. Examination is made immediately to determine the completeness of water drop-through for each of the samples. Emulsification at the interface should be slight, and be no greater in the sample under test than in the reference standard.

26. COMPATIBILITY OF EMULSIFIERS AND POST-EMULSIFICATION PENETRANTS. To check emulsifiers and penetrants for compatibility to insure that they will work properly together, the following procedure is used. Portions of penetrant and emulsifier are mixed in stoppered graduated cylinders. Tests are made with the materials at 65° F and again at 120° F. In one set of tests at each temperature, penetrant and emulsifier are mixed in equal proportions, and in another set the proportions are two volumes of emulsifier and one of penetrant. In all cases the resultant mixture should be a clear solution.

27. STABILITY OF PENETRANTS TO TEMPERATURE. Penetrants may be subjected to temperatures outside the normal range of temperatures of use, usually during shipment or storage. It is important that no significant change take place under such circumstances, that would affect the performance of the penetrant when returned to normal operating temperatures. The following tests may be absolute tests or they may be made in comparison with reference standards.

(a) STABILITY TO HIGH TEMPERATURES. Weigh 100 ml. of the penetrant into a 250 ml. beaker and subject to the following temperature cycle: 4 hours at 130° F followed by two hours at a room temperature between 65° F and 85° F. At the end of this time the sample should show no appreciable precipitation of insoluble material (or no more than shown in the reference standard). The beaker should be reweighed, and the sample should show no large loss of weight (or no larger than the reference standard).

(b) STABILITY TO COLD TEMPERATURES. Subject 100 ml. of the penetrant in a 4 oz. oil bottle to the following temperature cycle: 4 hours at 0° F followed by 2 hours at a room temperature between 65° F and 85° F. At the end of this time there should be no separation of constituents and no precipitate of insoluble material (or no more than shown by the reference standard).

Similar tests may be made on emulsifiers, if desired.

28. DISPERSIBILITY OF WET DEVELOPERS. It is highly desirable from an operating standpoint that wet developers in a suspension that has stood unused overnight be readily re-dispersed to a uniform suspension with no residue of undispersed developer in the bottom of the container. The following test was devised to make a determination of this property, usually in comparison with a reference standard.

Four hundred ml. of a suspension of the wet developer (and of the reference standard if a comparison test is to be made) are made up according to the manufacturer's instructions. Each sample is placed into a 1 pint clear glass bottle, capped, and put on a 60 cycle per second horizontal vibrator for 3 hours to settle out. At the end of this time the samples are re-dispersed by inverting the bottle and then righting it by hand, but without shaking it otherwise. The inversion is repeated until no sediment remains on the bottom of the bottle. The number of inversions is an indication of the ease with which the developer bath can be redispersed and furnishes a basis of comparison with other suspensions or with a reference standard.

29. WETTING ABILITY OF WET DEVELOPERS. Since the surface of parts after penetration and washing are usually not free of all oiliness, it is important that wet developers have sufficient wetting ability to give a smooth continuous film over such surfaces. The test for this property is conducted as follows:

Five drops of a 3% solution of white mineral oil (185 seconds viscosity, Saybolt) in trichlorethylene are placed on a 4″ x 4″ test panel cut from hot rolled steel sheet (in as-rolled condition). The panel is set at a 45° angle to the vertical and allowed to dry for 5 minutes. Five ml. of the developer suspension are then poured onto the panel above the oil spot and allowed to spread over and beyond the oily area. The panel, still at 45°, is then placed in an oven at 225° till dry. The developer film should be smooth and not peeled back from the oil area.

30. REMOVABILITY OF WET DEVELOPERS. Hot rolled 4″ x 4″ steel panels are used as in the preceding test. The water-washability fixture is used. The test panels are cleaned with acetone before use. Five ml. portions of the developer suspension and of the reference standard, if a comparison is being made, are poured on separate spots on the panel which is held at a 45° angle (in the drain station of the fixture). The panel, still at 45°, is placed in an oven at 225°F till dry. It is then cooled and placed in the wash position on the fixture and washed with 1 liter of cold tap water at 65°F ± 5°F. The panel is allowed to dry at room temperature and then examined under oblique white light to evaluate and compare the completeness of removal of the developer film from the surface.

Easy removal of wet developer residual films is often important when such a film would interfere with a subsequent process to be performed on the part after inspection.

31. SURFACE UNIFORMITY OF WET DEVELOPERS. Wet developers should produce a uniform film of developer after drying on the surface of parts. To check the ability of a wet developer to do this satisfactorily, 25 ml. of the developer mixture are poured over a 4″ x 4″ hot rolled panel held at a 45° angle. After 5 minutes of draining the panel, still at 45°, is dried in an oven at 225°F. When dry, it is examined for uniformity of the dried developer film on the surface. Comparison to a reference standard sample similarly prepared is usually desirable.

32. CORROSION TEST FOR WET DEVELOPER. This is an accelerated test to determine whether the wet developer has any tendency to corrode parts with which it remains in contact. The test specimen is a small block of 2024-T3 aluminum alloy, about 3/8″ x 3/4″ x 2″. Two sides of the block are filed clean with a *clean* file and the block placed immediately into approximately 50 ml. of developer in a 150 ml. beaker or 125 ml. Erlenmeyer flask. The developer is heated to boiling and boiling continued for 15 minutes. Caution: when boiling, the developer tends to bump and spatter. Lowering the heat when boiling commences is of some help. The block is then removed, washed with cold water and examined for any sign of corrosion or pitting. Again, comparison to a reference standard may be desirable.

Tests for Physical Properties

33. SPECIFIC GRAVITY. This test is used as a control or uniformity test for penetrants and emulsifiers. The test is made with a hydrometer in accordance with ASTM Standard D-287. Results are expressed in terms of A.P.I. gravity. These readings can be converted into density or weight per gallon figures, if desired.

34. VISCOSITY. Viscosity is a property of interest in the use of penetrants and emulsifiers. It is also a property which should not vary, outside reasonable limits, from lot to lot of a particular product, and is therefore another measure of uniformity. The property measured is the kinematic viscosity, and the method used is that of A.S.T.M. Standard D-445, using the Cannon-Fenske viscometer. Fig. 182 illustrates the viscometer tube with a sample

Chapter 17

TESTS FOR EVALUATION AND CONTROL

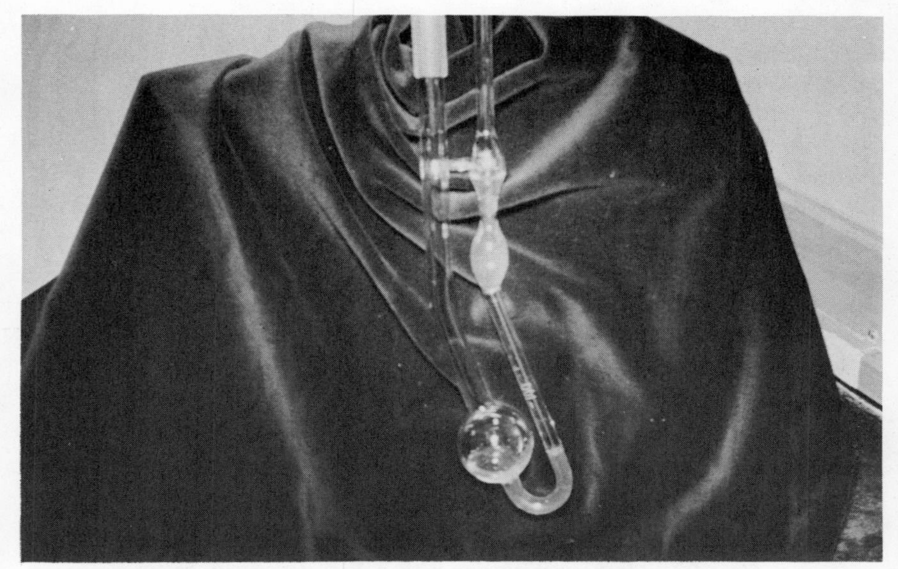

Fig. 182—Tube of Cannon-Fenske Viscometer, shown without its surrounding water bath.

of penetrant flowing through it. In conducting the test, this tube is immersed in a constant temperature bath maintained at 100°F. Viscosities are reported in centistokes, the unit of kinematic viscosity.

35. Flash Point. Flash point of penetrants and related materials are important from a safety standpoint and also as a control test. Flash points of most penetrants and materials are made in the closed-cup test apparatus using the Pensky Martens Flash Point Tester according to the method of A.S.T.M. Standard D-93, or in the Tag closed cup tester. In the test, the liquid is placed in a brass container or cup heated electrically or by a gas flame at a specified rate. The cup is covered, the cover supporting a fixture which holds the thermometer, with bulb in the liquid being tested, and supports the small test flame. At intervals, by moving a lever, a window in the cover is opened and the test flame brought to the opening. The temperature is recorded when this application of the flame ignites the vapor in the cup. Fig. 183 illustrates the apparatus.

36. Water Content. Water content of water-wash penetrants and emulsifiers is of interest as a quality control test, since initial water content should not exceed that required by the formulation

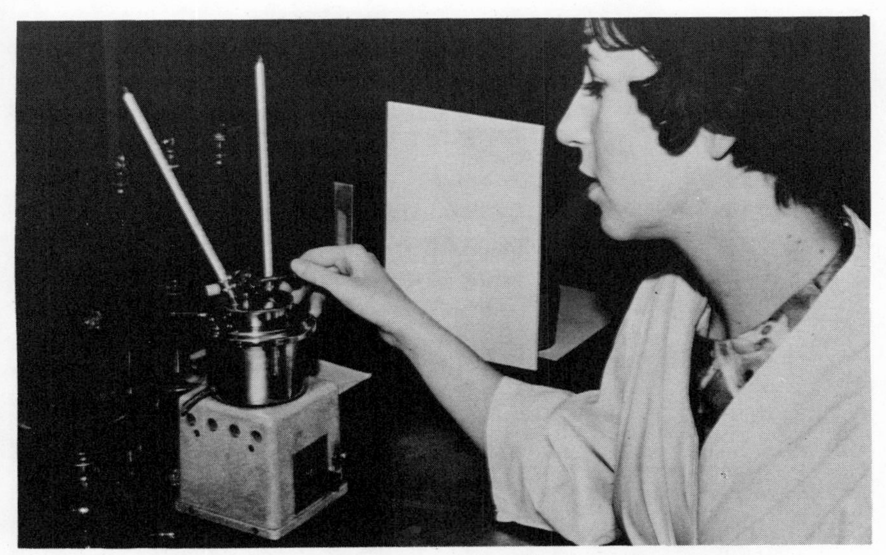

Fig. 183—Flash-point testing with a Tag closed cup tester.

of the material. It is also of interest as a measure of contamination in used materials. (See Section 42, following.)

Water content is determined by the method of A.S.T.M. Standard D-95. In this test 100 ml. of the material is put into a boiling-flask with 100 ml. of water-free xylene. The flask is connected to a reflux condenser in such a way that the condensate drops into a 25 ml. graduated tube, in which the water settles out. Excess condensed xylene overflows from the trap back into the boiling-flask. Boiling is continued till no more water comes over—usually about an hour. After cooling, the volume of water is read in the graduated tube of the trap. The volume in ml. is the percent of water—by volume—present in the sample.

37. SULPHUR CONTENT. Because of the possible damaging effect of sulphur on certain nickel alloys, sulphur content of some penetrants, emulsifiers and developers must be determined. This determination is made by the method of ASTM Standard D-1552. Special equipment is required for making this test, in which the material is heated at high temperature. Sulphur is converted to sulphide and the amount determined by titration with Sodium Iodate solution.

38. CHLORINE CONTENT. Chlorine is another element which may damage certain metals or alloys in some applications. Determination of chlorine content is therefore required in the case of penetrants, emulsifiers or developers to be used for the inspection of such materials. Chlorine content is determined by the method of ASTM Standard D-808. The material is burned with oxygen under pressure. Chlorine in the sample is converted to the form of a chloride and its amount determined by usual wet gravimetric chemical analysis methods.*

Operating Control Tests.

39. PURPOSE OF CONTROL TESTS. In the chapters dealing with the various materials used in making penetrant inspections by the several available methods and techniques, the problems of deterioration of these materials in use were discussed. To insure continuing dependable results, the operator must have a means of being sure that materials—penetrants, emulsifiers and developers—are performing as they are supposed to.

There is therefore a need for tests by which the fitness for continued use of the various materials can be determined. The series of tests to be described are intended to provide a ready means for checking materials for harmful deterioration.

These tests have been developed by Magnaflux Corporation and are strictly applicable only to their products. Some tests, however, such as water content, are general and can be applied to any material.

40. SENSITIVITY TESTS. Since the principal concern of the operator of a penetrant test system is assurance that the ability of the system to detect flaws continues unimpaired, a ready and reliable overall check for sensitivity is desirable. However, as has been pointed out at length, no fully satisfactory test of this type has so far been devised. Parts containing known defects can, after careful cleaning, be re-processed, but it is impossible to be sure that very fine discontinuities have been sufficiently well cleaned for sensitivity test purposes. If not thoroughly cleaned, failure of the system to reproduce the original indication is not a reliable warning that the system is not performing properly.

Comparative tests of used materials against new materials as reference standards, made on cracked aluminum blocks or plated strips, are the best over-all tests for sensitivity yet available. (See Sections 14 to 20 incl., this chapter.)

*Here see Appendix III for further information on Chlorine testing.

41. FLUORESCENT BRIGHTNESS DETERIORATION IN PENETRANTS. Fluorescent brightness of penetrants may deteriorate during use due to contamination of the penetrant bath with acids from any source, or possibly due to prolonged exposure to ultraviolet light (or sunlight). Overheating of the penetrant can also result in reduction in fluorescent brightness. If such deterioration is suspected, comparison tests in the photofluorometer, using new material of the same type as a reference standard, can be made as described in Sections 7 to 9 of this chapter. Reduction of fluorescent brightness so measured should be not more than 15% of the original. Visual comparison under black light of filter-paper specimens prepared as described should show no discernible difference in brightness from that of new penetrant. Since the eye cannot detect small differences in brightness in such a test, any loss which the eye *can* detect is in the neighborhood of the 15% mentioned above, or greater.*

42. WATER CONTAMINATION TEST FOR PENETRANTS. Since water is the most common contaminant causing deterioration of water-wash penetrants in use, tests for water content at intervals of two or three weeks is desirable. Water content determination is made by distillation with xylene, according to ASTM Standard D-95.

If the water content of the penetrant sample reaches 75% to 80% of the maximum tolerance of the particular penetrant being used (See Water Tolerance Test, Section 24, this chapter), the penetrant should be discarded in order to obviate the danger of complete functional failure of the penetrant in use. In the case of penetrants having high tolerance for water the point for discarding may be somewhat higher than 75%. Thus penetrant having a water tolerance of 5% should be discarded when water content reaches 4%, whereas one having a 20% water tolerance can be used at least until the water content rises to 16% or possibly 18%.

43. EMULSIFIER SENSITIVITY TEST. As in the case of penetrants, a direct check for performance of used emulsifiers as part of the penetrant system can be made only with cracked test specimens, comparing results with similar specimens using new emulsifier as well as new penetrant and developer.

44. FLUORESCENCE OF EMULSIFIER. The principal contaminant of the emulsifier is penetrant. This contamination is unavoidable in

*Here see Appendix III for further information regarding this test.

the nature of the operation, but must be watched so that it does not go too far. Fluorescence of the emulsifier can be determined by the photofluorometer using prepared filter paper test specimens. Relative luminance compared to the original emulsifier gives a measure of the amount of penetrant in the emulsifier.

A quicker test and one which can be performed by the operator to keep a continual check on the emulsifier bath is made by direct comparison with known mixtures of emulsifier and penetrant. A set of standard mixtures containing respectively 0, 5, 10, 15, 20, 30 and 40% of penetrant are made up in clear glass-stoppered test tubes or glass bottles. A similar container of emulsifier drawn from the bath in use is compared under black light with this series, and the nearest match selected. The percent of contamination is thus directly indicated with sufficient accuracy for practical purposes.

Contamination of 10% is probably the safe maximum permissible for critical inspections, though the emulsifier will still function with much higher degrees of penetrant contamination. For some inspections, the upper limit may be as high as 20% to 25%. However, penetrant-contaminated emulsifier usually requires increased emulsification time for equivalent results.

45. EMULSIFIER WATER CONTENT. Contamination of emulsifier with water changes its properties so that emulsification times set up for proper inspections are no longer applicable. The water content test is made by ASTM D-95 distillation method. From 18% to 20% water content is the maximum permissible for continued use.

46. WET DEVELOPER CONCENTRATION CONTROL TESTS. There are two types of wet developer currently supplied by Magnaflux Corporation—Type 3 and Type 5. These are prepared by mixing with water in prescribed proportions.

Type 3 developer comes as a dry powder and is mixed one pound to three or four gallons of water. The powder is stirred into the water to form a smooth suspension. In use the concentration of the bath may change, usually due to evaporation of water. Strength of bath can be checked by use of a comparator kit, consisting of a small glossy black plate on which the used developer is applied, and a similar plate on which developer of known strengths is displayed.

In making the test, a small amount of the developer from the well-mixed bath is poured on the test plate held at 45° to the vertical, and the plate dried in that position in the drier. The appearance of this streak is compared with those on the standard plate, and either developer powder or water added to the bath to bring it to the desired concentration.

Type 5 developer, also a dry powder, is mixed wtih water in a similar manner, but in somewhat greater concentration. One third to one pound per gallon is recommended. The mixture is somewhat thicker than the type 3, and concentration check is more accurately made by a different method. The streak test should not be used.

To check concentration of the type 5 bath the following equipment is needed:

(a) A scale or balance with metric system weights, capable of weighing 200 grams to the nearest 0.1 gram.

(b) A 100 ml. volumetric flask, or a 100 ml. pipette and a beaker of 150 ml. capacity.

To make the test proceed as folows:

(a) Agitate the developer bath till it is thoroughly mixed, but be careful not to beat many fine bubbles of air into the suspension.

(b) Weigh the clean, dry flask or the beaker to the nearest 0.1 gram; or balance it with an equivalent tare weight.

(c) Fill the flask exactly to the line with developer bath suspension; or pipette 100 ml. into the beaker. Wipe outside of flask or beaker dry.

(d) Weigh the filled flask or beaker to the nearest 0.1 gram.

(e) Subtract the amount of the tare weight of the flask or beaker (unless a special balancing tare weight was used).

(f) Move the decimal point two places to the left. The resulting decimal number is the specific gravity of the suspension.

(g) From the table below determine the pounds per gallon of developer in the suspension, and add water or developer powder as indicated to bring the suspension to the specified strength.

TABLE OF CONCENTRATIONS

Specific Gravity	Concentration lb./gal.
1.018	0.33
1.021	0.4
1.026	0.5
1.031	0.6
1.037	0.7
1.042	0.8
1.047	0.9
1.052	1.0
1.057	1.1
1.063	1.2

A high concentration of developer can be lowered by adding water to the mixture. If the concentration is too low, add powder and stir thoroughly.*

47. DEVELOPER FLUORESCENCE. A serious source of contamination of both wet and dry developers is from penetrant from whatever source. Periodically, samples of developer from the bath in use, spread out in a shallow pan, should be examined in the darkened inspection area with a black light. Spots of fluorescence in the developer indicate contamination, and can produce false and misleading indications by adhering to a part undergoing inspection. If there is evidence of such contamination the only remedy is to discard the bath or tank of developer and start fresh.

48. DEVELOPER COATING. From time to time a check on the wet developer should be made to make sure that it is still producing an even film of developer on drying. Perform the surface uniformity test, Section 31, this chapter. If the results indicate uneven or splotchy distribution of developer, the bath has gone out of control and should be discarded.

49. DEVELOPER WETTING ABILITY. Sometimes an old wet-developer bath, to which numerous adjustments have been made, no longer functions as it should due to inability properly to wet the surface of parts which may be slightly oily. Perform the wetting ability test, Section 29, this chapter. If uneven wetting is indicated, the bath should be discarded, since the results show that the proportion of wetting agent and developer powder are not correct. Addition of either more developer or water cannot correct this situation.

*Here see Appendix III for an additional test for developer concentration.

50. OPERATOR ALERTNESS. The tests here described have been devised to give the operator some definite means of checking the performance of materials which he is using to make penetrant inspections. He should, however, always be alert to any behavior of these materials that differs from normal performance. If the materials do not perform as they are intended to do, no dependable inspection results can be expected.

51. CONTROL OF COLOR-CONTRAST PENETRANTS. The tests which have been described are limited to fluorescent penetrant materials. Color-contrast pentrants as ordinarily used for spot-checking, do not suffer the same hazards of contamination as do penetrants that are used in open tanks for production purposes. Color-contrast penetrants used in open tanks would be subject to some of the same types of deterioration as described for fluorescent penetrant materials, but to date no similar series of control tests has appeared necessary.

APPENDIX I

PENETRANTS

1. GENERAL. During the six years since this book was first published (1963), there have been few really significant changes in the design of penetrants or the techniques of their application. Principal improvements have been in the direction of increased sensitivity, improved methods of washing or removing excess penetrant from test surfaces, and in research leading to a better understanding of penetrant and developer performance.

2. HIGH SENSITIVITY WATER WASH PENETRANTS. Penetrants of the water-wash type (i.e., with emulsifier incorporated in the penetrant) are now available which are the equal of the P.E. type penetrants for many applications—especially in fine tight cracks. They do not, however, replace P.E. penetrants for shallow open defects. Their advantage lies in the elimination of the emulsification step for many applications where P.E. penetrants have been used.

3. SELF-DEVELOPING CHARACTERISTICS OF SOME PENETRANTS. Such penetrants would be attractive in that they would eliminate the development step. However, self development is in fact a misnomer. Some penetrants with high dye content will give visible indications without development. The higher the dye content of the penetrant and the larger the defect, the stronger will be the indications produced. However, if developer is applied to such indications they will be amplified in visibility in the same way as indications produced with any penetrant.

Such penetrants do not eliminate the need for development and may fail to produce indications of very fine defects unless a suitable developer is also used.

4. MAXIMUM OPERATING TEMPERATURES. There is a demand for a penetrant which can be applied to parts which are hot—of the order of 200 to 300°F. The problem here lies mainly in the fact that temperatures in this range rapidly destroy the fluorescence of the dyes used in penetrants. Currently there are no penetrants available that are formulated to perform at such temperatures.

If tests *must* be made at higher than recommended temperatures, high sensitivity penetrants should be used, as these have a high dye concentration. The test should be conducted as *rapidly* as possible so that indications are produced and read before the effect of the heat has entirely destroyed the fluorescence of the dye.

It is inevitable that some loss of sensitivity will occur, but by following the above procedures, results are likely to give some useful indications. It should be realized, however, that the higher the temperature at which the test is conducted, the greater the loss of sensitivity that will occur, and the more rapid the rate at which sensitivity declines. At this time it is not recommended that tests with existing penetrants be conducted at temperatures above 175°F.

Work on the formulation of penetrants that *will* perform well at high temperatures is in progress, but so far no such penetrants are in commercial production.

5. WATER TOLERANCE. Modern water-wash penetrants and emulsifiers should have a high level of water tolerance. This term has, however, been misinterpreted by some users who confuse it with water content. A penetrant as it comes from the manufacturer may contain some proportion of water in its formulation—either by deliberate inclusion, or because of small amounts of water occurring in commercial materials which are ingredients of the formula. This water content—usually not over 1.5% to 2.0%—has no adverse bearing on the performance of the penetrant.

The property of importance to the user is the ability of the penetrant to "tolerate" contamination by additional water during use, without destroying its ability to perform satisfactorily for defect detection. Source of such water is commonly splash-over from the wash station, usually adjacent to the penetrant tank.

High water tolerance, therefore, refers to water which the penetrant can absorb *in addition* to that originally present.

Water additions to water-wash penetrants and emulsifiers will, when the "tolerance" limit is reached, cause the material to change its physical properties completely—thickening or even gelling, and eventually separating into its several constituents. When this occurs the material is no longer fit for use and must be discarded. Obviously a penetrant or emulsifier which can "tolerate" a high proportion of added water, and still be usable, is *economically* superior to one which becomes unusable after small amounts of added water.

Water tolerance is not a factor in the use of P.E. penetrants, since water does not mix with these, but simply drops through and forms a layer at the bottom of the tank, without interfering with the performance of the penetrant.

6. X-RAY OPAQUE PENETRANTS. A penetrant has been developed which shows considerable opacity to the passage of X-rays, and has some attractive possible applications. Unfortunately, the cost of such a penetrant is extremely high, excluding it from use except for very special applications. Better delineation of size and shape of voids in light metals such as magnesium, aluminum and titanium can be achieved by applying the penetrant, and washing and drying the part before x-ray examination. Best results are obtained with x-rays in the 40 K.V. range.

Other applications include graphite shapes and glass and ceramic parts. A most promising use is in combining leak detection with x-ray examination of glass-encapsulated electronic devices. X-rays are used to detect bad connections or misplacement of elements. If the device is first immersed in the x-ray-opaque penetrant, washed, and dried, and then x-rayed, the penetrant which will have entered cracks or poor seals will be visible in the radiograph.

APPENDIX II

DEVELOPERS

1. GENERAL. Since 1963, when this book first was published, considerable work has been done in analyzing the mechanism by which a developer magnifies a fluorescent indication. It has long been obvious that a suitable developer enlarges and greatly enhances the brilliance of a fine fluorescent indication, making it much more readily visible to the eye. Exactly how and in what magnitude this effect is produced has not been understood.

W. E. Thomas, in his Lester Honor Lecture before The Society for Nondestructive Testing in October of 1963, presented the result of some of the work which offers an explanation of the mechanics of developer action and an estimate of the gain in visibility obtained through the use of a developer. The reader is referred to the original paper for details of the analysis and calculations involved.* We will point out here only some of the conclusions which resulted.

If we consider a very fine crack such as is produced in the plated

Fig. 184—White light photograph of crack 2 microns wide by 80 microns deep at 75x magnification.

---

*Nondestructive Testing, November-December, 1963, "An analytic Approach to Penetrant Performance" by W. E. Thomas.

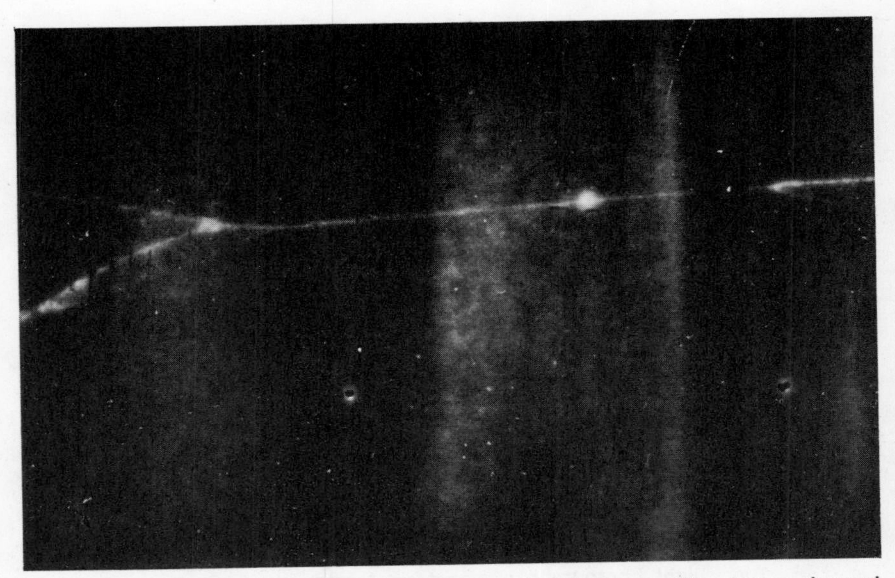

Fig. 185—Black light photograph of crack 2 wide microns by 80 microns deep at 75x magnification after applying penetrant.

test panels now in general use for evaluating penetrant and developer performance, its dimensions might be 2 microns in width and 80 microns in depth (0.00008 inches by 0.003 inches). Fig. 184 is a photomicrograph of such a crack at 75x magnification. When processed with fluorescent penetrant and examined under black light, the same area appeared as shown in Fig. 185.

When a dry powder developer was applied, having particle size of 0.2 to 0.4 microns in diameter (which basic particles may clump together in aggregates of 50 to 100 microns in size), the same area photographed under black light appeared as shown in Fig. 186. This developed indication has a width of 0.020 inches, compared to the crack width of only 0.00008 inches.

Such amplification is the more remarkable when one considers that the volume of the crack, and therefore the total penetrant available to make the indication, is only 0.00000024 cubic inches per inch of length. Of this probably no more than half is drawn back out during development. Volume of the developer film, assuming it to be 0.001 inch thick, is 0.00002 cubic inches per inch. It is evident from Fig. 186, that not all of the developer particles are fluorescent; but the above volume considerations, assuming that the voids between the developer particles is 50% of the total de-

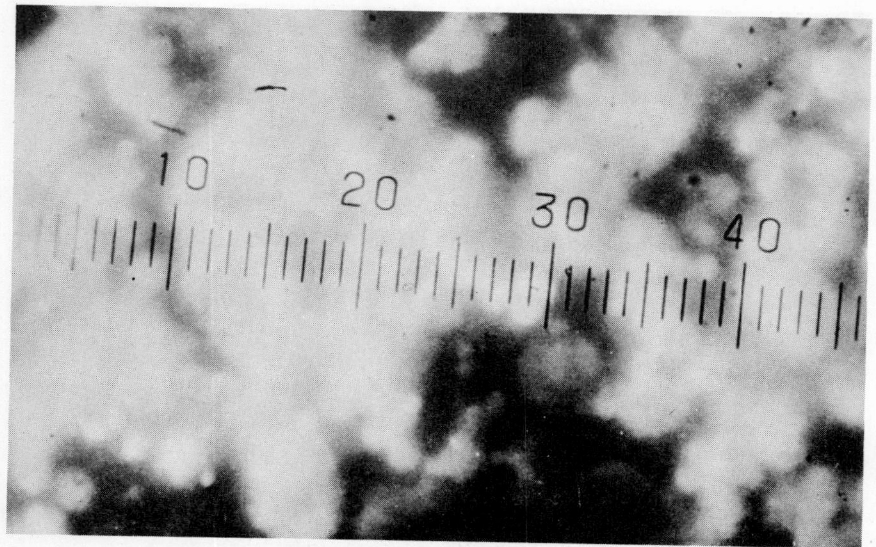

Fig. 186—Black light photograph of penetrant treated crack, 2 microns wide by 80 microns deep, at 75x magnification after application of developer.

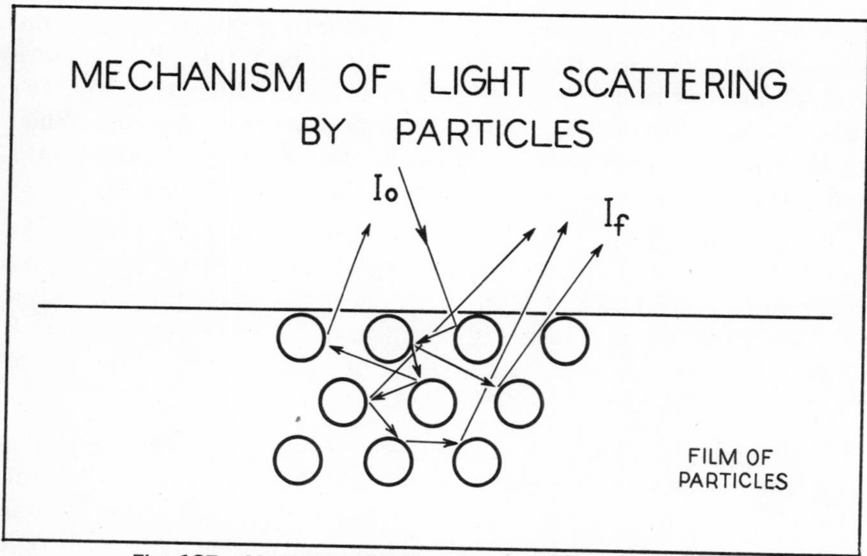

Fig. 187—Multiple reflection phenomenon of developer.

veloper volume, indicate that the penetrant available is filling no more than 2.4% of the maximum possible volume in the developer film. Yet a wide and brilliantly visible fluorescent indication is produced!

When we consider how very thin the film of penetrant on the surfaces of the developer particles must be, we realize that some other magnifying process must be occurring. This can be explained by the phenomenon of multiple reflection from particle to particle, and, therefore, through many very thin layers of penetrant. Fig. 187 illustrates diagramatically how this occurs, starting with the single incident ray of black light, I_o. The total emission of fluorescent light is shown by the smaller arrows, I_f, after multiple reflection among the particles.

Calculations indicate that the total factor of gain in perceptibility may be as high as 600 times the undeveloped fluorescent indication.

The developer, therefore, increases the perceptibility ("see-ability") of the indication by two means:

1. It increases the *width* of the indication, and

2. It increases the brightness by the scattering process.

In this case we have assumed that the dry, fluffy developer powder is used. Action of other developers is similar though the exact nature and amount of visibility gain will depend on the composition, size and shape of the developer particles.

2. SOLUBLE DEVELOPERS. Developers are now in use which consist of clear solutions in either water or organic solvents. The need for keeping a developer powder in uniform suspension in the bath is thereby eliminated. The developer solution is applied to the surface after penetration and washing; this is dried in the drier if water is the solvent. As the liquid evaporates, the dissolved solid material separates out as a fine powder, after which development action takes place as with normal dry developers. If the liquid used is an organic solvent, the solution of partially dried penetrant helps the process, just as in the case of developers suspended in solvents.

Advantages of this developer are:

(1) It is completely and easily removed from all test surfaces: smooth, rough or chemically treated. This is accomplished by the fact that the coating is *dissolved* off the part when dipped or sprayed with water, or solvent.

(2) Being completely soluble, there is no need for agitation of the developer bath. Once the developer powder is dissolved

in the water, the bath is clear, free of particles and ready for use.

(3) Since there are no particles in the prepared soluble developer bath, there can be no separation or stratification of solids as can occur with the standard pigmented water dispersible developers.

(4) In addition there is no selective dragout of developer ingredients.

The physical appearance of water soluble developer bath is that of a clear yellow liquid. Being water based, the prepared bath is non-combustible, it does not give off fumes or odor and it evaporates slowly; it can be used in large unventilated areas and it presents no air pollution problems.

3. DEVELOPMENT TIME. Experience has shown that for most applications development time of 5 to 10 minutes is adequate, regardless of the time required for penetration. Very few cases have been noted where longer development produced any increase in brightness of the indications, even when the latter are very fine.

If solvent developers are used, 10 minutes is a maximum development time, as indications tend to continue to spread. Fine indications may spread in time until they lose definition and contrast. They then become harder to see, and finally become completely invisible.

4. DRYING TIME WITH WET DEVELOPER. When the wet water base developer is applied over the surface of the part, and the part is placed in the drying oven, developing action begins quickly and is probably complete by the time the surface is completely dry and before the *penetrant* has had time to lose its fluidity. Longer drying time can then do little harm, except for the fading of the fluorescent dye under continued heating.

Similarly, with solvent developers, development occurs as the solvent dries. In addition, the solvent dissolves and keeps the penetrant liquid, thus aiding development, which is complete when the volatile portion of the solvent liquid has evaporated. Indications should be read promptly. Spreading of indications occurs slowly, but does occur as time goes on.

5. EFFECT OF SURFACE ROUGHNESS ON DEVELOPERS. It has been noted that on very smooth or polished surfaces, the dry fluffy developer sometimes does not adhere sufficiently to produce adequate developing action. As penetrant exudes from a very fine crack there may not be enough "stickiness" present to trap developer powder. This would be particularly true on vertical surfaces. On somewhat rougher surfaces, however, the surface itself traps sufficient powder for the purpose.

On smooth or polished surfaces, therefore, wet or solvent developers are often preferable.

Appendix III

EVALUATION TESTS FOR PENETRANTS AND DEVELOPERS

1. Black Light Measurement. The Weston or G.E. light meters, which have been in use for determining the intensity of the black light radiation on a test surface, do not measure black light directly. The photocells are sensitive to both white light and the short blacklight wave lengths. They are calibrated, however, in foot-candles of *white* light and therefore measure *all* the radiation which passes the black light filter covering the mercury arc plus any ambient white light. Because these filters are quite uniform the results of the test are reproducible at any given time. However, as the light source deteriorates, the *black light* wave lengths may not fall off at the same rate as the remainder of the wave lengths. A meter which actually measures black light, 3650 Å, has therefore considerable merit.

Such a meter is now available, though not in general use. It is calibrated in micro-watts per square cm., and is filtered so that it responds only to the wave band closely around 3650 Å. Thus a reading on this meter is a direct measure the true energy in the 3650 Å band range that falls on the test surface, in terms more meaningful than foot-candles. The foot-candle unit applies properly only to white light.

2. Standard Crack Specimens for Penetrant Tests. Chapter 17, Sections 18, 19, and 20, describe steel strips on which a coating of brittle iron has been plated. This coating, the thickness of which can be measured, is then cracked by bending over a standard curved block. Currently these strips have been replaced by brass panels plated with nickel and chromium. (See Chapter 4, Section 33.) The plating may be thin or thick depending on the *depth* of crack desired. After plating, the panels are bent to produce cracks, much in the manner that the iron-plated strips are bent. (Chapter 17, Section 19, P. 410.) Bending cracks the plating to the base metal. Width of cracks can be varied by the bending radius, and can be measured. Depth is known from measurement of the plating thickness. Thus "natural" cracks of known width and depth are produced.

These panels are more convenient to use and store than the iron-plated strips. Panels can be obtained from Scientific Control Laboratories, Chicago, Illinois. They are usually furnished in sets having panels of three different plating thicknesses, thus giving a range of crack depths.

The panels do not give absolute results and results are not reproducible from panel to panel. It is necessary, therefore, to treat one-half of the panel with the test materials, and the other half with standard materials, using the same procedure for both, and comparing the resultant indications.

This is a test only of overall system performance. If it is necessary to determine which material is faulty, i.e., penetrant, emulsifier or developer, one must test each material separately, using standard materials for the rest of the system. To check a penetrant, treat one-half of the panel with the suspected penetrant plus standard emulsifier and developer, and treat the other half completely with standard materials. Similarly, for emulsifiers and developers, use standard materials substituting only the suspected one.

Processing and evaluation are critical to the success of this test, so the operator should be familiar with good inspection techniques. He may have to establish his own emulsification technique to use the plate-cracked panels to best advantage. The cracks in these will likely be very different from those found in normal production parts and the surface is very smooth so less than normal emulsification will probably be required.

This test is the most important in the series of tests applied to used penetrant system test materials, since it shows whether or not all materials are performing as intended, or if not, which material is at fault.

3. WATER TOLERANCE TEST. (See also Section 5, Appendix I) This test applies mainly to emulsifiers and water washable penetrants. Water will not normally mix with P.E. penetrants, but falls through to form a layer on the tank bottom. If a P.E. penetrant shows signs of over removability, and will accept more water than its standard, it probably is contaminated with emulsifier, and should be replaced. Water washable penetrants and emulsifiers are designed to accept some water and still remain useable. Water is often splashed into these materials accidentally during use. This test simply and quickly determines whether excessive water contamination has occurred.

Water contamination is usually not seriously harmful to performance until the water tolerance point is reached. Then, however, the material usually becomes cloudy or separates into two layers which will not perform in a useable manner. Materials in this condition *must* be replaced. Smaller amounts of water will cause change, usually in viscosity and washing, but these effects normally are not enough to require replacement of a well engineered material.

A simplified method of checking water contamination is applied to penetrant baths that have been in use. It quickly and simply checks to see whether water contamination is approaching a dangerous level. Water tolerance of the unused penetrant should be determined by the more accurate alternate test.

The procedure for the quick test is as follows:

Using a 100 ml glass mixing cylinder, add an amount of water equal to about 50% of the original water tolerance of the test sample (previously determined) and fill to the 100 ml mark with the penetrant. Invert the cylinder several times to mix the contents and check for cloudiness. If the graduations on the opposite side of the cylinder can be read through the contents of the cylinder, the liquid can be considered clear. If a more exact estimate of the remaining water tolerance is desired, increments of 25, 50 and 75% of the original water tolerance can be added in separate steps, and the sample then checked for cloudiness after each addition. (Example —If a given material has an original water tolerance of 20% as measured by the alternate procedure given below, the following procedure would be used: 1) Add 10 ml of water (50% of the original tolerance) to 90 ml of penetrant. 2) Mix thoroughly. 3) check for cloudiness. If the mixture is cloudy, it is readily apparent that it already has been contaminated to an extent in excess of one-half of the water the original penetrant is capable of taking without reaching the failure point. If the mixture is clear, it is apparent that the amount of water present in relation to its water tolerance is still in a safe, usable amount.

A more precise method of determining water tolerance follows. This method can be used to determine the tolerance for water contamination (not total percentage of water content, which would include water present in the new penetrant) of unused or new penetrants. This figure must be known in order to use the quick test just described.

About 15 ml of the penetrant to be tested are weighed (to the nearest 0.1 gm) into a 50 ml beaker. The beaker is placed on a magnetic stirring unit, the rate of stirring being rapid enough to create a deep vortex in the liquid. A narrow beam microscope illuminator is placed behind the beaker, shining through the liquid but not directly into the eyes of the observer. Water is added very slowly from a burette calibrated to 0.05 ml, while the stirring continues.

When the light transmission first shows haziness, the volume of added water is measured on the burette, and the percent by weight of the water required to cause break-down of the penetrant (as evidenced by the haziness of the test sample), is calculated. 1 ml of water is assumed to be 1 gm in weight.

The test penetrant should be at 26°C ± 1°. The specific gravity of the penetrant must be known so that the water tolerance figure can be converted from a weight to a volume basis, which is the customary basis for expressing the percent tolerance for added water.

4. FLUORESCENT BRIGHTNESS MEASUREMENT. Fluorescent brightness is probably the most important property of a penetrant —whether new and unused, or, in the bath while in use. The method of measurement described in Chapter 17, Sections 7, 8 and 9, has been improved by employing a different method of sample preparation in place of the filter-paper test specimens. This new method is not yet in general use, but its advantages in reproducibility and its closer simulation of actual penetrant use conditions make it a desirable improvement. Details of this test will be available in the near future.

A quick and simple test has also been devised which can be used to monitor gross loss of fluorescence of a penetrant during use. This is a simplified test, using the cheapest equipment available that will give valid numbers. It must only be used to compare various samples of the same material, and even then, results can be trusted only within ± 5%. This is still two to four times better than visual observation, and thus warrants the expense of using the instrumental measurement. Further, instruments have more or less constant sensitivity while human observers vary greatly in sensitivity.

In this test a Weston Model 703, Type 8 (or 6A) illumination meter with Viscor filter is used. 10 microliters of the penetrant are diluted volumetrically to 25 ml with reagent grade xylene. The diluted penetrant is poured into a 50 ml beaker. The beaker is placed on the light-sensing cell of the meter, and a 100 watt inspection black light with Kopp #41 filter positioned over the beaker. Two specimens are prepared, one from the penetrant bath and one of new penetrant of the same batch.

The test should be performed in darkness. The meter with the standard sample in place is moved in relation to the black light until it reads a convenient value near the top of the scale—say 20 foot-candles. By replacing the standard with the beaker containing the diluted test sample a reading is then obtained which can be directly compared with the standard reading, to show proportionate loss (or gain) of fluorescence in the bath.

Loss of fluorescence in a penetrant usually occurs because the penetrant either has been contaminated by some substance, or heated. Contaminants may enter a little at a time, as residue on parts, or all at once, when some foreign material is added accidentally. Penetrants can absorb relatively large amounts of solvents or oils, but usually experience a decrease in fluorescence in proportion to the amount added. Some solvents, acids, or strongly colored substances, are much more likely to reduce fluorescence. One per cent by volume may be enough to completely kill the fluorescence of a penetrant.

Some users heat penetrant in the tanks to speed penetration, but the more common cause of heat degradation is the dipping of hot parts in the penetrants. Although these hot parts may not heat all the penetrant, that portion at the surface of the part often will reach 200 or 300° F. Repetition of this process will eventually seriously reduce the fluorescence.

It is also possible for penetrant fluorescence to increase with use due to evaporation of volatile portions of the penetrant. Such a penetrant will probably be more viscous than new, it will be slower to penetrate, and require more time to wash.

5. Wet Developer Concentration Test. Chapter 17, Section 47 describes a test to check the concentration of the wet developer* bath by determining its specific gravity by weighing a measured

*NOTE: This test does not apply to water soluble type developers.

portion. A more reliable test has been developed in which 100 grams —to the nearest 0.10 gm.—of the thoroughly mixed bath is evaporated to dryness in a weighed flat-bottomed dish, such as a glass petrie dish. The percent of solids by weight is thus obtained. The following table gives the relationship between percent of solids by weight to pounds per gallon of bath:

TABLE XVI

½ lb per gallon —	6.8% solids
¾ lb per gallon —	8.2% solids
1 lb per gallon —	10.7% solids
1¼ lb per gallon —	13.0% solids
1½ lb per gallon —	15.2% solids
1¾ lb per gallon —	17.4% solids
2 lb per gallon —	19.4% solids
2¼ lb per gallon —	21.2% solids

In the case of soluble developers, the specific gravity is taken with a hydrometer. It is a quick, easy test to run, but is not reliable for testing the solid-suspension type. This is because wet developer suspensions are gels which become more viscous at higher concentrations or when subjected to shear by a pump or mixer. In many cases these gels become stiff enough to prevent free movement of the hydrometer and cause incorrect readings. However, the hydrometer test must be used for water soluble developers.

The following table relates the specific gravity to the pounds of solids per gallon.

TABLE XVII
SPECIFIC GRAVITY VS. POUNDS PER GALLON OF WATER SOLUBLE DEVELOPER

Developer Concentration (Pounds per gallon of water)	Density Reading (22°C) (Using proper hydrometer)
3.00	1.093
2.00	1.071
1.50	1.054
1.00	1.038
0.75	1.028
0.50	1.020
0.25	1.010

6. Tests for Chlorine Content of Penetrant Materials. As mentioned in Chapter 17, Section 38 chlorine in small amounts has been determined by ASTM Method D-808. This method is, however, slow and not sensitive enough to determine accurately the small amount of chlorine now considered significant. A better method is badly needed which can determine very small amounts of chlorine with accuracy. Methods are under development to accomplish this end, but are not ready for publication at this writing.

Appendix IV

COLOR-CONTRAST TECHNIQUES

1. General. Chapter 10 describes color-contrast penetrants and discusses their place in the group of penetrant testing methods. Some newer techniques have been developed during the past years which have increased the sensitivity and therefore the usefulness of the color-contrast testing techniques.

2. New Color-Contrast Technique. One of the weaknesses of the older conventional method was that excessive bleeding and rapid spreading of penetrant re-issuing from a discontinuity reduced the definition of the indications and tended to hide indications of fine cracks. The new technique acts to fix indications before they have time to spread, arresting their spreading and leaving a clean-cut pattern of even very fine indications.

The procedure employs a special penetrant which is applied in the usual manner, as shown in Fig. 188, after the test surface has

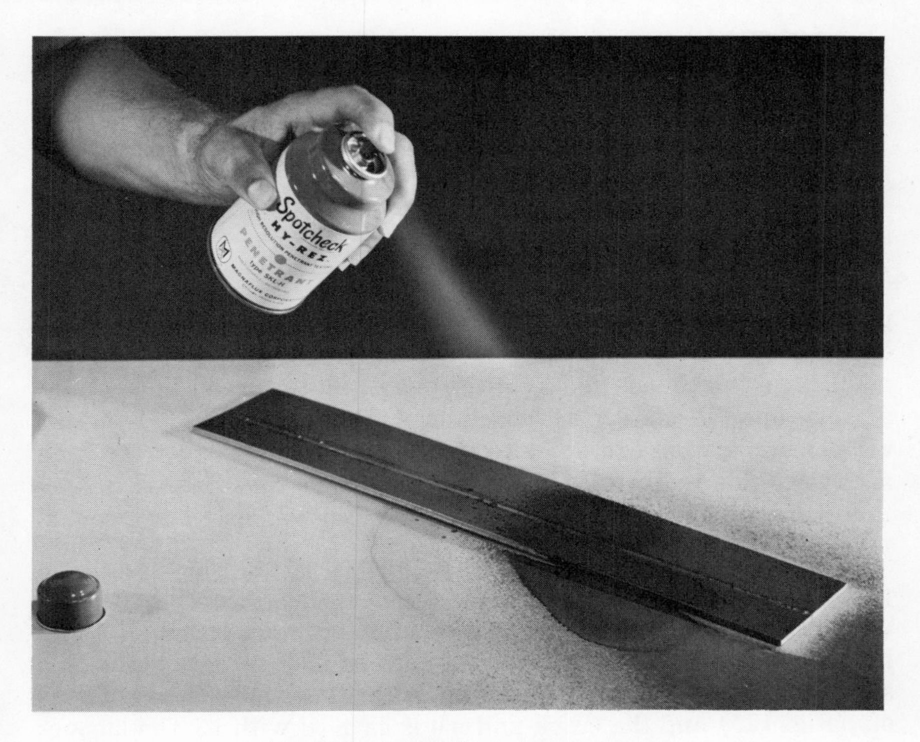

Fig. 188—Application of penetrant.

been properly cleaned and dried. Excess is wiped off with a cloth moistened with a solvent remover. The specimen is then allowed to dry, the penetrant liquid being quite volatile. Drying may take place in a drier. The difference here, from the conventional procedure, is that the penetrant is designed to dry completely in the defect, and quickly enough that little or no spreading has time to occur.

A volatile solvent suspended white developer is then applied by spraying (Fig. 189). The solvent dissolves and extracts the dry

Fig. 189—Application of developer.

penetrant from the defects. Being very volatile, the developer liquid evaporates so rapidly that development is practically instantaneous and little or no time is given for the penetrant to spread. Indications of very fine defects can be observed while they form, and the developer application can be halted before too heavy a layer can hide such very fine indications. The indications are thus fixed in a fine-line pattern of dry penetrant in the white developer background.

A variation of this technique is to incorporate in the developer a proportion of clear lacquer. After the developer has dried the indication pattern is permanently fixed (removable, of course, with lacquer solvent). Alternatively, the pattern may be sprayed with a strippable lacquer—after drying this film of lacquer can be stripped off (Fig. 190) and the crack pattern is carried with it. The lacquer film containing the indications can be filed for future reference. Figure 191 shows such a film. These techniques also are used with fluorescent penetrants, when desired.

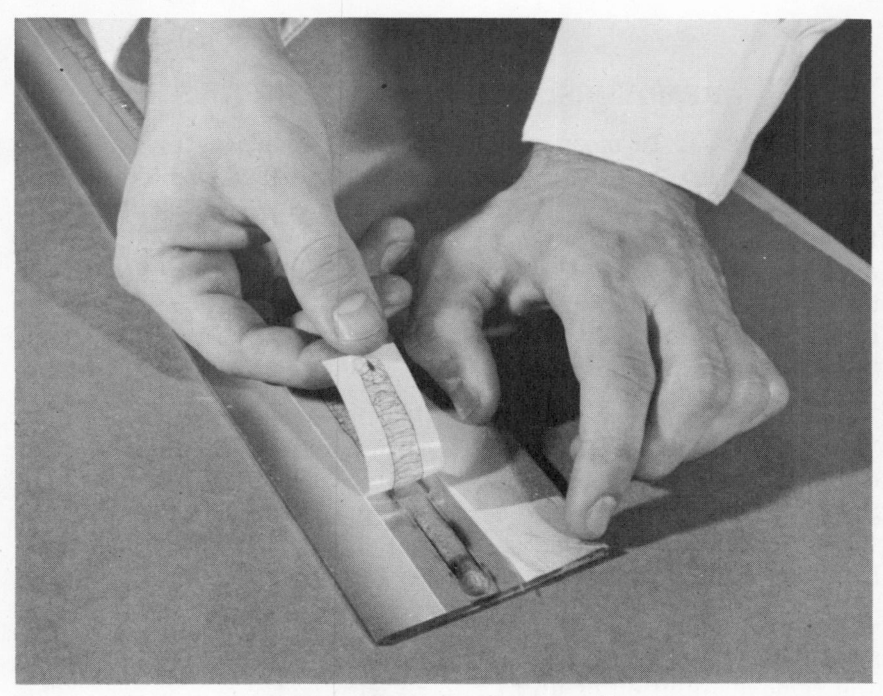

Fig. 190—Stripping off lacquer film.

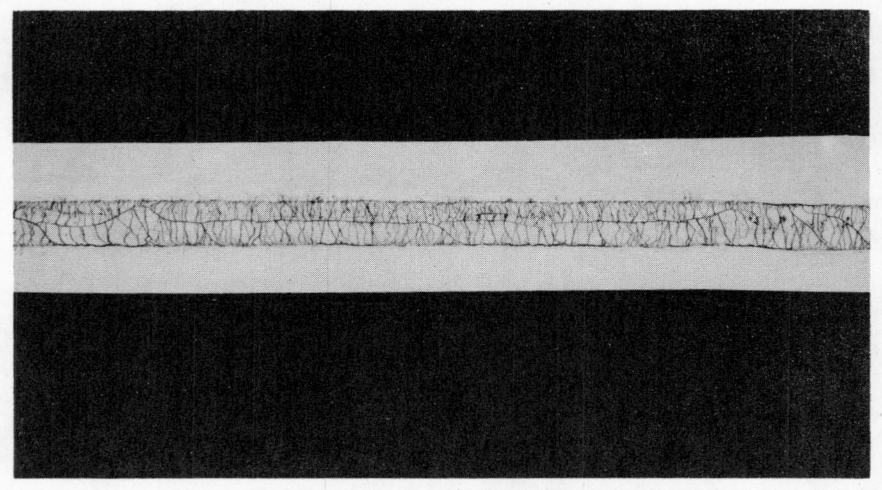

Fig. 191—Stripped lacquer film with indications.

Appendix V

REMOVERS, CLEANING TECHNIQUES

1. General. In most commercial use of the penetrant method, cleaning the excess penetrant from the test surface was almost universally done with water, with the aid of an emulsifier. The emulsifier was either incorporated in the penetrant (water-wash type) or applied as a separate step. (Post emulsification type). In the earliest tests, and increasingly in the last few years, attention has been given to other methods of cleaning the penetrant from the surface before developing indications.

2. Removers. This work has led to the development of so-called "removers," which are characterized by incorporation of either an emulsifier or a solvent in the water with which the part is washed. Some of these methods are remarkably effective. The amount of the materials added to the wash water may be very small, varying from a 1:4 dilution all the way down to 1:500 and even beyond.

Removers may be applied by spraying or by dipping. In the spraying technique, airless spray guns are one of the most effective, and remover dilution of up to 1 to 49 with water can be used. The hydro-spray gun is also satisfactory for this system.

Removers may also be applied in an open tank by dipping. Here a much lower dilution rate is used, around 1 to 9. Agitation is necessary, best accomplished by vigorous agitation of the bath liquid, rather than "sloshing" the part about in the bath. Contamination of the remover bath with penetrant occurs, but tolerance of the remover for penetrant contamination is quite high. When this tolerance limit is reached, the bath must be renewed.

Cleaning by this remover method makes over-washing—i.e., removal of penetrant from defect by prolonged washing—almost impossible. On the other hand, cleaning is quite rapid, spraying time being from one to two minutes, depending partly on degree of surface roughness.

When the spraying technique is used on an expendable basis, as in an automatic tunnel washer, remover can be automatically injected into the wash water in the correct amount. When the recovery and re-use of spray wash water is important, a "batch" dilution system is used and the batch recirculated, and discarded only when penetrant content reaches the limit of good performance, as in the open tank dip method.

One advantage of this system of cleaning is that fluorescent brightness of indications before development is noticeably higher than in conventional water-emulsifier cleaning. Developer, of course, effects the usual magnification in perceptability.

APPENDIX VI

EQUIPMENT

1. GENERAL. Equipment design trends have been largely in the direction of special units for difficult-to-handle parts. The development of new penetrants, developers and cleaners has also required changes in equipment for applying these improvements. A detailed discussion of some of these equipment designs and modifications would be of no particular interest in the present discussion.

2. ELECTROSTATIC SPRAYING. One improvement that promises to be of general interest and importance is the use of the electrostatic gun for the application of penetrants, emulsifiers, and developers. Mention has already been made of the use of the electrostatic principle in applying dry developer powders. Use of this principle for penetrants and other liquids is an advance, particularly in the economy of consumption of these materials.

The electrostatic principle has long been used in paint spraying techniques, and equipment for the purpose has been well developed and is available commercially. The process charges the droplets of liquid as they leave the spray gun. When directed to a surface carrying an opposite charge, they are attracted and all are drawn to the charged surface. Thus there is little spray dissipated in the air around the operation, nor is there waste of material because of it. In spraying penetrant or solvent developers which sometimes may be inflammable when the mist or vapor is mixed with air, the fire hazard is greatly reduced by this technique. Hazards to operator health and comfort are also reduced. The annoying or even harmful effect of breathing-in the spray-filled air, which is unavoidable due to scattering of spray when ordinary spraying systems are used, is eliminated.

Broad surfaces, essentially flat shapes (sprayed from both sides) and cylindrical shapes are best covered by this method. Where recesses occur, the spray may not cover them at all, but be attracted to the nearer surface.

Economy in amount of material used is at best advantage for very short penetration times (1-3 min.). When longer times are used (15-30 min.) enough excess material is recovered through run-off to make material costs of most other applications more nearly compatible.

3. BLACK LIGHT PHOTOGRAPHY. In Chapter 9, Section 23, instructions are given for making black-and-white photographic records of black light fluorescent indications. Color photography for this purpose results in some striking pictures, but they are not easy to produce. For those who may want to try their hand at color photographs, however, the following suggestions will be helpful and of interest.

4. ULTRAVIOLET PHOTOGRAPHY OF FLUORESCENT INDICATIONS IN COLOR. The basic problem in ultraviolet photography of fluorescent indications in color is showing the brilliant display of the fluorescent indication to the best advantage, without losing part shape and the general feel of how the scene appears to the naked eye.

Some of the elements of the photography, such as camera, film type, lens setting, and filter, can be held constant under varying conditions. Lighting and exposure time, however, necessarily vary with part shape and color, background color, and position and brilliance of the fluorescent indication. Since it is impossible to apply a simple formula (or, for that matter, a complicated formula) to these interacting variables, *experimentation is necessary with every black light photograph of fluorescent indications.*

Equipment

A 4 x 5 or larger view camera is in our opinion the best for this type of photography. However, a 35mm camera has some advantages. A larger f-stop may be used, because of the shorter focal length lens, and on making test exposures this speeds up the process considerably. Film is quite inexpensive, and the experience gained from exposing one 20- or 36-exposure roll can of course be applied to future exposures on larger cut film. In many instances the 35mm slide will be sufficient to do the job.

It is essential to have a rock-steady tripod and total darkness except for the actual lights used in making the photographs.

An ultraviolet light source such as the standard 400 watt or 100 watt Magnaflux flood makes an excellent light for photography when used over the part as general black light illumination. When a difficult part such as a tube is involved, it may be necessary to add one or two black light spots to dig in and light an area not illuminated by the flood.

A good black light photograph also needs some white light exposure to bring out the outline and contour of the part. The white light can be supplied by one or more #2 photofloods; it is usually bounced off a ceiling or wall to give it a soft quality and avoid bright reflections or highlights.

A K2 filter is used over the lens for all exposures involving a black lighting source. (The filter is removed for the white light exposure.)

Kodak Ektachrome Type B (32 ASA) is a good film to use, and the exposure data which follow are based on the use of this particular film.

Procedure

Arrange a photoflood to provide bounce light on the subject. Two or more floods from different angles might be necessary. Using a light meter, compute the exposure necessary to make a normal white light color photograph. For the white light exposure, use about one-third of this figure.

Place the 400-watt black light about two feet above the subject, making certain that the fluorescent defect area is well illuminated. If needed, add an additional black light spot or two.

With the lens set at f-16 and the filter in place, make a series of exposures, such as 2, 4, 8, 16 minutes. (With a 35mm camera, the f-stop will be larger and the times correspondingly shorter.) After making each individual black light exposure, close the shutter, turn off the black light, and remove the filter to make the white light portion of the exposure as computed. Vary the length of the white light exposure too in these tests. When the films are processed, it will be obvious if the white light is too strong (too much part definition and fluorescent indications weak by contrast) or too weak (dark, underexposed part and background, brilliant indications).

Comment

The above information used as a guide should give the photographer a basis for beginning to make good black light pictures in color. Experience should bring improvement in lighting technique and in ability to estimate limits of exposure time within which the best black light photograph of a given subject will fall. It should be borne in mind, however, that experimentation will always be necessary with each new set-up involving black light photography.

APPENDIX VII

BIBLIOGRAPHY

1. KULIN, S. ANDREW, *"Fluorescent Inspection of Tungsten."* Electronics, July, 1943.

2. CATLIN, F. S., *"Fluorescent Method Detects Leaks in Process Vessels."* Chem. & Met. Eng., August 1943.

3. WALSH, D. P., *"Practical Tool Inspection & Quality Control Methods."* Tool Engineer, Dec. 1946.

4. BLACKWELL, H. RICHARD, *"Contrast Thresholds of the Human Eye."* Journal of the Optical Society of America, Vol. 36, No. 11, Nov. 1946.

5. THOMAS, W. E., *"Inspection Methods Using Magnaflux and Zyglo in Production Industries."* Nondestructive Testing, Fall Issue, 1947.

6. HITT, WILLIAM, *"The Value of Scientific Inspection to Industry."* Western Machinery & Steel World, July 1948:108.

7. WOLDMAN, N. E., *"Some Notes on Fatigue Failures in Aircraft Parts."* Iron Age, 1948 #24:97.

8. ASTM *"Symposium on Usefulness and Limitations of Samples."* ASTM Proceedings, Vol 48:857.

9. CATLIN, F. S., *"Black Light Inspection of Castings."* Foundry, August 1949.

10. BARTH, V. C., *"C.&N.W. Intensifies Inspection of Equipment Parts."* Railway Mech. Engr., Oct. 1949.

11. MCMASTER, R. C., & WENK, S. A., *"A Basic Guide for Management's Choice of Nondestructive Tests."* A.S.T.M. Special Publication No. 112, 1950.

12. WALTERS, A. L., & MCMASTER, R. C., *"Some Observations on Problems in Fluorescent Penetrant Inspection."* Paper presented at Society for Nondestructive Testing National Meeting, Detroit. Oct. 1951.

13. PEDRICK, A. S., *"Railroad Maintenance Inspection."* Nondestructive Testing, Fall Issue, 1951.

14. SWEET, J. W., *"Weldment Inspection in Aircraft Construction."* Nondestructive Testing, Fall Issue, 1951.

15. *"Automatic Conveyorized Unit Used in Black Light Inspection."* Foundry, Dec. 1951:102, 225.

16. BUCKMAN, W. B., ROBINSON, A., GEIST, C. M., *"Fluorescent Penetrant Inspection and Magnetic Particle Inspection of Jet Engine Parts and Aircraft Parts."* Nondestructive Testing, Winter Issue, 1951-1952.

17. MCDOWELL, J. K., *"Nondestructive Testing as Applied to Tank Parts Inspection."* Nondestructive Testing, Winter Issue, 1952:4.

18. GILL, STANLEY A., *"Various Inspection Methods Used in Heat Treating Shops."* Metal Treating, May-June, 1952.

19. WENK, S. A., COOLEY, K. D., KIMMEL, R. M., *"Photoelectric Scanning of Fluorescent Indications."* Nondestructive Testing Summer Issue, 1952.

20. BLACKWELL, H. RICHARD, *"Studies of Psychophysical Methods for Measuring Visual Thresholds."* Journal of the Optical Society of America, Vol. 42, No. 9, Sept. 1952.

21. MCMASTER, R. C., *"Nondestructive Testing as Applied to Tank Parts Inspection."* Edgar Marburg Lecture. ASTM Proceedings, Volume 52:617.

22. RICE, GORDON, *"Lowered Production Costs Through the Use of Dy/Chek or Spek/Check."* Nondestructive Testing, March, 1953:16.

23. GILBERT, LEW & BUNN, WM. B., *"Inspection Techniques for Quality Welding."* Welding Journal, July 1953.

24. *"Improved Tools Expedite Magnetic Particle and Penetrant Inspection."* Metal Progress, Jan. 1954.

25. OYE, L. J., *"Nondestructive Testing of Structures."* Welding Journal, March 1954.

26. HAIWORTH, A. R., *"Testing for Fluid Tightness."* Power and Works Engineering, May 1954.

27. DEMER, L. J., *"Fatigue Crack Detection Methods."* W.A.D.C. Technical Report 55-86, Jan. 1955.

28. MIGEL, HAMILTON, *"Magnetic Particle, Penetrant and Related Inspection Methods as Production Tools for Process Control."* Steel Processing, Feb. 1955:86.

29. NASH, L. M., *"Quality Control of Light Metal Castings with Fluorescent Penetrant Inspection."* Modern Metals, March 1955:44.

30. MCCUTCHEON, D. M., *"Testing Inspection and Quality Control."* Metal Progress, March 1955:141.

31. RHODE, F. W., *"Development of the New Post-Emulsion Fluorescent Penetrant Inspection."* Nondestructive Testing, 1955 No. 3:27.

32. PENNEY, C. O., *"Nondestructive Testing on the Denver and Rio Grande Western Railroad."* Nondestructive Testing, 1955 No. 4, :33.

33. WILSON, T. C., *"Nondestructive Testing of Refinery Equipment."* The Plant Engineer, July 1955.

34. PATTERSON, N. C., *"Armco Avoids Accidents With Lifting Inspection Program."* Power Eng., Nov. 1955:80.

35. WALSH, D. P., *"Penetrant Inspection Method."* ASME Handbook, Sec. 93, 1955.

36. VAN DUZEE, G. R., *"New Nondestructive Test for Magnesium Alloy Castings."* Materials and Methods, Jan. 1956.

37. CATLIN, F. S. *"Nondestructive Sample Testing for Cracks Aids Heat-Treat."* Metal Treating, March 1956.

38. ROLL, KEMPTON H., *"Latest Methods for Inspecting Lead Linings."* Chemical Engineering, Nov. 1956.

39. MCPARLAN, JOSEPH L., *"How Nondestructive Testing Aids Power Station Maintenance."* Power Eng., March 1957.

40. PARKER, D. W., & SCHMIDT, J. T., *"Brightness of Fluorescent Penetrants, Its Measurement and Influence in Detecting Defects."* Nondestructive Testing, 1957 No. 6:330.

41. TURNER, RICHARD P., *"Leak Prevention Through In-Process Leak Detection."* Welding Journal, Dec. 1957.

42. *"Penetrant Inspection."* Welding Handbook, 4th Edition, Section 1, 8.36, 1957.

43. OLIVER, R. B., TOLSON, G. M., & TABOADA, A., *"The Use of Penetrants for Inspection of Small Diameter Tubing."* A.S.T.M. Symposium on Nondestructive Tests in the Field of Nuclear Energy. Special Technical Publication No. 223. 1957.

44. *"Fluorescent and Dye Penetrant Method."* Air Force Manual T. O. 33 B1-2-1-2, 1957.

45. MILLER, R. W., *"A Method for Evaluating Materials Used in Penetrant Flaw Detection."* Welding Journal, Jan. 1958 :30.

46. de Forest, T., *"Penetrant Testing."* Nondestructive Testing, 1958, No. 4:333.

47. Kleint, R. E., *"An Evaluation of the Effectiveness of Penetrants."* Nondestructive Testing, 1958, No. 5:421.

48. Betz, C. E., & Ellis, Greer. *"Fluorescent Penetrant Inspection."* A.S.M. Metals Handbook, 1958.

49. Betz, C. E., *"Sources of Defects."* Nondestructive Testing, July 1958.

50. *"Penetrant Inspection."* CAA Quality Control Digest No. 2, U. S. Govt. Printing Office. Nov. 1958.

51. *"Black Light Is Bright in Shop Work."* Automotive Service Digest, April 1959.

52. *"Nondestructive Testing"* by J. F. Hinsley. P. 320. McDonald & Evans, Ltd., London, England. 1959.

53. Betz, C. E., *"The Nondestructive Testing Engineer—Today's Career Oportunity."* S.N.T. Lester Lecture 1959. Nondestructive Testing, 1960, No. 1:15.

54. Heneghan, Paul S., *"Some Observations of Phenomena Related to Penetrant Detection of Cracks."* Nondestructive Testing, 1960, No. 2:121.

55. *"Zyglo Magic Tool Proves Safety Guard on Mixers.* The Grand Central Technical Report, Feb. 1960.

56. Nishikawa, Sakata, et al., *"The Application of Ultrasonic Irradiation to Fluorescent Penetrant Inspection Processes."* Proceedings, Third International Conference on Nondestructive Testing, Tokyo, Japan, March 1960. P. 684.

57. Shimadzu, Nakamura, Sakata, et al., *"The Standardization of Magnetic Particle and Penetrant Testing."* Proceedings Third International Conference on Nondestructive Testing, Tokyo, March 1960. P. 251.

58. Alburger, J. R., *"Fluorescent Penetrant Methods of Detecting Microflaws."* Ibid., P. 692.

59. Skeie, K. A., *"ABC's of N.D.T.'s."* Air. Accident and Maintenance Review, Feb. 1960.

60. *"New Tools Aid Turbine Checks."* Airlift, Feb. 1960.

61. Walsh, D. P., *"Nondestructive Testing Materials."* National Safety News, April 1960.

62. Hausman, F., *"Tested Your Machines for Flaws Lately?"* American Machinist/Metal Working Manufacturing, May 1960.

63. *"Tests for Safety and Reliability of School Buses,"* School Bus Trends, Aug. 1960.

64. WALSH, D. P., *"Reducing Maintenance Costs Through Inspection."* Mining Congress Journal, Aug. 1960.

65. *"Proper Testing Can Improve Quality."* Industrial World, Nov. 1960.

66. NORTHGROVE, J., *"Penetrant Methods."* Techniques of Nondestructive Testing (HOGARTH, C. A., & BLITZ, J.), Butterworth, London, England, 1960.

67. JOHNSON, L., *"How to Find Leaks Fast."* Motor Service, Feb. 1961.

68. *"Preventive Maintenance for Air Safety."* Airport/Services Management, March 1961.

69. BARBER, NICK, *"Reliability of Nondestructive Testing in Airline Maintennace."* Paper presented at Western States Meeting, S.N.T., March 1961.

70. KASTNER, J., & DICKERSON, M. H., *"Penetrant Evaluation Test Using Johanson Gauge Blocks."* Nondestructive Testing, 1961, No. 4:275.

71. GRAHAM, BRUCE, *"Evaluation of Penetrant Systems."* Paper presented at National Meeting, S.N.T., Detroit, Michigan, Oct. 1961.

72. BOGART H. G., *"The Place for Nondestructive Testing in the Field of Plant and Equipment Overhaul."* ASME, Winter-Annual Meeting, Nov. 1961.

73. *"Nondestructive Testing,"* by WARREN J. MCGONNAGLE. McGraw-Hill, 1961.

74. ALBURGER, J. R., *"Theory and Applications of Liquid Tracers."* Nondestructive Testing, 1962, No. 2:91.

75. KASTNER, J., *"Relation of Fluorescent Color to Ambient Illumination."* Nondestructive Testing, 1962, No. 3:182.

76. COTTRELL, K., & SHARPE, R. S., *"The Use of Carbon Tetrachloride as a Radiopaque Penetrant."*

77. MCCAULEY, ROY B., & VAN WINKLE, Q., Technical Documentary Report. WADD-TR-60-520 Part I, March 1962.

78. DALE, D., *"The Crack of Doom."* Sports Car Graphic, May 1962.

79. SKEIE, K. A., *"The Road to Real Reliability."* Western Aerospace, Nov. 1962.

80. *"Magnetic Particle and Penetrant Inspection."* Precision Metal Molding, March, 1963.
81. ERICHSEN, W. J. and BILLINGS, G. W., JR., *"How to Use Liquid Penetrant Tests."* Metal Progress, September, 1963.
82. THOMAS, W. E., *"An Analytic Approach to Penetrant Performance."* ASNT Lester Honor Lecture, 1963.
83. PARKER, D. W., *"Penetrant Testing of Plastics."* Plastics Design & Processing, January, 1964.
84. BETZ, CARL E., *"Getting the most from Penetrants."* Quality Assurance, March, 1964.
85. TURNER, RICHARD P., *"Nondestructive Testing by Electrical, Magnetic Particle, and Penetrant Methods."* Presented at the 19th Engineering Conference of the Technical Association of the Pulp and Paper Industry, July, 1964.
86. ALBURGER, JAMES R., *"Porosity Detection and Suppression in Penetrant Inspection Processs."* Materials Evaluation, August, 1965.
87. MCFAUL, HOWARD J., *"Effect of Finishing Processes on Detectability of Surface Flaws by Penetrant Process."* Materials Evaluation, December, 1965.
88. *"Invisible-Crack Detection Means Dependable Carbide Performance."* Cutting Tool Engineering, July/August, 1966.
89. SCHMIDT, J. T., *"A New Method for Measuring Fluorescent Brightness and Color."* Materials Evaluation, December, 1966.
90. CAMPBELL, W. B. and MCMASTER, R. C., *"Derivation of Penetrant-Developer Resolution."* Materials Evaluation, May, 1967.
91. HOLLAMBY, D. C., *"The Comparison of the Various Methods of Penetrant Inspection."* Testing, Instruments and Controls, November, 1967.
92. LAUTZENHEISER, C. E. and WATSON, P. D., *"The Effects of Chlorinated Solvent Cleaning on Weldments."* Welding Journal, December, 1967.
93. SKOGLUND, H. N. and MAGDALIN, C., *"Gillespian Approach to Penetrability."* Materials Evaluation, December, 1968.
94. ALBURGER, JAMES R., *"Dual Sensitivity Inspection of Penetrants and High Resolution Developers."* Materials Evaluation, April, 1968.
95. SHERWIN, AMOS G., *"Classification of the High-Sensitivity Water-Washable Fluorescent Penetrant."* Materials Evaluation, November, 1968.
96. LOMERSON, EDWIN O., JR., *"Statistical Method for Evaluating Penetrant Sensitivity and Reproducibility."* Materials Evaluation, March, 1969.

SUBJECT INDEX